Compiled by William Green

The World Guide to
COMBAT PLANES
TWO

Illustrated by Dennis Punnett and John Weal

With contributions by Roy Braybrook, John Fricker
Kenneth Fulton and Philip Robins

DOUBLEDAY AND COMPANY INC.
Garden City, New York

PRINTED IN GREAT BRITAIN

Introduction

FEW PERIODS in aviation history have witnessed greater changes in combat aircraft requirements and development than has the past decade. As the threat of global conflict has receded, the limited war assuming ever increasing importance, accent has changed from the strategic bomber and the interceptor fighter intended specifically to counter its threat, to the multi-purpose tactical warplane. With the growth in effectiveness of early warning and defensive missile screens, the high-flying strategic bomber has lost its supremacy, its deterrent role being assumed by the intercontinental ballistic missile, and remaining warplanes of this type have been obliged to drop from economical cruise altitudes to a mere few hundred feet in order to remain, temporarily at least, a viable means of attack. At such altitudes their lightly-built structures are buffeted by turbulence and their range is reduced to perhaps one-third of normal values, placing deep penetration targets outside their radii. Proposed successors intended for the high-speed, low-altitude mission have so far failed to offer true strategic ranges, and thus the strategic bomber is now widely considered a dying breed.

This changed accent is posing major problems for the power plant designer who is faced with the demand for optimum propulsion performance from loiter to dash and from terrain-following to the highest attainable altitudes, and it is also providing the impetus for the development of new airborne tactical weapons. Relatively few years ago, atomic encroachment was obvious in virtually all areas of weapon development, but today it is the tactical weapon with conventional warhead that has priority, and tremendous effort is being expended on airborne weaponry, which ranges from cannon and machine guns using the Gatling principle of revolving barrels to the first tactical missiles with true stand-off capability, such as the television-guided version of the Anglo-French Martel.

Limited wars, and that being waged in Vietnam in particular, have not only served to accelerate the development of new airborne weapons; they have provided the reason for the evolution of entirely new categories of warplane, such as those designed specifically for counter-insurgency tasks, and the fighting helicopter which, in its advanced aerial fire support form, bids fair to rival the fixed-wing fighter in importance over the next decade. However, the limited wars have had little influence on the development of strategic reconnaissance aircraft, and those intended for maritime patrol and anti-submarine warfare. So-called "ferret" missions, normally undertaken just outside territorial limits, are regularly performed by aircraft of East and West, but it seems unlikely that overflights of hostile territory such as were conducted with the Lockheed U-2 remain practical, despite the advanced nature of the U-2's successor, the SR-71, and orbital vehicles will presumably supplant the manned aircraft for such aerial surveillance in the immediate future. In the realm of anti-submarine warfare, the steadily increasing deployment of nuclear-powered underwater vessels is posing new problems, necessitating the development of new ASW systems and new airframes to house them.

In this second volume, all these facets of combat plane development are surveyed, an attempt is made to place them in perspective, and the aircraft, weapons and power plants fulfilling the previously-mentioned tasks and currently under development as potential successors to present equipment are described and illustrated.

London, September 1966

WILLIAM GREEN

Contents

AIRBORNE ARMAMENT	page 7
BOMBER DEVELOPMENT	25
CURRENT BOMBERS	33
RECONNAISSANCE AIRCRAFT DEVELOPMENT	73
CURRENT TACTICAL RECONNAISSANCE AIRCRAFT	91
MARITIME PATROL AND ANTI-SUBMARINE WARFARE AIRCRAFT DEVELOPMENT	117
CURRENT PATROL AND ASW AIRCRAFT	127
COUNTER-INSURGENCY AIRCRAFT	154
COMBAT HELICOPTER DEVELOPMENT	172
POWER PLANTS FOR COMBAT AIRCRAFT	190
INDEX	208

Acknowledgements

The sources of some of the photographs appearing in this volume are as follows: Aircent (pages 92 and 94); Aireview (pages 60, 62, 75, 80, 88, 90, 91, 96, 106, 125 and upper 174); Amilpress (page 107 lower); B-R Photos (pages 126 lower and 173); Leo J. Kohn (page 29); T. Matsuzaki (pages 36, 44 upper and 46); S. P. Peltz (page 52); F. G. Swanborough (page 127); Bo Widfeldt (pages 163 and 175 lower); G. Williams (page 168).

AIRBORNE ARMAMENT

THE postwar development of armament for combat aircraft might be summarised as a mixture of delayed decisions, protracted and expensive research programmes, a multitude of cancellations, and an occasional flash of ingenuity which turned an indifferent weapon into a great one. In Britain, for example, it took almost ten years from the end of the war to put a 30-mm. cannon in service, following which an immense effort was undertaken to produce a family of air-to-air weapons, eventually resulting in only two modest types of guided weapon being available for present-day R.A.F. interceptors. As for air-to-surface armament, insofar as Britain is concerned it is only now that a start has been made to replace the traditional 3-inch rocket, virtually unchanged since the Typhoons swept the panzers from Normandy. To add insult to injury, the vast sums spent on armament development in the United Kingdom have not only failed to produce any major breakthrough in technology; they have forced Britain to purchase from abroad the simplest of weapons, such as the SNEB/MATRA rocket battery, the Nord AS 30, the Bullpup and the Sidewinder!

Historically, the first really effective airborne armament was the machine gun, but this was largely abandoned more than twenty years ago in favour of the cannon which, due to its explosive ammunition, is far more effective against armour or self-sealing fuel tanks. The U.S.A. alone persisted with machine guns on first generation turbojet fighters (the F-80 and F-84), and this was emulated by Fiat with the Italian Air Force's version of the G.91, but Korea proved the need for heavier firepower, and cannon thus came to be used on some later F-86 Sabre and the Century Series fighters. Strangely enough, the humble machine gun is now enjoying a resurgence of interest as a result of the shift in planning from a European war to various levels of conflict in the regions bordering on the Indian Ocean.

Two principal threats are considered: a major drive south by Chinese forces, and a spread of the counter-insurgency type of warfare now being experienced in Vietnam. In either case it is not expected that there would be any serious air opposition, and the main target would be personnel, especially, in the "human wave" attack situation. Under the circumstances the best armament is light (for carriage on small, low-cost aircraft), and it must have a very high rate of fire. The cannon can produce similar effects through fragmentation on hard ground, but its explosive energy may be lost in sand, and foliage may cause premature fuzing. Work is consequently in progress on a whole series of machine-

The hand-held 20-mm. cannon, seen here installed experimentally on a U.S. Army UH-1B Iroquois, took a new lease on life with its application to helicopters for COIN warfare.

(Left) An F-4C Phantom II firing the 20-mm. General Electric M-61 Vulcan rotary cannon mounted in SUU-23/A ("Vulpod") pods on the underwing pylons. Note the shell cases trailing beneath the aircraft. The Vulcan cannon are used in conjunction with a General Electric ASG-22 gun sight.

guns to supersede the regular Colt-Browning **M-3**, which fires 1,100 rounds per minute of 0.5-in. calibre ammunition. Hughes has produced a 0.3-in. calibre twin-barrel **Heligun**, firing

(Below) The gun tray of the MiG-15bis with one 37-mm. and two 23-mm. cannon.

4,000 rounds per minute, while the General Electric **Minigun** of the same calibre utilises the Gatling principle of six revolving barrels to achieve a cyclic rate of 6,000 rounds per minute. In addition, it may be assumed that considerable work is in progress on even smaller calibres. Some clue to the trend may be obtained from current army equipment, one of the most important of recent developments being the 0.223-in. **AR-15** rifle evolved by the Armalite Division of Fairchild-Hiller. Due to the lightness of the bullet, extremely high velocities are attained, and the Armalite rifle has been said to be capable of killing simply by shock effects in grazing wounds. These low calibre weapons were first used operationally by Indonesian infiltrators against British troops in Brunei, and the later Colt **M-16** is now being used by some U.S. troops in Vietnam in place of the standard 0.3-in. **M-14**. The ammunition fired by the **M-16** has also been used in the development of a new General Electric **Minigun** pod, which can provide an aircraft with a rate of fire of 10,000 rounds/min.

By comparison with these light weapons, a cannon is inherently more flexible in operation, being able to inflict severe damage on most types of air or surface targets, and it is likely to remain a permanent fit on high performance fighter-bombers. With the 30-mm. **Aden,**

DEFA, and **Oerlikon** guns, and the U.S. 20-mm. **M-39,** the West has virtually standardised on developments of the war-time Mauser MG 213C, and it seems likely that this was also the basis for the current Russian 30-mm. cannon. The American preference for a lighter shell is presumably based on requirements emphasising low ballistic drop and high rate of fire (**M-39**: 1,500 rounds per minute) for effectiveness in dogfight-style combat, but it is debatable whether these qualities offset the decrease in explosive weight when it comes to shooting at a bomber. Ammunition of 20-mm. calibre has been retained for the General Electric **M-61 Vulcan** rotary cannon, which represents virtually the only major post-war advance in the field. Fed by two belts of ammunition, the **Vulcan** provides the F-104, F-105, B-52H, and B-58 with a built-in rate of fire of nominally 6,000 rounds per minute, and the gun is now available in **SUU-23/A** "Vulpod" form for under-wing attachment to aircraft such as the F-100, F-105 and F-4C, the "Vulpod" containing a 1,200-round linkless ammunition feed system. The U.S. Navy's latest cannon development is the Hughes **HIPEG,** a podded version of the brilliant twin-barrel **Mk.11** Marquardt gun with 750 rounds of 20-mm. ammunition, which discharges at over 4,000 rounds per minute. This is a rather lighter installation than the "Vulpod", being designed for use by attack planes such as the A-4, or by helicopters.

The acid test of combat invariably explodes many of the most cherished peacetime theories, and the Vietnam conflict has certainly served to vindicate the protagonists of the gun as aircraft armament. Their views had for so long been eclipsed by those of the missiles-for-all-purposes factions, and the opinion was widely held that the gun was as obsolete in air-to-air combat as the bow-and-arrow on the modern battlefield. Aerial skirmishes over North Vietnam have resulted in some disenchantment with AAMs. Distinguishing enemy from friendly aircraft in air-to-air combat using active homing missiles has presented a serious problem, and one which was emphasized in the spring of 1965 when a U.S. Navy F-4B Phantom II was destroyed by a Sidewinder fired by another

(Above) An SUU-11/A 7.62-mm. Minigun pod, weighing 320 lb. when loaded with ammunition, mounted beneath the wing of an A-1E Skyraider.

Phantom II during an encounter with North Vietnamese MiG-17s over the Gulf of Tonkin. Reliable identification of aircraft over Vietnam is demanding visual "eyeballing" at which ranges it is too late to launch missiles, and for the close-in, high-*g* manoeuvring of air-to-air combat, fixed guns are once more considered essential. Guns have also proved to be of extreme importance in air-to-ground strike missions, both for flak suppression and as an accurate means of hitting troops in the open.

Rocket projectiles have, of course, an advantage over cannon shells in attacks on hardened emplacements, armoured vehicles or ships, in that they carry a larger warhead, and that their speed results in better penetration and less ballistic drop at long range. Unguided rockets can also be used by interceptors (the British 2-in. rocket was developed mainly for this purpose), the fighter then normally being removed from the bomber's field of fire. Probably as a result of early difficulties with guided weapons, the Soviet Union developed a 210-mm. rocket for air-to-air use. This

(Above) MATRA Type 116 *launching pods beneath the wing of an Indian Mystère IVA. Each pod houses* 19 *SNEB 68-mm. rockets.*

weapon appears to have been employed without effect during an encounter between MiG-17s and A-1H Skyraiders over Vietnam in mid-1965, one of the MiG-17s being shot down when its pilot attempted to fight on the Skyraider's terms, at low speed and low altitude.

The normal types of rocket warhead are armour-piercing (using a tungsten core), fragmenting, blast, shaped charge, and HESH. The shaped charge is essentially a blast warhead with a concave forward face covered by a thin sheet of copper; exploded at the optimum stand-off distance, this will send a high-energy beam of metal particles through a considerable thickness of armour, possibly up to four times the warhead diameter. The HESH (High Explosive Squash Head) works simply by squashing a great mass of explosives close to the armour prior to detonation, after which the tank crew may be disabled by fragments thrown from the inner face, or die of fright! These various means of penetrating armour are ingenious, but it should be remembered that the squash head may be defeated by a double skin of armour, and that other warheads may incapacitate the tank crew without destroying the vehicle itself. In addition, rockets have been used with flare heads,

concrete heads for practice or knocking holes in mud forts, and with napalm, which was employed with limited success by the R.A.A.F. in Korea.

The principal unguided rockets at present in use are the 68-mm. **SNEB,** the 80-mm. **Hispano** and the U.S. 2.75-in. FFAR (Folding Fin Aircraft Rocket), originally known as the Mighty Mouse, and 5-in. **Zuni.** Following development by the U.S.A.F. at Wright-Patterson AFB, Northrop is now manufacturing a special 2.75-in. warhead which will eject a cloud of tiny winged darts or *flechettes.* In addition, the spin-stabilised **AIR-2A Genie** is carried by a number of interceptors including U.S.A.F. Air Defence Command F-101Bs and R.C.A.F. CF-101Bs. Its nuclear warhead can accommodate miss distances of over 1,000 ft. The **Genie** is now being developed with a large conventional warhead as an air-to-surface area saturation missile for use in Vietnam.

BOMB DEVELOPMENTS

Although rockets are useful for delivering small warheads accurately, the free-fall bomb is still the normal way to land a reasonable weight of explosive on a large target at minimum cost. Due to the availability of a whole range of nuclear warheads, the heavyweight bombs developed toward the end of World War II have now been discarded, and almost all of those now in use lie in the range 500–2,000 lb. (aside from practice bombs of around 25 lb.). The normal British weapon is the 1,000-lb. bomb, of which two are carried externally by a Hunter, six internally by a Canberra or four by a Buccaneer, and up to 35 by the Victor. The corresponding U.S.A.F. bombs, the **M-117** and **Mk.83,** weigh 750 lb. and 1,000 lb. respectively, and the B-52s operating from Guam against insurgent areas in Vietnam have been modified to take fifty-one 750-pounders, twenty-seven of which are carried in the weapon bay, and the remainder on two underwing pylons. Further modifications carried out early in 1966 enable the B-52's weapon bay to accommodate up to eighty-four 500-lb. or forty-two 750-lb. bombs in addition to the twenty-four 750-lb. weapons on the pylons.

Weapons for an all-out war bear little resemblance to the original 10,000-lb. 20-kiloton "Little Boy" that was dropped on Hiroshima; nine years after the end of the war the F-86H was flying with a 100-kiloton atomic bomb weighing only 1,200 lb., and the standard NATO thermonuclear weapon now mounted on the F-104G has a yield of one-megaton and weighs 2,000 lb.

The main concern at the present time is, however, the counter-insurgency operation, and in this context the need is for area coverage by tactical anti-personnel weapons, which has in the past been obtained by the use of fragmentation heads with VT fuses, or fire-bombs (napalm). In this application the VT (variable time) fuse is simply a miniature radar which triggers the warhead at a preset height above the ground. The fire bomb is commonly a drop tank, filled with fuel and a special additive, and ignited by an inertia fuse and a phosphorus grenade. It has been argued that its effectiveness against well-trained troops in prepared positions would be far less than its spectacular fireball suggests, but there is no doubt of its usefulness against troops caught in the open during an attack, and it has been used extensively in Vietnam, the most common napalm weapon being the 750-lb. **BLU-1/B.** Use of the fire-bomb is frowned upon in many countries, and it is not normally stocked by the R.A.F., although it is very easily manufactured.

Aside from the ease with which troops in slit trenches can protect themselves against fire-bomb attacks by simple coverings, these weapons have the disadvantage of ineffectiveness in jungle, and in addition they only produce a very narrow streak of fire. For these reasons a great deal of development work is being directed at more sophisticated types of bombs, which can wipe out the enemy over a relatively wide area. Much of the pioneer work in this field has been carried out at the U.S. Naval Ordnance Test Station at China Lake, where a whole range of cluster bombs has been developed. Typical of these new weapons is the cylindrical 1,000-lb **Gladeye,** composed of seven canisters which can be released singly, in ripple, or as a salvo. Each canister can contain a fragmentation warhead, anti-radar chaff, or leaflets. **Sad-**

(Above) Twin Zuni rocket launchers and a Bullpup-A ASM mounted on an F-8E Crusader.

eye is a 750-lb. low-drag cluster bomb of conventional streamlined shape with tail fins, and may presumably be released at greater height for low level bursts. Thirdly, NOTS have produced a bomb designated **Rockeye,** which takes the form of ninety-six shaped-charge bomblets (modified from the warhead of the 2.75-in. rocket), stacked around a Zuni motor which disperses them after release. This weapon would obviously be more effective than conventional bombs against hard-skinned targets, since it overcomes the problem of inaccurate delivery.

The U.S. Navy is also attempting to advance the state-of-the-art in conventional bomb fusing which has remained virtually unchanged since World War II, and development has been concentrated on a new type of electrical fusing. This enables the pilot to set the bomb fuse remotely for proximity, contact or delayed burst. However, initial operational trails in Vietnam were accompanied by the loss of several aircraft as a result of premature bomb

(Above) A P-3A Orion of the U.S. Navy with its arsenal, including Mk.44 torpedoes, 1,000- and 2,000-lb. class mines, Mk.54 depth bombs, a Mk.101 nuclear depth bomb, rockets, flares, etc.

Not much is known of U.S.A.F. activities in this field of bomb development, although **Lazy Dog** is reported to be an anti-personnel weapon which scatters shrapnel over a wide area. The U.S. Army Weapons Command has been engaged in developing armament such as rocket launchers and grenade dispensers for helicopter use, and much of this is obviously applicable to low speed fixed-wing aircraft. In addition, Weapons Command is testing small winged bombs that scarcely penetrate the ground, and iron-cased "grenades" the size of golf-balls, which are dropped in batches of 1,000 from containers weighing only 100 lb. The requirement in this case is to deny an area to the enemy, without rendering it permanently unsafe to friendly troops. This is achieved by fusing arrangements that result in the grenade becoming lethal as a minute land-mine for a period of eight hours after the drop, after which time a chemical action renders it inert.

Notwithstanding the wide variety of weapons under development for brush-fire wars, the need remains for bombs which can deliver heavy conventional warheads, but which overcome the basic faults of inaccurate delivery and danger to the low-flying aircraft. Where ground fire is encountered, a steep dive attack is ruled out and the bomb must be released in a low fly-over. This has the disadvantage that the bomb strikes the ground at a grazing angle, so that small errors at release result in considerable miss distances, in addition to which the attacking aircraft is low over the bomb at detonation. One cure is to employ a retarded bomb, equipped with a drag device which enables the aircraft to leave the bomb behind, and which results in the bomb impacting at a steep angle and consequently with greater accuracy. Para-frag bombs (i.e., with braking parachutes and fragmentation warheads) were used with some success against targets such as bridges in Korea, and the retarded-fall **Snakeye** is now being evaluated in Vietnam. The **Snakeye** is a Mk.80 series bomb with four metal airbrakes at the rear, which normally lie flat against the sides of the bomb and open umbrella-fashion on release from the aircraft, permitting extremely low-altitude delivery. However, its use has been res-

explosion, electromagnetic radiation from the aircraft carrier's radar possibly having armed the bombs, the proximity of one to another in a salvo release being sufficient to activate the proximity fuses.

tricted by the heavy North Vietnamese small arms and automatic weapons fire.

Largely as a result of losses due to flak in the Korean War, attention turned to the idea of a bomb which could be guided to the target from a considerable distance, so that the fighter would never come within range of small-calibre weapons. One of the missiles to derive from this programme is the **AGM-12 Bullpup** which is remarkable in that it can be handled as a normal piece of ammunition and fitted to an aircraft without any system checks, in spite of which it achieves a reliability of over 90 per cent. The **Bullpup A (AGM-12B)** is a 250-lb. warhead placed in a canard-layout airframe, and fitted with command guidance, the pilot moving a miniature control column to issue steering corrections to the weapon over a microwave link, so that the missile flies down a straight line to the target. In essence, command guidance is the simplest possible form of control, but it has a number of drawbacks. The pilot may become confused if the enemy fires tracer at him, because he is tracking the **Bullpup** by means of flares at the rear, and cloud cover provides a limiting factor. In addition the launch aircraft must dive toward the target, thus losing the immunity of low level flying, and it is furthermore difficult to see how a visually command-guided missile can be used for a nuclear warhead with air burst without blinding the pilot.

Originally designed to fulfil a U.S. Navy specification for an anti-shipping missile, the first production version of the **Bullpup** employed a very simple type of guidance and had a range of six miles. This model has been in use on the AF-1 Fury and A-4 Sky-hawk, and has been adopted by the Royal Navy for fitment to the Scimitar and Sea Vixen. An improved version, the **AGM-12C Bullpup B**, armed with a 1,000-lb. warhead and weighing 1,785 lb. (compared with the earlier 570 lb.) is now in service with both the U.S.N. and U.S.A.F., while the **AGM-12D** with interchangeable conventional and nuclear warheads is in service use. Development includes the use of offset attacks and blind delivery, the A-6 Intruder having a special facility known as BAGS (Bullpup All-

(*Above*) *Twelve 750-lb. general-purpose bombs pylon-mounted beneath the wing of a B-52 Stratofortress. In addition to 24 pylon-mounted bombs, the B-52 can carry 42 750-pounders internally.*

weather Guidance System). Both of the earlier versions have seen action in Vietnam, where it has been found that the larger miss distance of **Bullpup A** made it ineffective against targets such as bridges, whereas the more advanced guidance of **Bullpup B** produced highly satisfactory results.

EUROPEAN WEAPONS

Although command guidance had been tested in the early days of British GW research, the concept was discarded as not warranting further development, and it was left to France to build up a substantial lead in this field. With an eye on both air-to-air and air-to-surface applications, Nord Aviation initiated a family of

(Above) The AGM-28 Hound Dog turbojet-powered stand-off missile is a standard weapon with the U.S.A.F.'s B-52 bomber force.

fore be fitted with two alternative guidance systems, namely an anti-radar homing head by Electronique Marcel Dassault, and a TV guidance system by Marconi. Using the anti-radar version, and aircraft such as the Mirage IVA will be able to blast a way through defence networks, while the TV model will enable precision attacks to be made without abandoning the safety of "nap of the earth" flying, and without incurring the nuclear flash problem of line-of-sight command guidance. The Martel will be carried by a variety of aircraft, ranging from the HS.801 maritime patroller to the Jaguar, Buccaneer, and F-4K Phantom.

Sweden's main contribution in this field has been the **Rb** (Robot) **04,** a heavy subsonic command-guided missile, which is mounted on the A 32A Lansen for use against shipping. At the present moment trials are in progress of the **Rb 05,** which is a lighter, supersonic weapon intended for the A 60 and the AJ 37A Viggen. Generally similar in appearance to the **AS 30,** this missile has been designed for highly accurate delivery in offset attacks at low level, and is seen in some quarters as a possible back-up to the **AS 37/AJ 168 Martel** programme.

In the U.S.A., progress in guided bombs has roughly paralleled (and in certain respects advanced over) work in Europe. The U.S. Navy already has the **AGM-45A Shrike** anti-radar missile (ARM) at operational status, although initial use of this weapon in Vietnam proved ineffective. Although continued development of the **Shrike** ARM is being funded by the U.S. Navy, a more effective ARM is obviously needed, and consideration is being given to the development of several AAMs, such as the **AIM-47A Falcon,** as interim ARMs pending development of an entirely new type. The **Walleye** TV-guided glide bomb is currently under active development. A possible successor to the **Bullpup,** the **Walleye** is claimed to deliver a 1,000-lb. warhead with an accuracy of 6–7 yards, and the final guidance phase is automatic, to overcome transmission difficulties when both missile and launch vehicle are at low level, the pilot of the launching aircraft controlling the missile only until he has focussed its TV camera on the target. In addition, the 50-

command-guided missiles, notably the 320-lb. **AS 20** which is carried by both the Etendard and Fiat G.91, and the 1,125-lb. **AS 30,** used by the Mirage IIIE, *Kriegsmarine* F-104Gs, and R.A.F. Canberras. This highly successful programme is being followed up by joint development with Germany of the inertially-guided **AS 33,** and the **AS 34** which is believed to have infra-red terminal homing for use against tanks. A follow-on to the **AS 30** is planned by Engins MATRA in collaboration with Hawker Siddeley Dynamics, two companies with excellent experience in the air-to-air field. This new weapon, designated **AS 37/AJ 168 Martel** (an acronym for Missile Anti-Radar Television), is intended for operation by the air forces and navies of the United Kingdom and France against a wide range of surface targets, and will there-

(1) **North American AGM-28B Hound Dog:** *Propulsion:* One 7,500 lb. Pratt & Whitney J52-P-3 turbojet. *Guidance:* NAA Autonetics inertial. *Launch weight:* 9,600 lb. *Warhead:* Thermonuclear. *Dimensions:* Length, 42 ft. 6 in.; span, 12 ft. 2 in.; max. diam., 28 in. *Range:* 690 mls. (2) **Hawker Siddeley Dynamics Blue Steel Mk.1:** *Propulsion:* Bristol Siddeley Stentor liquid-fuel rocket motor. *Guidance:* Elliott inertial. *Launch weight:* Not available. *Warhead:* Thermonuclear. *Dimensions:* Length, 35 ft. 0 in.; span, 13 ft. 0 in.; max. diam., 50 in. *Range:* Not available. (3) **Kipper:** *Propulsion:* One turbojet. *Guidance:* Inertial. *Launch weight:* Not available. *Warhead:* Thermonuclear. *Approximate dimensions:* Length, 30 ft.; span, 14 ft.; max diam., 36 in. *Approximate range:* 200 mls. (4) **Kennel:** *Propulsion:* One 5,000 lb. RD-9 turbojet. *Guidance:* Autopilot and radar homing. *Launch weight:* Not available. *Warhead:* Approx. 1,000 lb.H.E. *Approximate dimensions:* Length, 30 ft.; span, 16 ft.; max. diam., 60 in. *Approximate range:* 80–90 mls. (5) **Kangaroo:** *Propulsion:* One turbojet. *Guidance:* Inertial. *Launch weight:* Not available. *Warhead:* Thermonuclear. *Approximate Dimensions:* Length, 46 ft.; span, 28 ft.; max. diam., 60 in. *Approximate range:* 250 mls.

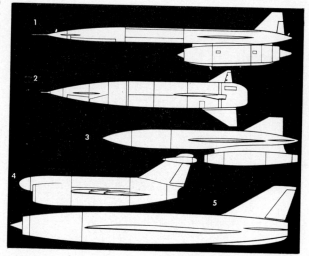

mile **AGM-53 Condor** TV-guided missile is being studied for A-6A and F-111B application, and somewhat further in the future is the **SRAM** (Short Range Attack Missile), intended for such widely differing types as the Phantom II, the F-111, and FB-111, and the B-52 and B-58. Boeing and Martin are prime contenders for the SRAM contract, with Aerojet-General, Lockheed and Thiokol competing for the propulsion system contract, and total SRAM development cost is expected to total $170.1 million (£60.75 million).

Before leaving the subject of tactical missiles, it may be of interest to recall one of the most ingenious concepts in this field, the regrettably defunct **Wagtail**, which proposed a unique solution to the problem of an aircraft required to deliver a nuclear weapon for air-burst, without climbing above 200 ft. and without destroying itself in the ensuing explosion, The idea of **Wagtail** was to fire the missile rearwards as the aircraft passed over (or abreast of) the target, after which the inertially-controlled missile would then tip on end and fire itself vertically into the air before falling back and detonating over the target!

In view of the pre-eminent position of the strategic ballistic missile, the development of guided weapons for long-range bombers has now virtually ceased, although a fresh appraisal will clearly be made in the event of the U.S.A.F. obtaining a go-ahead for the AMSA (Advanced Manned Strategic Aircraft) programme to replace its G and H model Boeing B-52s. Rather surprisingly, the present B-58's weapon load consists purely of a free-fall bomb pod, but the B-52 carries an offensive load supplemented

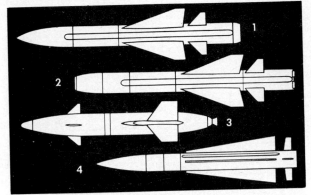

(1) **MATRA-Hawker Siddeley AS. 37 Martel:** *Propulsion:* Solid-propellant rocket. *Guidance:* Electronique Marcel Dassault passive homing. *Launch weight:* Not available. *Warhead:* H.E. *Approximate Dimensions:* Length, 13 ft.; span, 4 ft.; max. diam. 15 in. *Range:* Not available. (2) **MATRA-Hawker Siddeley AJ.168 Martel:** *Propulsion:* Solid-propellant rocket. *Guidance:* Marconi TV homing. *Launch weight:* Not available. *Warhead:* H.E. *Approximate dimensions:* Length, 13 ft.; span, 4 ft.; max. diam., 15 in. *Range:* Not available. (3) **Robot 04C:** *Propulsion:* Solid-propellant rocket. *Guidance:* Radio command. *Launch weight:* 1,390 lb. *Warhead:* 660 lb.H.E. *Dimensions:* Length, 14 ft. 7 in.; span, 6 ft. 8 in.; max diam., 19.4 in. *Range:* 2.5–3 mls. (4) **Saab 305A:** *Propulsion:* Solid-propellant rocket. *Guidance:* Radio command (line of sight). *Launch weight:* 660 lb. *Warhead:* H.E. *Dimensions:* Length, 11 ft. 7 in.; span, 2 ft. 8 in.; max. diam., 12 in. *Range:* Not available.

by **ADM-20C Quail** decoys and **AGM-28B Hound Dog** missiles. The **Quail** is powered by a J85-GE-7 turbojet, giving it a range of 256 miles and a ceiling of 50,000 ft., where its autopilot leads it through programmed manoeuvres to simulate B-52 patterns, and its radar reflecting devices enable it to simulate the full-size bomber. The **Hound Dog** is an inertially-guided Mach 2.0 weapon with a maximum range of 690 miles and a nuclear warhead. Its prime mission is to suppress defences and allow the B-52 to penetrate to top-priority targets.

Unlike the Hound Dog, which is turbojet-powered, the Hawker Siddeley **Blue Steel** weapon carried by the Vulcan B.2 is fitted with a rocket engine, with separate chambers for acceleration and cruise. Although this form of power plant obviously results in a higher cruise speed, it has the incidental disadvantage that the missile engine cannot be used to improve the bomber's take-off performance. The **Blue Steel** has an Elliott inertial navigation

system and a range of 100–200 miles, depending on the release altitude. Russia has four principal types of large air-to-surface missiles: the **Kitchen** mounted on Blinder, the **Kangaroo** on the Tu-20 (Bear-B), the **Kennel** on the Tu-16 (Badger B), and the **Kipper** on the Tu-16 (Badger C). The only one of these known to have been exported is the **Kennel**, which is carried in pairs and is assumed to be an anti-shipping missile. This weapon is in service with the Indonesian and UAR air forces, and could represent a threat to merchant shipping in the event of open war, although it would presumably offer little danger to the sophisticated defences of major naval units.

AIR-TO-AIR WEAPONS

Reference has already been made to cannon and unguided rockets which can be used in the air-to-air mode. The cannon is basically suited to the high accelerations and brief firing opportunities that occur in close-in combat, and it overcomes the main difficulty of rockets as rear defence weapons for bombers (viz., the problem of passing through a zero speed phase). The unguided rocket, on the other hand, is useful as an interceptor armament since it effectively takes the fighter outside the range of the bomber's rear gunner. In round numbers, a rocket might be fired from a range of 1,000 yards, rather than the 500 yards of a cannon. However,

(1) **Maxson AGM-12B Bullpup:** *Propulsion:* One 12,000 lb. Thiokol/RMD LR58-RM-4 liquid-fuel rocket. *Guidance:* Pilot command via radio link. *Launch weight:* 571 lb. *Warhead:* 250 lb. H.E. *Dimensions:* Length, 10 ft. 6 in.; span, 3 ft. 3½ in.; max. diam., 12 in. *Range:* 7 mls. (2) **Martin AGM-12C Bullpup:** *Propulsion:* One Thiokol/RMD LR62-RM-2 liquid-fuel rocket. *Guidance:* Pilot command via A.W. system. *Launch weight:* 1,785 lb. *Warhead:* 1,000 lb. H.E. or nuclear. *Dimensions:* Length, 13 ft. 7 in.; span, 4 ft. 0 in.; max. diam., 18 in. *Range:* 10 mls. (3) **Martin AGM-12D Nuclear Bullpup:** *Propulsion:* One Thiokol/RMD LR62-RM-2 liquid-fuel rocket. *Guidance:* Offset command via proportional radio link. *Launch weight:* Not available. *Warhead:* Nuclear or H.E. *Dimensions:* Length, n.a.; span, 3 ft. 3½ in.; max. diam., 13 in. *Range:* Not available. (4) **Martin Walleye:** *Propulsion:* None. *Guidance:* Visual command with TV homing. *Launch weight:* 1,100 lb. *Warhead:* H.E. *Dimensions:* Length, 11 ft. 3½ in.; span, 3 ft. 9½ in.; max. diam., 15 in. *Range:* 4–5 mls. (5) **NOTS AGM-45A Shrike:** *Propulsion:* NAA/Rocketdyne Mk. 39-Mod-0 solid-propellant rocket. *Guidance*. Texas Instruments S-band passive homing. *Launch weight:* 390 lb. *Warhead:* H.E. *Dimensions:* Length, 10 ft. 0 in.; span, 3 ft. 6 in.; max. diam., 9 in. *Range* 8–9 mls. (6) **Nord AS.12:** *Propulsion:* One Nord solid-propellant rocket. *Guidance:* Wire (can be employed with semi-automatic infra-red tracking). *Launch weight:* 165 lb. *Warhead:* H.E. *Dimensions:* Length, 6 ft. 1½ in.; span, 2 ft. 1½ in.; max. diam., 7.1 in. *Range:* 4.6 mls. (7) **Nord AS.20:** *Propulsion:* Cordite-type boost and sustainer charges. *Guidance:* Visual radio command (line of sight) with optional optical aiming/infra-red guidance. *Launch weight:* 309 lb. *Warhead:* 66 lb. H.E. *Dimensions:* Length, 8 ft. 6 in.; span, 2 ft. 7 in.; max. diam., 9.9 in. *Range:* 4 mls. (8) **Nord AS.30:** *Propulsion:* Solid-propellant rocket. *Guidance:* Visual radio command (line of sight) with optional optical aiming/infra-red guidance. *Launch weight:* 1,146 lb. *Warhead:* 550 lb. H.E. *Dimensions:* Length, 12 ft. 8 in., span, 3 ft. 3 in.; max. diam., 13.4 in. *Range:* 7.5 mls.

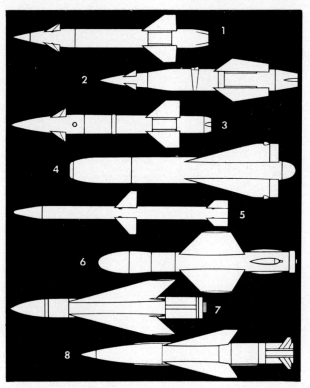

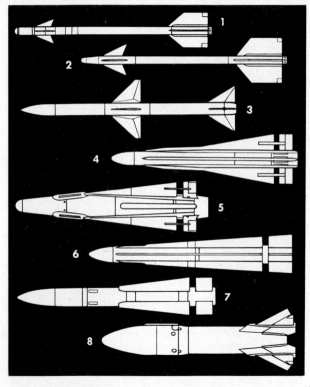

(1) **Philco AIM-9B Sidewinder 1A:** *Propulsion:* One Naval Propellant Plant solid-propellant rocket. *Guidance:* Philco infra-red homing. *Launch weight:* 160 lb. *Warhead:* 10 lb. H.E. *Dimensions:* Length, 9 ft. 4¾ in.; span, 1 ft. 9 in.; max. diam., 4.8 in. *Range:* 2.3 mls. (2) **NOTS AIM-9C/D Sidewinder 1C:** *Propulsion:* One Rocketdyne Mk.18-Mod-1 solid-propellant rocket. *Guidance:* (AIM-9C) Semi-active radar, (AIM-9D) infra-red homing. *Launch weight:* 187 lb. *Warhead:* H.E. *Dimensions:* Length, 9 ft. 6 in.; span, 2 ft. 0 in.; max. diam., 4.8 in. *Range:* 10 mls. (3) **Raytheon AIM-7E Sparrow III:** *Propulsion:* One Rocketdyne Mk.38-Mod-0 solid-propellant rocket. *Guidance:* Raytheon CW semi-active radar homing. *Launch weight:* 400 lb. *Warhead:* 60 lb. H.E. *Dimensions:* Length, 12 ft. 0 in.; span, 3 ft. 3½ in.; max. diam., 8 in. *Range:* 13.8 mls. (4) **Hughes AIM-4F Super Falcon:** *Propulsion:* One 6,000 lb. Thiokol M-46 solid-propellant rocket. *Guidance:* Infra-red homing. *Launch weight:* 145 lb. *Warhead:* 40 lb. H.E. *Dimensions:* Length, 6 ft. 11 in.; span, 2 ft. 0 in.; max. diam., 6.6 in. *Range:* 6 mls. (5) **Hughes AIM-26A Nuclear Falcon:** *Propulsion:* One Thiokol M-60 solid-propellant rocket. *Guidance:* Semi-active radar homing. *Launch weight:* 203 lb. *Warhead:* (-26A) Nuclear, (-26B) H.E. *Dimensions:* Length, 7 ft. 0 in.; span, 1 ft. 8 in.; max. diam., 11 in. *Range:* Not available. (6) **Hughes AIM-47A Falcon:** *Propulsion:* One Lockheed Propulsion solid-propellant rocket. *Guidance:* Infra-red and pulsed Doppler radar. *Launch weight:* 800 lb. *Warhead:* Interchangeable H.E. or nuclear. *Dimensions:* Length, 12 ft. 6 in.; span, 3 ft. 0 in.; max. diam., 13.2 in. *Range:* 115 mls. (7) **Hughes AIM-54A Phoenix:** *Propulsion:* One Rocketdyne solid-propellant rocket. *Guidance:* Radar homing. *Launch weight:* 1,000 lb. *Warhead:* H.E. *Dimensions:* Length, 13 ft. 0 in.; span, 3 ft.; max. diam., 15 in. *Range:* Not available. (8) **Douglas AIR-2A Genie:** *Propulsion:* One 36,000 lb. Aerojet solid-propellant rocket. *Guidance:* None. *Launch weight:* 835 lb. *Warhead:* 1.5 KT nuclear. *Dimensions:* Length, 9 ft. 7 in.; span, 3 ft. 3½ in.; max. diam., 17.4 in. *Range:* 5.75 mls.

both of these weapons fall short of modern interception needs. What is really wanted is a missile that can be launched from considerable ranges ahead, abeam, or below the target, so as to overcome any inferiority in fighter speed or altitude, and to enable interception to take place with the minimum of delay. Furthermore, the missile should be completely proof against jamming, and should destroy the bomber instantly. Whereas it might have been sufficient at one time to damage the target sufficiently to cause it to turn back for base, it is now of the utmost importance that the enemy should have no opportunity to arm and launch a stand-off nuclear weapon—the bomber must be obliterated without warning. It follows that a considerable weight of explosive is needed to achieve the necessary results. Instead of the 0.2 lb. of a 30-mm. cannon shell or the 2 lb. of an unguided rocket, a weight

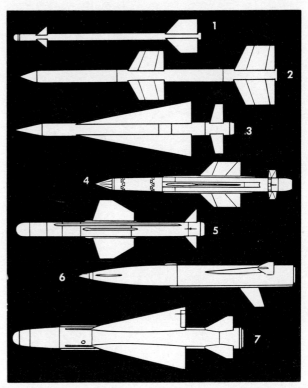

(1) **Atoll:** *Propulsion:* One solid-propellant rocket. *Guidance:* Infra-red homing. *Approx. launch weight:* 150 lb. *Warhead:* 7–10 lb. H.E. *Dimensions:* Not available. *Range:* 2–3 mls. (2) **Awl:** *Propulsion:* One solid-propellant rocket with booster. *Guidance:* Probably infra-red. *Launch weight:* Not available. *Warhead:* H.E. *Approximate dimensions:* Length, 15 ft.; span, 4 ft. 6 in.; max. diam., 10 in. *Approx. range:* 5 mls. (3) **Ash:** *Propulsion:* One solid-propellant rocket. *Guidance:* Probably infra-red. *Launch weight:* Not available. *Warhead:* H.E. *Approximate Dimensions:* Length, 10 ft.; span, 3 ft. 6 in.; max. diam., 9 in. *Range:* Not available. (4) **Hawker Siddeley Firestreak:** *Propulsion:* One solid-propellant rocket. *Guidance:* Infra-red. *Launch weight:* 300 lb. *Warhead:* H.E. *Dimensions:* Length, 10 ft. 5 in.; span, 2 ft. 5.4 in.; max. diam., 8.75 in. *Range:* 5 mls. (5) **Hawker Siddeley Red Top:** *Propulsion:* One solid-propellant rocket. *Guidance:* Infra-red. *Launch weight:* Not available. *Warhead:* H.E. *Dimensions:* Length, 11 ft. 5¾ in.; span, 2 ft. 11¾ in.; max. diam., 8.75 in. *Range:* 7 mls. (6) **MATRA R.511:** *Propulsion:* One 2-stage (1st stage 3,530 lb. and 2nd stage 440 lb.) Hotchkiss-Brandt solid-propellant rocket. *Guidance:* Semi-active radar. *Launch weight:* 396 lb. *Warhead:* 55 lb. H.E. *Dimensions:* Length, 10 ft. 1½ in.; span, 3 ft. 3½ in.; max. diam., 10.25 in. *Range:* 4.5 mls. (7) **MATRA R.530:** *Propulsion:* One 18,740 lb. 2-stage Hotchkiss-Brandt solid-propellant rocket. *Guidance:* Semi-active radar or infra-red. *Launch weight:* 429 lb. *Warhead:* 60 lb. H.E. *Dimensions:* Length, 10 ft. 9¼ in.; span, 3 ft. 7¼ in.; max. diam., 10.25 in. *Range:* 3.7 mls.

(Above) The 200 "black boxes" of the F-106A Delta Dart's MA-1 system arrayed behind the interceptor's armament of two AIM-4E Falcon radar homers (upright) and two AIM-4F Falcon infra-red homers (horizontal). The infra-red search and tracking system can be seen immediately ahead of the windscreen.

of 20 lb. is the minimum usable, and then only if delivered with fantastic accuracy!

As in the case of air-to-surface missiles, the easiest method of control is to use command guidance, the pilot merely passing left/right and up/down corrections to the weapon over a microwave link, while the signals are turned into fin movements by reference to a gyro aligned with the fighter's axes prior to launch.

This system can be very effective in short-range line-astern attacks in clear daylight conditions against a steady unescorted target, and it is difficult to jam the guidance link because the missile antenna can have a very high gain (i.e., it only accepts signals coming from the direction of the launching aircraft). On the other hand, the interceptor may be shot down by escorting fighters while it is committed to a steady course, and efficient attacks from ahead or abeam demand range information, which can be denied by the bomber's counter-measures. In addition, it has been argued that this concept is unsuitable for single-seat fighters, due to the double task of flying the aircraft and controlling the missile, and the rate of firing is obviously low. Command guidance is, however, used on the 315-lb. Nord **AA 20,** or **Type 5103,** which is still employed by training units of the *Armée de l'Air* and by Aquilon and Etendard squadrons of France's *Aéronavale.* In addition, the early Russian **Alkali** missile, seen on the Sukhoi Su-9, MiG-17, and MiG-19, may well use guidance of this type, but has probably now been removed from service.

Beam riding is a development of command guidance in which the pilot merely aims his aircraft at the target by means of the normal gunsight, and the missile flies down a specially modulated radar beam aligned with the fighter axis. The radar signal is received by an antenna at the rear of the missile (which incidentally permits a nicely streamlined forebody), and examined for frequency modulation and phase shift, from which the missile's position relative to the beam axis is deduced, allowing appropriate corrective action to be taken. In principle, this makes matters easier for the fighter pilot, permits a higher firing rate, and could presumably be developed for beam attacks somewhat more readily than command guidance. Unfortunately it retains most of the disadvantages of the latter approach, perhaps the most important being unsuitability for manoeuvring targets, and lack of accuracy at long range. Both of the systems discussed above are based on correcting guidance errors as they appear from the position of the fighter, so that miss distances increase with firing

Rocket launcher pods produced by Engins MATRA have been adopted for some two score aircraft types, and examples of these launchers are the Type 120 (inboard) and Type 181 (outboard) beneath a G.91R wing (right), and (below, right) Type 125 launchers on the same aircraft.

range. For instance, if the average weapon misses by 10 ft. when fired from 1,000 yards, the miss distance from 3,000 yards will be 30 ft. which would require an extremely heavy warhead to achieve worthwhile effect. The main example of the beam rider is the British **Fireflash**, which was evaluated by the R.A.F. and relegated to GW training duties with a Swift Mk.7 squadron.

In view of the severe limitations on missiles using these simpler forms of guidance, attention has turned to various types of homing weapons, which place less restraint on the fighter after launch, can be used effectively against manoeuvring targets, and have miss distances virtually independent of firing range. The method of steering used is termed "proportional navigation", which is derived from the old mariner's rule that if another vessel maintains a constant bearing, then there will be either a collision, or the two are travelling on parallel courses at the same speed. In practice the missile is made to turn so that the target's bearing is fixed, by applying lateral accelerations proportional to the rate of change of target bearing. Since the computation is based purely on the relative bearing of the bomber without regard to range, conventional jamming has no effect aside from making it difficult for the fighter to compute whether the bomber is within firing range.

Aside from the optical homing system tested in the MATRA **R.511,** the main forms of guidance in this category are radar and infra-red. Radar homers may be either fully- or semi-active, the former acting as both transmitter and receiver, while the latter relies on the fighter radar illuminating the target. The fully-active radar weapon has the advantage that the launch aircraft can break off immediately the weapon is released, but its guidance range is limited by the small size of radar dish, and its bad-weather performance may be restricted by the short-wavelength emission

(Left) The immense variety of ordnance loads that may be carried by a modern tactical fighter is graphically illustrated by this photo of an F-4C Phantom II with the various external stores that it can carry. The missiles are Bullpups, Sparrow IIIs and Sidewinders, and the stores in the third row from the nose of the aircraft are Minigun pods.

required by this small dish. In contrast, a semi-active missile benefits from the larger dish of the fighter radar to operate on longer wavelengths and to produce a greater range. Both types of radar guidance are theoretically capable of all-round attacks, but their use at low altitude is affected by ground return, and their miss distance is spoiled by radar "glint". This phenomenon results in the radar missile seeing its target not as a single point reflecting transmissions, but more as a "great shivering jelly covered in sequins", the missile first being attracted by one part, then another. In contrast, the infra-red weapon will normally see only the jetpipe, and in the case of a multi-engined aircraft it will home on to one particular nozzle! The miss-distance is consequently much reduced, and the weapon has the additional advantage of less interference at low level, but infra-red will not penetrate cloud, and therefore some back-up armament is normally required. It also has the drawback that all-round attacks are only feasible if the target is hot (i.e., flying at high supersonic speeds).

Although by no means the best of the infra-red homers, the **AIM-9 Sidewinder** is almost undoubtedly the simplest, cheapest, and most ingenious. Developed by NOTS at China Lake, this missile was first fired in September 1953, and has now been produced in massive quantities (well over 60,000 examples of the **AIM-9B Sidewinder 1A** alone) by Philco, General Electric, and licences in Germany and Japan, for use by over fifteen air forces and navies. The **Sidewinder** is unusually light (160 lb.), and can be handled much as a normal round of ammunition. Most of the secrets of the original production version are now known to the Communist world, but it remains a highly classified piece of equipment, and less technical information has been made public than

(*Right*) *A Saab 305A* (*Robot 05A*) *test round mounted beneath a Saab 35A Draken being used in the development programme of this missile. Primarily a clear-weather air-to-surface weapon, the Rb 05A can also be used for the interception of certain flying targets. Possessing a Swedish-design proximity-fused warhead and a Saab-designed microwave radio link, the Rb 05A is guided by a pilot-operated stick, the pilot keeping a tracking flare on the missile on the line of sight to the target.*

on more sophisticated missiles such as the **Firestreak.** However, one item which is apparent from external examination, and which serves to illustrate the ingenuity that went into the design, is the use of wind-driven gyroscopes on the aileron tips. The effect of these novel devices is to sense any rolling motion and automatically apply a corrective aileron angle, thus eliminating one entire branch of the normal servo-control system. Other simplifying concepts have been used throughout the weapon, and it might be assumed from this approach that the final performance is substantially degraded as a result, but this is not borne out by experience. The **Sidewinder** proved its effectiveness firstly in 1958 when Chinese MiG-17s were shot down in the Quemoy area, and again later, under tragic circumstances, when a B-52 was accidentally destroyed as a result of a training mishap. Still more recently, in April 1966, a Phantom II shot down the first MiG-21 over North Vietnam with two of three **Sidewinders** launched.

Although the Quemoy encounter vindicated U.S. faith in this rather primitive weapon, it had one disastrous consequence in that one **Sidewinder** buried itself in the fuselage of a MiG without exploding and was carried back for exhibition in Peking (or so it is widely believed). If true, this reflected badly on the missile as it then was, since it implied that failures had occurred in the prox-

imity fuse, contact fuse, and self-destruct systems! Be that as it may, the fact is that within two years Russia had produced a very similar weapon, code-named **Atoll,** with the same canard layout, but apparently powered by a somewhat more slender rocket motor. Examination of these weapons mounted on the MiG-21 reveals that not only is the **Atoll** virtually identical with the **Sidewinder** in all basic features, but this also applies to the design of the launching shoe, and such minor items as the safety device to render the warhead inert while the aircraft is on the ground.

The British opposite number to the **Sidewinder 1A** is the Hawker Siddeley Dynamics **Firestreak,** which employs none of the short-cut techniques of the American missile, and is consequently more effective in certain respects, but far more expensive, costing perhaps £11,000 or $30,000 in comparison with **Sidewinder's** £850 or $2,400. Like most infra-red homers, it is a tail-attack weapon, limited to firings in a narrow cone from which it can look down the target's jetpipe to the hot parts of the engine. Its main advantages over **Sidewinder** are probably that it carries a much heavier warhead, places far less restriction on fighter manoeuvring at launch, and that it is able to home on to a bomber seen against a bright background, thanks to its use of more advanced infra-red technology. The French equivalent is the MATRA **R.530,** which

(Above) AIM-9 Sidewinder AAMs mounted on an F-8D Crusader. Undoubtedly the most widely used of all air-to-air missiles, the Sidewinder has no more electronic components than a domestic radio and only a score or so of moving parts. It has been adapted for surface-to-air application as the Chaparral.

may alternatively be fitted with semi-active radar homing, and which is employed by the Mirage IIIC, the R.A.A.F. Mirage IIIO, and the French *Aéronavale* F-8E(FN) Crusader. Infra-red guidance is also the basis of the **AIM-4C Falcon**, which weighs somewhat less than the **Sidewinder**, and is a more compact design for internal stowage on U.S.A.F. Air Defence Command aircraft such as the F-101 and F-102. The current production version is designated **AIM-4F** or **HM-58**, and is in service with the U.S.A.F., the R.C.A.F., and the Swedish Air Force. In the last case, the missile is designated **Rb 28,** and mounted on the J 35F Draken in combination with the **Rb 27 (AIM-4E** or **HM-55)** semi-active radar version, which has also been selected for the Swiss Mirage IIIS. Probably the most advanced infra-red homer in the world is the Hawker Siddeley Dynamics **Red Top** equipping R.A.F.

Lightning F. Mk.6s, which is capable of all-round attacks on high speed targets. This operational flexibility may, however, be rivalled by the latest **Sidewinder 1C (AIM-9D),** which is also being built with an alternative semi-active radar head (**AIM-9C**).

Promising to rival Sidewinder's success in universal acceptance is the **AIM-7E Sparrow III,** utilising semi-active radar homing. This weapon has been in service with the U.S. Navy's Phantom II for several years, and has now been ordered for U.S.A.F. and British versions of the same aircraft, the latter order apparently amounting to 2,500 rounds. Further evidence of the **Sparrow's** future is provided by its selection as standard armament for the F-104S Starfighter for the Italian Air Force, and the U.S. Navy has initiated development of a more advanced version, the **AIM-7F,** with an improved warhead and new motor. Semi-active guidance is also the basis of the **AIM-26B** nuclear **Falcon** arming Air Defence Command F-102s. The development of fully-active radar missiles now appears to have been abandoned in view of the limited ranges obtainable, but may possibly be resurrected as the terminal phase of a multi-stage guidance system.

Looking into the future, air-to-air missiles will require longer ranges, which in turn will demand very sophisticated types of guidance. One example of this forthcoming generation is the Hughes **AIM-47A** weapon, derived from the **Falcon** and fitted to the Lockheed YF-12A Mach 3.0 interceptor. If reports of a 100-mile range capability are well founded, then the weapon is almost certainly initially guided by course-setting commands fed in from the fighter's computer prior to release, while terminal homing is a hybrid system of infra-red and coherent pulse Doppler radar. A similar hybrid guidance system is believed to be used by the U.S. Navy's **AIM-54A Phoenix,** six of which will be carried by the F-111B. Development of the Rocketdyne solid-propellant rocket motor for the **Phoenix** was reportedly troubled by temperature and vibration problems in 1966, however, which may delay service introduction of this weapon, the development programme having already slipped one year.

BOMBER DEVELOPMENT

WITH the dropping of the first atomic bomb on Hiroshima in 1945 the manned bomber became—at least for a time—the most important of all aircraft. There grew out of this a number of élite service branches: Strategic Air Command in the U.S.A., the *Aviatsiya Dalnovo Deistviya* in Russia, the V-Force in Britain, and the *Forces Aériennes Stratégiques* in France. Run on a quasi-wartime basis so that they could respond to attack in a matter of minutes, these commands became the spoiled children of their governments, with the best of men and material lavished upon them. In terms of effectiveness, the U.S.A.F.'s S.A.C. has undoubtedly been the leader, and shows every indication of retaining this position. Having learned a painful lesson at Pearl Harbour, the U.S.A. is determined never to be caught with its aircraft on the ground again, and a proportion of SAC's force was therefore always in the air, with nuclear weapons in the bomb-bays, and targets already assigned until mid-1966 when it was decided that there would be sufficient warning of a missile attack to get the bombers airborne. If any single factor is responsible for the fact that the Communists have attempted no widespread aggression during the past twenty years, then the credit almost certainly belongs to these American bombers.

However, in the opinion of many informed observers, the supremacy of the strategic bomber is now approaching its end. The development of surface-to-air missiles effective up to more than 60,000 ft. has forced the two super-powers to cut back on bomber development and build hundreds of ICBMs for burial in underground silos, where they would be virtually immune from attack, and whence they could strike with relatively negligible risk of interception. To remain a viable means of attack, the remaining bombers have been obliged to drop from economical cruise altitudes to a mere few hundred feet, where their lightly-built structure is buffeted by turbulence and their range is reduced to perhaps one-third of normal values. New designs have admittedly been proposed that are intended specifically for flight at high speeds and low level, smoothing out the gusts by using well-swept, short-span wings, but these can still only offer a radius of a few hundred miles: the deep strategic targets can nowadays only be reached by missiles. Pending a breakthrough in nuclear propulsion, it thus appears that the bomber will become relegated to tactical missions and brush-fire wars, where its ability to deliver a heavy load of explosive at minimal cost, and to carry out reconnaissance duties, give it a significant advantage over the missile.

The period immediately after the end of World War II saw the principal bomber forces on terms of technical parity, with Britain abandoning its own Lincoln in favour of the Boeing B-29 (re-named the Washington), and the Soviet Union copying the B-29s which had landed on their territory after raids on Japan. Known as the Tu-4, and allotted the NATO code-name of "Bull", this aircraft represented a tremendous improvement over indigenous designs, not only on account of its sheer size, but also for its economical engines, pressurised crew compartments, and General Electric fire control. This system enabled the numerous barbettes to be directed from remote aiming windows, and was clearly used as the basis for the defensive armament of all succeeding Russian bomber designs up to the supersonic "Blinder".

The first major phase in development beyond the B-29 set an extremely difficult problem, since the attainment of greater ranges (which were necessary for deep penetration into the Soviet Union, or conversely to attack the prime metropolitan areas of the U.S.A. over the Arctic) was incompatible with the high fuel consumption of the turbojet engines required to give the bomber a reasonable chance of evading interception. In Britain the decision was deferred until more economical engines such as the Rolls-Royce Avon became available, which was a logical approach in view of the preoccupation with a war in Europe. The U.S., having just fought a war in the Pacific, and faced with the possibility of a war that excluded Europe, had to match any range that Soviet bombers might achieve, and therefore produced the ultimate in piston-engined bombers, the Convair B-36. Designed to the unprecedented specification of a 10,000-mile range with a 10,000-lb. bomb load, the B-36 grossed over 300,000 lb., eventually rising to 410,000 lb., and managed for a time to elude U.S. interceptors during defence exercises by virtue of the extreme altitude conferred by its moderate wing loading and high aspect ratio. Whether this immense target would have had equal success against the MiG-15, which entered service in 1948, is open to dispute. Perhaps Russia's late start in the field of radar, coupled with the B-36's powerful defensive armament and use of counter-measures, would have given the bomber some degree of immunity.

The Soviet Union's own approach to heavy bomber development was to delay procurement of advanced designs until the mid-1950's, although the Il-28 light bomber had meantime gone ahead, and at least one heavyweight project, the Tupolev Tu-85, had appeared with straight wings and four VD-4K turboprops. The aircraft that became the mainstay of the strategic bombing force was the Tupolev Tu-20, which employed a unique combination of swept wings and turboprop power. This idea was completely ignored in the West because the swept wing was always held to be pointless at speeds below Mach 0.75, while propellors were felt to be inoperable above this speed due to shock losses on the supersonic tips. An unusual amount is known about this particular design because the engines were the responsibility of a team of expatriate German engineers who had previously worked at Junkers and the Bayerische Motoren Werke during the war, and were subsequently allowed to return to the West after the details of engine performance had lost their military intelligence value. It appears that the original design objective was a speed of Mach 0.85 at 36,000 ft., but US. intelligence sources now put the Tu-20's speed over the target at only Mach 0.76, and, in fact, when two of these aircraft were intercepted over Alaska in March 1964 they were only cruising at Mach 0.67. On balance, it appears that

Western technicians may have underestimated the potential of the propellor to some extent, but the Tu-20 would still have been an easy target for the F-89s and F-102s of the U.S.A.F. Air Defense Command. It might be concluded that the turboprop bomber was accepted by the *Aviatsiya Dalnovo Deistviya* merely because this was the only way to achieve the 4,500-mile radius to cover Los Angeles, Chicago, and New York without reliance on an immense tanker fleet. However, whatever the shortcomings of this design in regard to speed, its range was later to prove invaluable for maritime reconnaissance, making it a threat to major naval units at several thousand miles from Soviet bases. At the same time, it became the basis for the Tu-114 transport, which has been a major factor in upholding Soviet technological prestige, making possible non-stop flights between Moscow and Havana in support of the Castro regime.

LIGHT BOMBERS

While the poor economy of early turbojets held up the development of pure jet bombers for strategic duties, no such restriction applied to the design of tactical aircraft, and new designs in this class soon appeared in response to requirements issued immediately after the end of the war. The first successful projects were the Ilyushin Il-28, the Tupolev Tu-14, and the North American B-45 Tornado, which all flew in 1947 and combined straight wings of moderate aspect ratio with first-generation turbojets slung underneath. The four-engined B-45 was a rather large aircraft for tactical duties weighing normally 82,600 lb. at take-off, and was only produced in small quantity. The twin-engined Il-28, on the other hand, became the standard light bomber for most air forces in the Communist Bloc. Powered by the Klimov VK-1 engine evolved from the Rolls-Royce Nenes exported to Russia in 1947, it was a very fruitful example of straightforward engineering, retaining a useful potency even as late as 1962, when the U.S. insisted on the withdrawal of these aircraft from Cuba along with the Shyster MRBMs, and evoking even more concern recently, in

1966, by their mere presence in some numbers on Hainan, within striking distance of the South Vietnamese capital of Saigon. The contemporary Tu-14, although generally believed less effective than the I1-28, was, nevertheless, adopted by Russia's naval air arm.

The Canberra flew at the end of 1949, and lacked both the ground-mapping radar and rear gun turret of its opposite numbers, but its low wing loading conferred a useful ceiling and manoeuvrability at altitude, while its low aspect ratio straight wing and clean lines resulted in a somewhat better critical Mach Number. Whether these qualities would have put it beyond the reach of the MiG-15 is debatable, since only the later photo-reconnaissance versions of the Canberra could have exceeded the 52,000 ft. ceiling of the Russian fighter. On the other hand the Canberra proved appreciably better than the U.S. light bomber projects of the period, and was selected for licence-production by Martin as the U.S.A.F.'s B-57. Aside from performance improvements arising from revised airframe sealing and slightly more powerful engines, the aircraft was extensively redesigned to provide more capability in the nocturnal interdiction role. Modifications included a revamped front fuselage with tandem seating for the two crew members, plus wing pylons, provision for eight 0.5-in. machine guns or four 20-mm. cannon in the wing, and a rotary bomb door. In Britain, development aimed at similar types of operation resulted in the Canberra B.(I).Mk.8, which retained the basic contours of the original three-seater nose, but had the pilot seated to port under a fighter-type canopy, and the second crew member located in the nose. Provision was also made for underwing stores, and for a detachable bomb-bay pack to contain four 20-mm. guns.

The French equivalent was the Sud-Aviation Vautour, a rather lighter design grossing normally 33,000 lb. in comparison with the Canberra's 51,000 lb. Intended from the outset to fulfil the roles of level bomber, close support aircraft, and all-weather interceptor with relatively minor changes to the basic aircraft, the Vautour utilised a swept wing which gave it transonic performance in dives. At the end of 1952, when the first of this type left the ground, the same stage had been reached by the 70,000-lb. swept-wing Douglas A-3 Skywarrior, which equips Heavy Attack Squadrons of the U.S. Navy. This aircraft will provide a nuclear capability on *Essex* and *Midway* class carriers throughout the 'sixties, and its closest equivalent in the Royal Navy is the Buccaneer, which is regarded in some quarters as a natural replacement for the Canberra. Aimed at high speed penetrations and blind attacks, the

(Right) Powered by two Klimov VK-1 centrifugal-type turbojets, the Tupolev Tu-14, known as the "Bosun" in the West, is a contemporary of the Il-28, but was only adopted by the Soviet naval air arm, the Morskaya Aviatsiya. Carrying four crew members, the Tu-14 entered service in 1949, and internal weapons loads include two torpedoes or four 1,000-lb. bombs. It is unlikely that many Tu-14s now remain in service.

(Left) The Sud-Aviation SO-4050 Vautour II.1B two-seat light bomber was one of three versions of the basic Vautour design manufactured. Forty Vautour II bombers were produced, these having an internal weapons bay capable of accommodating three 1,000-lb., six 750-lb. or 500-lb., or nine 200-lb. bombs, and four underwing pylons can each carry a Nord AS.30 ASM. Powered by two 7,720 lb.s.t. SNECMA Atar 101E-3 turbojets, the Vautour has a maximum speed of 685 m.p.h. at sea level.

Buccaneer features an Area Rule airframe, highly economical Rolls-Royce Spey turbofan engines, rotary weapons bay, nose radar, and a heavily loaded wing with flap blowing for low speeds. For land-based operation, a twin-barrel rocket motor can be fitted to give an additional thrust of 8,000 lb for 30 seconds. The only known Soviet design in this category to have achieved service status is the Yakovlev "Brewer", a high performance derivative of the Yak-25 series of aircraft. The "Brewer" is a replacement for the I1-28 discussed earlier, and achieves a reasonably short take-off run by virtue of two afterburning engines of the type used on the MiG-21. It effectively combines the very useful glazed nose of the Canberra with the radar mapping of the Buccaneer, by housing the radar in a ventral fairing below the pilot's cockpit. Whereas the far larger A-3 Skywarrior has space for a tricycle undercarriage to retract into the fuselage, and the Buccaneer is able to enclose the main gear in a thickened wing root, the "Brewer" employs a bicycle landing gear (as does also the Vautour) which makes it impossible to rotate the aircraft for unstick, and requires touch-down to be very carefully controlled in attitude.

One of the main stumbling-blocks in bomber development has been the difficulty of releasing weapons at high speed. Trials showed that the traditional bomb-bay with edge-hinged doors resulted in excessive drag, large pitching moments, unacceptable buffeting on the stores and airframe, and non-positive separation of the bomb. In the worst case, the weapon might batter around the interior before falling clear and missing the target by a considerable margin. A somewhat cleaner approach is to use bomb-bay doors that retract, rather than extending into the slipstream, and this has been done on aircraft such as the Canberra, Valiant and Victor, while the Breguet Atlantic has doors that slide over the outside of the fuselage. Further improvement can be effected by forcible ejection, either using the energy from a cartridge, or swinging the bomb clear of the bay on a parallelogram linkage before releasing it. Buffeting in the bay itself can be minimised by aerodynamic fixes at either end; for instance the A-3 Skywarrior has a spoiler or anti-buffet rake ahead of the bay, linked with the door actuation mechanism. However, these schemes are only minor variations on the traditional approach: a much more satisfactory performance can be achieved by the use of a rotary bay. This idea was patented by Martin and applied to the XB-51 project abandoned in favour of the Americanised Canberra in 1951. Other applications have included the B-57, the Buccaneer, and the P6M SeaMaster flying boat.

The rotary door certainly presents a far cleaner depression to the airflow, and it has the advantage that turn-around between flights can be speeded by the use of pre-loaded weapon doors, but this system may not be ideal for supersonic release. One solution might be to eject bombs through snap-action doors, but this is probably an inflexible arrangement in terms of bomb size. The most revolutionary approach so far attempted was the "linear" bomb-bay of the A-5 Vigilante, in which the weapon was carried between the two J79 engines and ejected through the base area below the fin, the end of the tunnel being covered by a jettisonable fairing to minimise the drag of the aircraft on the way out to the target. The bomb was located at the forward end of this tunnel, and two 275 U.S. gallon tanks stood directly behind it, all three stores being rigidly interconnected. These tanks were the first to be emptied in the strike mission, and on reaching the objective the whole bomb-tank assembly was ejected rearwards along rails by means of a catapult, the empty tanks acting as a stabilising tail for the weapon.

This scheme was highly ingenious, but it was finally abandoned

and all Vigilantes converted to the reconnaissance role. The reasoning behind this decision is not hard to visualise: loading the bomb into the tunnel must have been a relatively slow process, access rather poor, and the system was basically too inflexible for anything other than nuclear wars. In addition, there may have been something of a fuel-leak hazard in the weapon bay, and the bomb-tank assembly may have been broken up by the jet exhausts. However, in spite of the failure of the weapon delivery system, the A-5 has a number of advanced features which are likely to be employed on future high performance projects. These include the dorsal fuel tank which forms a rearward extension of the canopy lines on later Vigilantes, the high-lift wing with blowing on both the leading- and trailing-edges, and a rolling tailpiece to provide lateral control, as was later used on the TSR-2.

STRATEGIC BOMBERS
Although the B-47 did not have the highest performance of the first generation of strategic turbojet bombers, it was the most

(*Right*) *Although the Douglas B-26 Invader light bomber was withdrawn from U.S.A.F. service some two years ago owing to structural fatigue, this type remains in first-line service with the air arms of Chile, Colombia, Indonesia, Nicaragua, and Peru, and in its refurbished B-26K version with the Congo and Laos. The B-26 illustrated belongs to No. 1 Squadron of Indonesia's air arm. A number of B-26s have been rebuilt recently with reinforced centre spar sections and R-3350 engines in place of the original R-2800s.*

important historically as the jumping-off point for Boeing's progress to the immense B-52 Stratofortress, and through the C-135 series to the 707 commercial transport and possibly on to the SST. As explained earlier, the problem facing designers in the late 'forties was to achieve long ranges in spite of the high fuel consumption of the engines available, a difficulty that could only be alleviated by producing the lowest possible structure weight and the highest possible lift/drag ratio. If the critical Mach Number was to be reasonably high, the wing had to be swept back, but this restricted the aspect ratio (and hence the lift/drag ratio) through tip stalling. The greater the aspect ratio, the more aerodynamically efficient the wing in the cruise, but the greater the tendency for boundary layer air to drift outboard and stagnate at the tips, causing premature separations at low speeds or very high altitudes. In addition, the high aspect ratio so essential in cruise normally resulted in a severe penalty in structure weight. Boeing's approach was to use more sweep and a higher aspect ratio than many experts thought practical, and then to add six engines slung in four pods under the wing, using the engine installations to improve both aerodynamics and structure weight. Firstly, the pods and associated pylons acted as fences to stop the spanwise flow of boundary layer. Secondly, the weight of the engines produced inertia loads which acted to damp out flutter of the wings, which could consequently be built less stiff and hence far lighter than normal.

Partly because of its radical nature, the B-47 was slow to enter service, finally being issued to the 206th (Medium) Bomber Wing in mid-1951. It went on to be produced to the tune of approximately 2,030 machines, but the number on strength was gradually decreased from the peak of 1,800 in 1957 to half that figure in 1962, and the type was completely phased out in 1966. While it still represented the backbone of the SAC in the late 1950s, the B-47 was switched to the low level attack mode, and immediately encountered fatigue cracking in various parts of the structure, but especially at the vital wing-fuselage attachments. In order to increase their safe lives by 3,000 hours, eighteen hundred B-47s

were put through "Project Milk Bottle", which involved strengthening the inboard wings, adding doubler plates near the roots, and considerable improvements to the attachments themselves (the project being named after the shape of the new pins by which the wings were fastened to the fuselage).

Aside from extending the life of the B-47s, this programme also enabled them to carry out the special manoeuvres necessary to deliver nuclear weapons safely from very low altitudes. The simplest technique was the LABS (Low Altitude Bombing System) manoeuvre, which merely involved flying directly over the target, pulling up into a half loop at constant "g", and releasing at perhaps 70° to the horizontal. In a typical LABS (or over-the-shoulder) attack, the bomber might roll out at 15,000 ft. and the bomb carry on up to 22,000 ft. before falling back and exploding over the target. This produced an accurate delivery with the minimum demands on aircraft systems, but it gave defences around the target too much time for shooting down the bomber before it climbed to the release point. For this reason, it became the practice to compute the range to the target during the run-in, and pull up well short, releasing the bomb to carry on forward either at a shallow angle (long toss), or more accurately in a short toss at a steeper angle.

R.A.F. Bomber Command was quick to adopt American delivery techniques, but the British approach to strategic bomber design was far more conservative, beginning with the straight-wing Short Sperrin, virtually a 115,000-lb. scaled-up Canberra, which flew in 1951 as a precaution against the failure of the three V-bombers. The Valiant was somewhat faster than the B-47 (Mach 0.82, compared with Mach 0.75), but only weighed 175,000 lb. in comparison with the B-47E's 220,000 lb. It flew slightly earlier in 1951 than the Sperrin, and entered service in 1955, being later relegated to photographic reconnaissance and tanker duties. It was withdrawn from service due to wing spar fatigue at the end of 1964, with an average airframe life of only 2,500 hours. The Valiant benefitted from compound sweep in having sufficiently deep roots to bury its four Avon engines, and was thus quite clean aerodynamically, but its structure weight lacked the B-47's advantage of a flexible wing. Compound sweep was carried even further on the crescent-wing Victor, which flew in 1952 and was issued to the service in 1957. As a result of careful grading of thickness/chord ratio and wing sweep, the drag rise was considerably delayed, and the Victor is reputed to cruise at Mach 0.94 at up to 55,000 ft. Later production aircraft were modified to carry the Blue Steel missile, and were fitted with chaff-dispensers in the form of Whitcomb bodies on the upper wing surface. In 1965, the Victor Mk.1 was relegated to flight-refuelling duties to replace the Valiant.

The Vulcan progressed on virtually the same timescale as the Victor, but employed a delta wing which gave more fuel volume, a higher ceiling, and possibly a longer fatigue life through its inherent rigidity. Although this aircraft may well represent the ultimate in subsonic bombers in terms of speed and altitude, its unrefuelled radius of 2,300 miles is only some 15 per cent better than that of the B-47. The two bombers are in roughly the same weight category, but the Vulcan has 80,000 lb. of thrust compared to the 36,000 lb. of the B-47, the associated weight of powerplant obviously cutting heavily into the fuel carried, and thus largely offsetting the potential gains of the more economical twin-spool Olympus turbojets. Engines of the same thrust as the Olympus were developed by the Russians for their long-range bombers, but it is believed that the four-jet Myasishchev Mya-4 was only produced in token quantity in view of progress in ballistic missiles and the failure of this aircraft to attain sufficient range to threaten U.S. targets. The twin-engined Tupolev Tu-16, on the other hand, was manufactured in much the same quantities as the B-47, which it also resembled in weight and performance, although the range of the Tupolev design is believed to have been somewhat less.

The turbojet bombers already discussed would have been adequate for a war in Europe, but none approached the range of the B-36. In the search for a B-36 replacement, the U.S.A.F. considered two projects—the Convair YB-60 and the Boeing YB-52—which were very similar in design, although the YB-60 had the advantage of a normal wing-mounted main undercarriage, compared with the YB-52's bicycle arrangement of quadruple gears. Although the Convair aircraft also had the practical asset of retaining many sub-assemblies from the B-36, the verdict went to the Boeing design, which subsequently proved to be an outstanding weapon system. Since the B-52's entry into service in 1955 it has been continually improved, the latest version (B-52H) having turbofan engines, a Vulcan gun for rear defence, Quail decoys, Hound Dog defence-suppression missiles, and a structure which has been considerably revised to improve fatigue life at low levels. With a maximum loaded weight little short of 500,000 lb., the B-52H can achieve the remarkable unrefuelled high-altitude radius of approximately 5,000 miles, i.e., over twice that of the best V-bomber.

SUPERSONIC DESIGNS

If the attainment of really long ranges was difficult for subsonic turbojet bombers, it is well nigh impossible for their supersonic counterparts, which can only aim for lift/drag ratios of 7–8 in comparison with the B-52's 18, and which have engines of possibly three times the cruise specific fuel consumption. As a result of these difficulties, plus the vulnerability of high-flying aircraft to surface-launched missiles, and the comparative ease with which nuclear warheads can be delivered by ICBMs, most supersonic bomber programmes have been abandoned, and the few successful projects have only been manufactured in limited quantities.

The Soviet Union built only prototypes of the Myasishchev Bounder, a 300,000-lb. bomber intended to reach a modest supersonic speed on four unreheated 28,660 lb. turbojets. In 1959, this aircraft set up a number of load-carrying records (including one flight with a load of 121,760 lb.), but its airframe clearly lacked the subtle design required for supersonic cruising, and although afterburning was later fitted to the inboard engines, its performance did not warrant production. A British project

The Myasishchev-designed strategic bomber known as the "Bounder" in the West existed in several versions but failed to attain service status. This type was capable of short-duration supersonic dash performance but normally operated at subsonic speeds.

which was cancelled before it left the drawing-board was the Avro 730, a canard bomber designed to meet OR 330 and intended for service in 1964. Powered by eight Armstrong Siddeley P.176 turbojets clustered in two mid-span pods, the 730 would have cruised at Mach 2.5 and 65,000 ft. for a range of almost 3,000 miles. Had it not been axed in the famous 1957 White Paper, its costs would certainly have reached astronomical proportions, but it might have provided invaluable information for the Concorde SST.

The first successful example of the supersonic bomber was the B-58 Hustler, a 165,000-lb. delta-wing aircraft which entered service in 1960 with an arbitrary cruise limitation of Mach 2. Perhaps the most remarkable aspect of its design is the structure weight of only 14 per cent gross (about half the normal percentage) which is achieved partly through carrying one-quarter of the fuel in a jettisonable nuclear bomb pod under the fuselage. The B-58's unrefuelled radius is, however, limited to 1,200 miles including a 500-mile Mach 2.0 dash, and production was consequently

stopped at 116 aircraft and a cost of £1,145m. or $3,306m. The area-ruled Tupolev "Blinder" is probably slightly heavier than the B-58, and its swept wings should produce a better subsonic range, but it is thought to be only capable of Mach 1.4 at altitude. France's *Forces Aériennes Stratégiques* is based on the Mirage IVA, which is a smaller and more straightforward design, grossing only 70,000 lb., but it is capable of more than Mach 2.0, and a subsonic radius of over 1,200 miles. Sixty-two of these aircraft have been ordered, and the type entered service early in 1965, backed by twelve Boeing C-135Fs for flight refuelling.

The future course for bomber development is difficult to foresee, although variable-sweep wings and jet lift may well be used to improve airfield performance. The main issue is, however, whether a high-flying hypersonic aircraft is any less vulnerable than one cruising at marginally supersonic speed over the treetops. Britain's 100,000-lb. TSR-2 was designed to exploit the low-level defence loophole, combining a gust-damping, heavily-loaded delta wing and the most advanced contour-following equipment in the world. America's 525,000-lb. B-70 Valkyrie took the alternative approach of Mach 3.0 and 75,000 ft., using the compression-lift principle to improve lift/drag ratio, and turn-down wingtips for supersonic directional stability, but this too was abandoned, serving only in the research role. The SAC has now accepted a bomber version of the variable geometry F-111, the FB-111, for service from 1969–70, but as replacement for its G and H model B-52s and B-58s, the U.S.A.F. is still intent on an entirely new project known as AMSA (Advanced Manned Strategic Aircraft). As currently envisaged, the AMSA is in the size range of the Boeing B-47, will weigh 325,000 lb., and combine the performance of the FB-111 with the bomb load of the B-52: truly an intriguing prospect! Speed at altitude will be of the order of Mach 2.5, sufficient electronic penetration aids being carried to permit successful strikes against targets deep within the Soviet Union, and maximum payload of conventional weapons will be 128 750-lb. bombs.

(Right) A B-52G-80 Stratofortress (57-6480) in the camouflage finish applied to some Stratofortresses employed for operations over S.E. Asia. One hundred and ninety-three examples of the B-52G were manufactured, this being the first model of the Stratofortress to embody redesigned vertical tail surfaces. The B-52G and the later B-52H are scheduled to remain in U.S.A.F. Strategic Air Command service until the mid 'seventies. There are currently 38 B-52 Wings (one Wing having two squadrons and the remainder each having one squadron) but three one-squadron Wings will be disbanded by July 1967.

BOEING B-52 STRATOFORTRESS

Although the U.S.A.F.'s Strategic Air Command has a steadily diminishing force of manned bombers, the B-52 Stratofortress, which has now served with the Command for 11 years, is destined to continue to furnish a substantial proportion of the S.A.C.'s nuclear deterrent into the mid 'seventies. Constant refinement of equipment and tactical techniques have maintained the value of the B-52 as a retaliatory weapon, and this aircraft's versatility has been dramatically demonstrated by Guam-based B-52s which, although designed as long-range, high-altitude, deep-penetration bombers carrying nuclear weapons, have delivered huge tonnages of conventional bombs in precision high-altitude attacks on Viet Cong concentrations. At the present time there are 38 Wings of B-52 Stratofortresses in the S.A.C., but early production models are being progressively phased out, and by 1970 the active inventory will include only 18 Wings equipped with 255 late-model (G and H) bombers of this type.

B-52s in the active inventory have undergone progressive modifications to enhance their low-altitude capabilities, and during 1966

a proportion of the B-52 force was receiving weapons-bay modifications to enable 85 500-lb. or 42 750-lb. bombs to be housed internally as compared with a maximum of 27 750-lb. bombs accommodated previously. Together with the 24 pylon-mounted 750-lb. bombs, the modified weapons bay now enables the B-52 to transport no less than 60,500 lb. of conventional bombs. Future modifications will enable late-model B-52s to carry the forth-

The B-52D Stratofortress (56-0629) illustrated above is one of two that has been used in a development programme aimed at increasing the bomber's short-range conventional bomb load. Modifications have enabled 42 750-lb. or 84 500-lb. bombs to be housed internally.

coming SRAM (Short-Range Attack Missile) as primary armament. Following the basic concept of the smaller B-47 Stratojet, now phased out of the S.A.C. inventory, the Stratofortress's development was initiated in 1946, and the two prototypes flew on April 15 and October 2, 1952. Of the initial production order for 13 aircraft, three were completed as B-52As but the remainder were B-52Bs, the initial service model which joined the S.A.C.'s 93rd (Heavy) Bomb Wing in June 1955. Powered by the J57-P-19W, -29W or -29WA, the B-52B carried six crew members and was equipped with an MA-2 bombing-navigation system at an early service stage, defensive armament comprising four 0.5-in. guns in a

Bosch Arma MD-9 tail barbette with fully automatic radar detection and tracking. Fifty B-52Bs were built, these having now been phased out of the active inventory, and the B-52C which followed, the first example flying on March 9, 1956, differed primarily in the size of the auxiliary underwing tanks, each of which housed 3,000 U.S. gal. (2,498 Imp. gal.) of fuel, gross weight rising from 420,000 to 450,000 lb. Thirty-five B-52Cs were completed to be followed by 170 B-52Ds which differed solely in that they lacked provision for the installation of interchangeable reconnaissance packs in the weapons bay.

Improvements in the electronics, bombing and navigational systems resulted in a change in designation to B-52E, the first of 100 examples of which flew on October 3, 1957, and with a switch from the J57-P-29W turbojet, which offered 10,900 lb.s.t. dry and 12,500 lb.s.t. with water injection, to the J57-P-43W rated at 11,200 lb.s.t. dry and 13,750 lb.s.t. wet, the designation became B-52F. Eighty-eight B-52F Stratofortresses were built, the first flying on May 6, 1958, and the last being completed in November 1958 to bring production to 448 aircraft. In the meantime, a major weight-saving programme had been initiated, and the first model that this affected was the B-52G.

B-52G: Although resembling earlier models of the Stratofortress superficially, and retaining the J57-P-43W turbojets of its immediate predecessor, the B-52G was the end product of a programme of major structural redesign which resulted in a substantial increase in overall performance, including a 25 per cent increase in range. Some 10,000 lb. was saved in structural weight, and the redesign of the wing to permit fuel storage in nearly the entire in-spar area out to the external underwing tanks, permitted these tanks to be reduced in capacity to 700 U.S. gal. (583 Imp. gal.) with a useful reduction in drag. New vertical tail surfaces were provided

GENERAL ARRANGEMENT DRAWING: *A B-52G-105 Stratofortress of the U.S.A.F. Strategic Air Command*

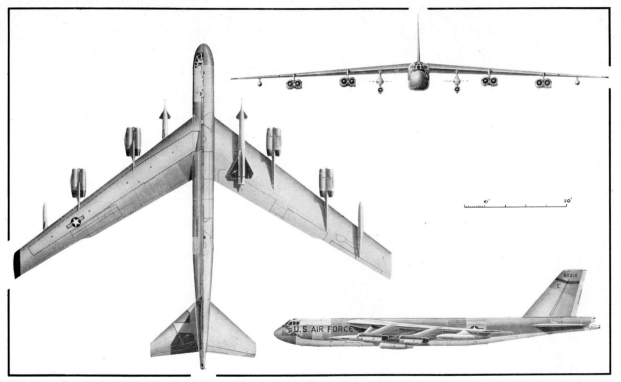

of substantially reduced height and broader chord, the ailerons were replaced by a system of spoilers for lateral control, and the gunner was moved forward from the tail to the crew compartment from where he monitored his weapons by television.

The first B-52G flew on September 26, 1958, and in the following year, a major improvement in the effectiveness of the aircraft was made by modifications permitting it to carry a pair of AGM-28A Hound Dog stand-off missiles on pylons between the inboard engine nacelles and the fuselage. Two AGM-28 missiles accounted for less than half the weight of the total weapons load of the B-52G which could also carry some 20,000 lb. of thermo-nuclear free-falling stores in its internal weapons bay, together with a number of ADM-20 Quail diversionary missiles. A retrospective modification programme provided other countermeasures in the form of ALE-25 pods housing chaff-dispensing rockets and mounted between the engine pods. The 193rd and last B-52G was completed on September 23, 1960 when this model was succeeded in production by the B-52H.

B-52H: The principal change embodied by the B-52H was the replacement of the turbojets by TF33-P-3 turbofans offering some

12 per cent improvement in fuel consumption. The switch to turbofans also permitted the elimination of some 10,000 lb. in water injection equipment, and still more weight was saved by replacing the quartette of 0.5-in. machine guns in the tail by single 20-mm. ASG-21 rotary cannon. The first of 102 B-52H Stratofortresses flew on March 6, 1961, and was delivered to the 379th Strategic Bomb Wing two months later, and the last aircraft of this type was completed in June 1962.

Power Plants: *Eight Pratt & Whitney TF33-P-3 turbofans each rated at 17,000 lb.s.t.*
Performance: *Max. speed, 630 m.p.h. at 40,000 ft. (Mach 0.95), 645 m.p.h. at sea level (Mach 0.85); average cruise, 565 m.p.h. at 36,000 ft.; max. unrefuelled range, 12,000* mls.; service ceiling, 55,000 ft.*
Weights: *Max. loaded, 488,000* lb.*
Dimensions: *Span, 185 ft. 0 in.; length, 157 ft. 6¾ in.; height, 40 ft. 8 in.; wing area, 4,000 sq. ft.*
*APPROXIMATE

(*Left*) *A B-52F Stratofortress (57-065). The B-52F is currently operated by the 7th, 320th, and 454th Bomb Wings of the Strategic Air Command, and these, together with the B-52Cs of the 99th, the B-52Ds of the 28th, 92nd, 306th, 340th, 484th, 494th, and 509th, and the B-52Es of the 6th, 11th, 17th, 70th, and 96th, are all scheduled to be inactivated between 1967 and 1971.*

CONVAIR B-58A HUSTLER

The first combat aircraft of delta configuration with podded power plants—and so far the only one—to attain production, the B-58A possesses no internal weapons bay, an area rule-conforming external pod containing weaponry, ECM gear, reconnaissance equipment and fuel in varying ratios from almost total fuel to almost wholly weapon, and offering the ultimate in mission flexibility. The crew members are carried in individual capsulated cockpits permitting escape at any speed or altitude, and the ASQ-42V bombing-navigation system, which combines Doppler, celestial and inertial navigation, supplies the aircraft position, heading, ground speed and track, attitude, steering data, distance to target and weapons release information. The rearmost crew member, the defence systems operator, is responsible for the operation of the various ECM equipment, radar chaff dispenser, and the 20-mm M-61 Vulcan cannon mounted in the flexible tail cone. Normal fuel capacity, including that housed in the pod, exceeds 15,000 U.S. gal. (12,490 Imp. gal.), and on a typical high-altitude mission, the aircraft cruises at approximately Mach 0.9 at 50,000–55,000 ft. to within 600 miles of its target, and then accelerates to Mach 2.0 for the run-in and escape.

The 43rd Bomb Wing was first activated with B-58As on March 15, 1960, and 10 of the pre-production aircraft were brought up to definitive production standards to augment the 86 genuine production examples of the Hustler, the last of which was completed in the autumn of 1962. Eight other pre-production aircraft have been converted as TB-58A dual-control trainers, the first of these flying on May 10, 1960. The TB-58A has the bombing-navigation system deleted, together with ECM and other defense systems, and the transparent glazing is extended so that the aircraft can be flown from either of the forward cockpits.

Currently scheduled to be phased out of the U.S.A.F. Strategic Air Command service in 1971, the B-58A Hustler was the world's

(Right) The B-58A Hustler possesses the distinction of having been the first strategic bomber to attain supersonic speeds. The accompanying photograph shows clearly the external mission pod which can house varying ratios of weaponry, fuel, countermeasures and reconnaissance equipment. A 20-mm. M-61 Vulcan cannon protrudes from the tail cone.

(*Above*) *The B-58A Hustler, which is currently scheduled to be phased out of U.S.A.F. Strategic Command service in 1971, equips two Bomb Wings, the 43rd and 305th, each with three squadrons. Only 116 aircraft of this type were manufactured.*

first service strategic bomber capable of attaining dash speeds of the order of Mach 2.0. Currently equipping the six squadrons of the 43rd and 305th Bomb Wings at Little Rock A.F.B. and Bunker Hill A.F.B. respectively, the Hustler was first conceived in 1949 and was awarded a development contract in August 1952. The initial contract called for 13 aircraft for test and evaluation purposes, and the first of these flew on November 11, 1956. Subsequently, an additional 17 test and pre-production aircraft were ordered which, followed by 86 production examples, brought the total quantity of Hustlers built to 116 machines.

Power Plants: *Four General Electric J79-GE-5B turbojets each rated at 10,000 lb.s.t. and 15,600 lb.s.t. with afterburning.*
Performance: *Max. speed, 1,385 m.p.h. at 44,000 ft. (Mach 2.1), 700 m.p.h. at sea level (Mach 0.92); range cruise, 595 m.p.h. at 40,000–50,000 ft.; tactical radius (Mach 0.9 to 500 mls. of target, Mach 2.0 to target and Mach 0.9 return), 1,200* mls.; service ceiling, 55,000 ft.*
Weights: *Max. loaded, 163,000–165,000 lb.*
Dimensions: *Span, 56 ft. 10 in.; length, 96 ft. 9 in.; height, 31 ft. 5 in.; wing area, 1,542 sq. ft.*
*APPROXIMATE

GENERAL ARRANGEMENT DRAWING: *A B-58A-10 Hustler (59-2451) of the 43rd Bomb Wing at Little Rock A.F.B., Arkansas*

DASSAULT MIRAGE IVA

Currently providing the backbone of France's *Forces Aériennes Stratégiques* and serving with the 91e and 93e *Escadres de Bombardement* respectively at Mont-de-Marsan and Istres, with a third *Escadre*, the 94e, in process of formation, the Mirage IVA medium-range supersonic bomber produced by Avions Marcel Dassault was originally conceived for the high-altitude nuclear strike role. Changed tactical considerations have, however, necessitated concentration on low-altitude penetration for which no airframe strengthening has been demanded as the basic structure possesses the necessary fatigue life, and the shape and loading of the wing provide adequate low-level gust-response characteristics. The minor modifications dictated by the new primary mission profile have been introduced progressively on the Mirage IVA assembly line and retrospectively on early production aircraft.

The Mirage IVA, 62 examples of which have been ordered for the *Armée de l'Air*, was designed for an unrefuelled radius of action

of the order of 800 miles, including Mach 1.7 dash, but normally operates with the C-135F tankers of *Escadron* 4/91. It differs markedly from the original Mirage IV-01 which, flown on June 17, 1959, was a somewhat smaller and lighter aircraft meeting a less ambitious requirement. The three pre-production aircraft that followed embodied considerable redesign, overall length was increased to provide additional fuselage space for fuel and avionics, and chordwise extensions to the leading edges and elevons resulted in a substantial increase in wing area. The first pre-production aircraft, the Mirage IVA-02, was flown on October 12, 1961, and the third, the Mirage IVA-04 which flew on January 23, 1963, was fully representative of the production model which followed less than 11 months later, on December 7, 1963.

Crewed by a pilot and navigator in tandem Hispano-Suiza-built Martin-Baker Mk.BM.4 ejection seats, the Mirage IVA is a fairly sophisticated aircraft, its equipment including TACAN, Marconi

(Left) A Mirage IVA of France's Forces Aériennes Stratégiques taking-off in maximum loaded condition with the aid of SEPR 844 liquid-fuel rockets. Two 550 Imp. gal. (660 U.S. gal.) auxiliary fuel tanks are seen mounted beneath the wings.

GENERAL ARRANGEMENT DRAWING: *A Mirage IVA of Escadron 1/91 "Gascogne" based at Mont-de-Marsan.*

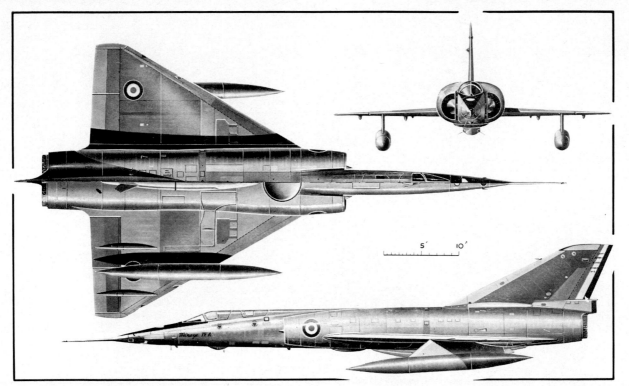

The Mirage IVA normally carries a single 2,200-lb. free-fall 50-kiloton bomb which, semi-recessed in the fuselage, is claimed to have no effect on performance. This photograph depicts the first production Mirage IVA with a dummy nuclear bomb under the fuselage.

Doppler navigational radar and CSF mapping radar, and Dassault navigation and bombing computer and countermeasures equipment, but the current service version lacks forward-looking terrain-avoidance radar, although consideration has been given to the possibility of equipping late production models with Dassault Antilope terrain-following and ground mapping radar for conventional-weapon-aiming and beacon-homing modes. The Mirage IVA's standard weapon is a single 2,200-lb. free-fall 50-kiloton bomb semi-recessed in the lower fuselage and detonated by chronometric fuse at high altitude or by radar at low altitude. Speed performance of the Mirage IVA is the same with or without the bomb, this being structurally heat-limited to Mach 2.2. The aircraft will eventually be adapted to carry up to four AS.37 Martel anti-radar missiles, and for the strike mission with conventional weapons provision is made for an external load of up to 16 1,000-lb. bombs—six under each wing and four under the fuselage —or a mix of bombs, missiles and fuel tanks. The Mirage IVA will normally use the hi-lo-hi mission profile for which the unrefuelled tactical radius (with maximum auxiliary fuel and nuclear

bomb) is of the order of 700 miles, tactical radius in the lo-lo case being about 450 miles. The normal attack mode is toss-bombing using the radar ground-mapping display, but a SFOM-Cotelec optical sight of inverted periscopic type offers the navigator a field of view through a glazed blister beneath the forward fuselage and could presumably be used for visual aiming.

Total internal fuel capacity is 3,080 Imp. gal. (3,700 U.S. gal.), this being housed mainly by integral wing tanks and fuselage tanks, the latter extending from the electronics bay to the engine faces, and occupying the belly of the aircraft between the wing leading and trailing edges except for the cut-outs for the undercarriage and engine accessory access bays. Fuel is also housed in the forward portion of the vertical tail surfaces, and may be supplemented by two 550 Imp. gal. (660 U.S. gal.) drop tanks. The Mirage IVA can use standard 7,875-ft. NATO runways, utilising six underwing-mounted SEPR 844 liquid rocket motors, but normally operates from 12,000-ft. runways, taking-off lightly loaded and topping up its fuel tanks in the air.

Power Plants: *Two SNECMA Atar 9K turbojets each rated at 10,360 lb.s.t. and 15,435 lb.s.t. with afterburning.*
Performance: *Max. speed, 1,454 m.p.h. at 40,000 ft. (Mach 2.2); max. stabilized speed, 1,122 m.p.h. at 60,000 ft. (Mach 1.7); tactical radius (with two 550 Imp. gal./660 U.S. gal. drop tanks), 1,240 mls. at 595 m.p.h. at 40,000 ft. (Mach 0.9), (without external fuel with supersonic target approach and subsonic cruise return), 770 mls.; climb to 36,100 ft., 4 min. 15 sec.; ceiling, 65,600 ft.*
Weights: *Empty, 31,967 lb.; normal loaded (with nuclear weapon and drop tanks), 69,666 lb.; max. loaded, 73,800 lb.*
Dimensions: *Span, 38 ft. 10¼ in.; length, 76 ft. 11¼ in.; height, 17 ft. 8½ in.; wing area, 839.584 sq. ft.*

(Above) An A-3B of VAH-2 refuelling an A-4C Skyhawk of VA-153. A weapons bay pack comprises hose-reel assembly and 1,300 U.S. gal. tank.

DOUGLAS A-3 SKYWARRIOR

Equipping five Heavy Attack Squadrons and scheduled to remain in the U.S. Navy's first-line aircraft inventory throughout the 'sixties, the A-3 has done more to change carrier warfare concepts than any other shipboard aircraft. The largest and heaviest aircraft ever planned for carrier operation, the A-3 three-seat attack bomber provided the U.S. Navy with true strategic bombing capability when it entered service with VAH-1 in 1956. A contract for two prototypes designated XA3D-1 was awarded on March 31, 1949, and the first of these flew on October 28, 1952, with 7,000 lb.s.t. Westinghouse XJ40-WE-3 turbojets. The unsatisfactory performance of the Westinghouse engine resulted in its replacement by the Pratt & Whitney J57-P-6 in the initial produc-

tion model, the A-3A, this power plant offering 9,700 lb.s.t. and 11,600 lb. with water injection. The A-3A was considered from the outset as an interim model for indoctrination, the development of shipboard procedures and operational techniques, etc., and only 50 had been built when production switched to the definitive A-3B. Five A-3As were subsequently modified for electronic counter-measures as EA-3As, and others were relegated to the training role under the designation TA-3A.

A-3B: Externally similar to the A-3A, the A-3B introduced the more powerful J57-P-10 turbojet and a number of equipment changes, and first entered service with VAH-2 in 1957, and in

(Left) An A-3B Skywarrior (Bu.No. 147655) of VAH-6, and (below, left) an RA-3B (Bu.No.144835) of VAP-61. Both aircraft are seen in the current Skywarrior configuration with fixed refuelling probe on the fuselage port side, and tail armament deleted.

addition to this unit currently equips Heavy Attack Squadrons (VAH-) 4, 6, 8 and 10. Capable of all-weather operation from carriers down to the size of the *Essex*-class, the A-3B has been launched at weights in excess of 80,000 lb., although normal maximum loaded weight is 73,000 lb. Almost the entire nose is occupied by the ASB bombing radar, and the bombing-navigation system permits a wide range of bomb modes and approach patterns including LABS attacks with automatic, semi-automatic or manual techniques. The box-like 15-ft. weapons bay which dictated the cross section of the fuselage accommodates a wide variety of ordnance loads up to a maximum of 12,000 lb., conventional bomb loads including four 2,000-lb., twelve 1,000-lb., or 24 500-lb. bombs, mines or depth charges on individual ejector racks. A spoiler or anti-buffet rake deflects ahead of the weapons bay simultaneously with the opening of the bomb doors to avoid buffeting. All A-3Bs were initially delivered with twin 20-mm. cannon in a Westinghouse radar-directed tail barbette, but this

GENERAL ARRANGEMENT DRAWING: *An A-3B Skywarrior (Bu.No. 147656) of Heavy Attack Squadron (VAH-) 2, the "Royal Ramparts", home-based at N.A.S. Whidbey Island, Washington.*

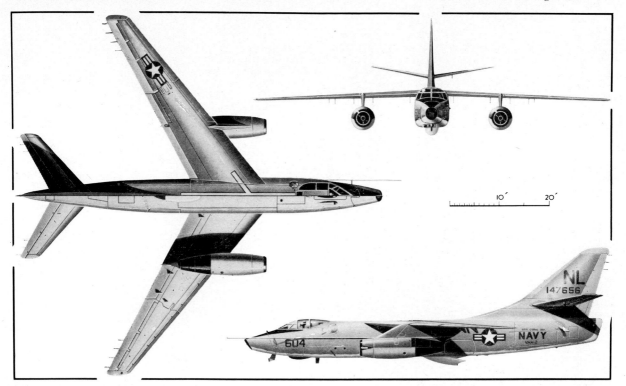

(Above) An EA-3B radar countermeasures aircraft of VQ-1.

has now been deleted from the majority of aircraft which employ the space previously occupied by this armament for radar chaff dispensers and other ECM equipment.

An in-flight refuelling probe is attached to the port side of the fuselage, and the standard A-3B may be adapted for the tanker role by the installation of a special weapons bay pack comprising a 1,300 U.S. gal. (1,082.5 Imp. gal.) tank and a hose-reel assembly, and a "Mobile Engine and Cargo Carrier" capable of housing the largest turbojet or 3,000 lb. of cargo may be inserted in the weapons bay for COD (Carrier On-board Delivery) tasks. A total of 164 A-3B Skywarriors was built, production switching in 1958 to the EA-, RA-, and TA-3B versions.

EA-3B: A seven-seat radar counter-measures and electronic reconnaissance development of the A-3B, the EA-3B flew on December 10, 1958, and 24 were built, these serving with Fleet Reconnaissance Squadron (VQ-) 1. Featuring a redesigned, pressurized fuselage, the EA-3B carries forward- and side-looking radar, infra-red scanner and other non-photographic reconnaissance and ECM equipment, and has stations for four electronics operators. The SLAR is housed in a long ventral fairing, additional internal fuel tankage is provided, and an in-flight refuelling probe is fitted.

RA-3B: Serving with Heavy Photographic Squadrons (VAP-) 61 and 62, the five seat RA-3B has a similar pressurized fuselage to that of the EA-3B, the space occupied by the weapons bay of the A-3B being utilised by a photo-navigator and photo technician, and various camera stations. Dual view finders and a master control in the cockpit permit single or multiple operation of all cameras by the pilot or photo-navigator, and a small bay aft of the pressurized photographic compartment houses photoflash bombs for night illumination. The prototype of the photo-reconnaissance version of the Skywarrior, the YRA-3B, flew on July 22, 1958, and 30 production RA-3Bs were built.

TA-3B: Flown on August 29, 1959, the TA-3B was the last version of the Skywarrior to be manufactured, 12 being built for operation by training squadrons VAH-3 and VAH-123. Embodying a pressurized fuselage accommodating a pilot, instructor and six pupils with individual radar bomb sights, the TA-3B enables pupils to be instructed in LABS bombing techniques, and the last example was delivered in January 1961.

Power Plants: Two Pratt & Whitney J57-P-10 turbojets each rated at 10,500 lb.s.t. dry and 12,400 lb.s.t. with water injection.
Performance: Max. speed, 610 m.p.h. at 10,000 ft. (Mach 0.83), 560 m.p.h. at 36,000 ft. (Mach 0.85); range cruise, 475 m.p.h. at 36,000 ft. (Mach 0.72); tactical radius (standard internal fuel), 1,050 mls. at 36,000 ft.; max. range (with auxiliary fuel tankage in weapons bay), 2,900 mls.; service ceiling, 41,000 ft.
Weights: Empty, 39,409 lb.; normal loaded, 73,000 lb.; max. 82,000 lb.
Dimensions: Span, 72 ft. 6 in.; length, 76 ft. 4 in.; height, 22 ft. 9½ in.; wing area, 812 sq. ft.

(Right) Canberra B.Mk.16s of No. 213 Squadron with the R.A.F.'s 2nd Tactical Air Force. The B.Mk.16 is, like the B.Mk.15, an up-dated conversion of the B.Mk.6 with external pylons for bombs or missiles but retaining some of the original B.Mk.6 radar aids. The nearer aircraft is fitted with a ventral pack housing four 20-mm. cannon.

ENGLISH ELECTRIC CANBERRA

Possessing the record among jet combat aircraft for production longevity, having been manufactured continuously for 12 years, the Canberra was Britain's first essay in the jet bomber field, and despite the fact that its prototypes were ordered 21 years ago—on January 7, 1946—it bids fair to remain in first-line operational service well into the 'seventies. Although conceived as a two-seater high-altitude light bomber utilizing radar bombing aids, it was to emerge in service form as a three-seater employing visual bomb-aiming, and it is now employed primarily in low-altitude tactical roles. The first of four two-seat prototypes, designated Canberra Mk.1s, was flown on May 13, 1949, and the initial production model, the Canberra B.Mk.2, which had flown in prototype form on April 23, 1950, entered R.A.F. service in May 1951, this having the original radar nose eliminated and a transparent nose for a bomb-aimer substituted. Three crew members were carried, with the pilot on the port side of the cockpit and the navigator and bomb-aimer seated side by side aft. Power was

provided by two Avon 101s each rated at 6,500 lb.s.t., and performance included maximum speeds of 518 m.p.h. at sea level (Mach 0.68) and 570 m.p.h. at altitude (Mach 0.82). Initial climb rate was 3,800 ft./min., and maximum operational ceiling was limited by aircrew breathing equipment to 48,000 ft. Internal fuel capacity was 1,377 Imp. gal. (1,654 U.S. gal.), which could be supplemented by two 244 Imp. gal. (293 U.S. gal.) wingtip tanks, and with an internally-housed bomb load of six 1,000-lb. weapons, range was 2,660 miles.

The impetus provided by the Korean conflict resulted in a rapid build-up of Canberra B.Mk.2 production, and A. V. Roe, Handley Page and Short Brothers all established production lines, A. V. Roe and Handley Page manufacturing 75 and 65 B.Mk.2s respectively, and Short Brothers going on to build later variants of the aircraft after completing 76 B.Mk.2s. The parent company manufactured 203 B.Mk.2s to bring total production in the U.K. to 424 machines, five of which were delivered to Australia as pattern aircraft for

(Above) A Canberra B.(I).Mk.8 of No.16 Squadron (foreground) flying in formation with Canberra B.Mk.16s of No. 213 Squadron.

licence manufacture by the Government Aircraft Factory, Australian production comprising 49 aircraft which, essentially similar to the B.Mk.2, were designated B.Mk.20s, and were mostly powered by Australian-built Avon 109s of 7,400 lb.s.t. One B.Mk.2 was also supplied to the U.S.A. to serve as a pattern aircraft for the Glenn L. Martin Company which had also acquired a manufacturing licence (see pages 60–62).

Fifteen ex-R.A.F. Canberra B.Mk.2s were delivered to Rhodesia and are still operated by No. 5 (Bomber) Squadron, and six other aircraft of this type supplied to the *Fuerzas Aérea Venezolanas* in 1953 and operated by that service's *Escuadron de Bombardeo* No. 39, were supplemented in 1965 by a further batch of reconditioned ex-R.A.F. B.Mk.2s. In R.A.A.F. service, the licence-built B.Mk.20 equips No. 82 Wing with Nos. 1 and 6 Squadrons at Amberley, Brisbane, and No. 2 Squadron at Butterworth, Malaysia, and is scheduled to remain as first-line equipment until 1969 and the availability of the General Dynamics F-111A.

Photo-reconnaissance and training versions of the B.Mk.2 were evolved as the P.R.Mk.3 (which see page 81) and T.Mk.4, the latter incorporating a new cockpit with side-by-side seats and dual controls, and 75 aircraft of this type being manufactured with others subsequently being converted from B.Mk.2 airframes. The Canberra B.Mk.5 was a target-marking version with a special nose radar installation and Avon 109 engines. It was also the first Canberra to feature integral wing tankage, but only one prototype was completed, the next bomber variant to attain production being the B.Mk.6.

B.Mk.6: Distinguished from the B.Mk.2 by 7,400 lb.s.t. Avon 109 engines and integral wing tanks raising internal fuel capacity to 2,277 Imp. gal. (2,735 U.S. gal.), the Canberra B.Mk.6 flew on January 26, 1954, and 88 were built by the parent company and a

GENERAL ARRANGEMENT DRAWING: *A Canberra B.(I).Mk.8 (WT341) of No. 16 Squadron with the R.A.F.'s 2nd Tactical Air Force in Germany.*

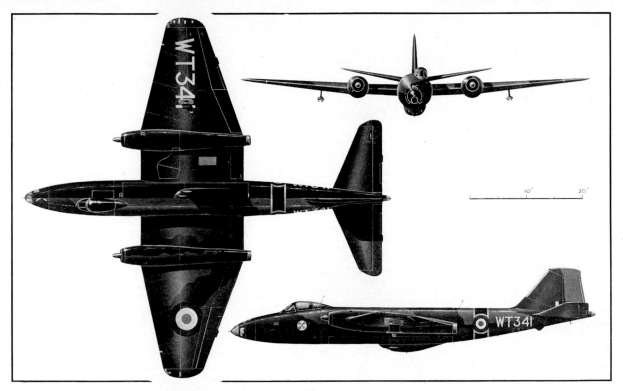

(Left) One of a small quantity of Canberra B.(I).Mk.8 bombers supplied to the Fuerzas Aérea Venezolanas in which service this type is operated alongside a number of earlier Canberra B.Mk.2s.

further 30 by Short Brothers. Of these, six were delivered to the *Fuerza Aérea Ecuatoriana* with which they still serve, and six went to the *Centre d'Essais en Vol* at Bretigny for use in connection with France's missile development programme. The Canberra B.Mk.6 was phased out of R.A.F. Bomber Command service in 1961, but 38 were converted to B.Mk.15 and 20 to B.Mk.16 standards for use by the R.A.F. overseas. The B.Mk.15, which is operated by Nos. 32, 73 and 249 Squadrons with the R.A.F.'s Near East Air Force, and by No. 45 Squadron with the Far East Air Force, introduced underwing attachment points for two 1,000-lb. bombs or two Microcell pods each housing 37 2-in. rockets, and various new items of equipment, including UHF and HF communications radio, a forward-facing F.95 camera in the nose and a G.45 camera in the starboard wing leading edge, a Decca rollermap with feed-in from the Doppler navigation radar, and more minor items. The F.24 camera originally mounted in the rear fuselage of the B.Mk.6 is retained, and the internal bomb load remains at 6,000 lb. The B.Mk.16, which equips No. 6 Squadron with the Near East Air Force and No. 213 Squadron with the 2nd T.A.F., is generally similar to the B.Mk.15 but retains some of the original radar aids of the B.Mk.6, and may have a ventral pack containing four 20-mm. cannon mounted in the rear half of the bomb-bay, the forward portion of the bay still housing three 1,000-lb. bombs.

This pack was first mounted on the B.Mk.6 conversion designated B.(I).Mk.6 to endow it with intruder capability.

B.(I).Mk.8: Whereas all production versions of the Canberra prior to the B.(I).Mk.8 were three-seaters, this model introduced major redesign in the form of a new two-seat forward fuselage in which

Power Plants: *Two Rolls-Royce Avon 109 turbojets each rated at 7,500 lb.s.t.*
Performance: *Max. speed, 580 m.p.h. at 30,000 ft. (Mach 0.83), 518 m.p.h. at sea level (Mach 0.68); range (interdictor role with combat allowances), 800 mls. at 403 m.p.h. at 2,000 ft.; ferry range (with two 244 Imp. gal./293 U.S. gal. wingtip tanks), 3,630 mls.; initial climb (at 55,134 lb.), 3,400 ft./min.; service ceiling, 48,000 ft.*
Weights: *Empty, 23,173 lb.; normal loaded, 50,992 lb.; max., 56,250 lb.*
Dimensions: *Span, 63 ft. 11½ in.; length, 65 ft. 6 in.; height, 15 ft. 7 in.; wing area, 960 sq. ft.*
Note: *Specification applies to B.(I).Mk.8 but is generally applicable to all similarly-powered bomber variants.*

the pilot was seated to port beneath a fighter-type canopy with a second crew member in the nose. A detachable pack housing four 20-mm. cannon was installed in the rear portion of the bomb-bay for the night interdictor role, and hard points were provided in the wing for a 1,000-lb. ordnance load on each of two pylons. The prototype was flown on July 23, 1954, and 74 production examples from June 1955, eight of these being delivered to the *Fuerza Aérea del Peru* to equip one *escuadron* of the service's *Gruppo* 21, and a

similar quantity being delivered to the *Fuerzas Aérea Venezolanas* in which they serve alongside earlier Canberra B.Mk.2s. In R.A.F. service, the B.(I).Mk.8 is operated by Nos. 3, 14 and 16 Squadrons with the 2nd T.A.F.; 66 similar aircraft were supplied to the Indian Air Force under the designation B.(I).Mk.58; 12 were supplied as B.(I).Mk.12s to the R.N.Z.A.F. to equip No. 14 Squadron at Ohakea, and six other B.(I).Mk.12s are operated alongside six B.(I).Mk.58s by No. 12 Squadron of the *Suid-Afrikaanse Lugmag.*

HANDLEY PAGE VICTOR

Representing the ultimate in transonic medium bomber design, the Victor has been manufactured in relatively small numbers for R.A.F. Bomber Command, and in its B.Mk.2 form equips Nos. 100 and 139 Squadrons, operating in the strategic reconnaissance role as the B.(S.R.)Mk.2 with No. 543 Squadron, all within No. 3 Group, the earlier B.Mk.1A having now been relegated to flight refuelling tanker duties. Possessing a unique cresent wing planform in which a constant critical Mach number is maintained from root to tip by means of graded sweepback, the Victor was designed to meet the requirements of specification B.35/46, but more than a decade elapsed between the initiation of design work and service introduction; a decade in which the Victor's concept was, in some respects, overtaken by developments in surface-to-air missiles and advances in interceptor capabilities which largely nullified the immunity stemming from a combination of high subsonic speeds and extreme altitudes envisaged by the specification. Thus, shortly after the service introduction of the definitive version of the Victor, the bomber's mission capabilities were extended to include low-level penetration.

The first prototype Victor flew on December 24, 1952, the initial production Victor B.Mk.1 following some three years later, on February 1, 1956 with 11,000 lb.s.t. Sapphire 202 turbojets, but another two years were to elapse before, in April 1958, the bomber entered service. The Victor B.Mk.1 could attain speeds only

marginally lower than Mach 1.0 at altitudes between 40,000 and 45,000 ft., maximum cruise performance including a speed of 607 m.p.h. at 45,000 ft. The B.Mk.1 was issued to four squadrons, Nos. 10, 15, 55 and 57, but only 66 had been manufactured when

(Below) A Victor B.K.Mk.1A of No. 55 Squadron with a Mk.20B refuelling pod beneath each wing. The fully converted tanker version also has a Mk.17 hose drum unit in the rear of the weapons bay.

(Left) A Victor B.Mk.2 of No. 100 Squadron equipped with auxiliary slipper tanks under the wings and deploying its drogue chute. Only two squadrons operate this Blue Steel-carrying strategic bomber, the other being No. 139 Squadron.

the appreciably more powerful B.Mk.2 appeared on the assembly line. During their career in first-line service, a number of B.Mk.1s were brought up to B.Mk.1A standards by up-dating internal equipment and providing countermeasures equipment in the extreme rear fuselage, and these are, in turn, being modified for the flight refuelling role as B.K.Mk.1As.

B.K.Mk.1A: The premature retirement of the R.A.F.'s Valiant tankers as a result of fatigue problems resulted in the choice of the Victor B.Mk.1A for conversion as a successor offering, in its definitive form, three-point refuelling. The prototype conversion was flown in the summer of 1964 and, as the B.K.Mk.1A, the conversion has been issued to Nos. 55 and 57 Squadrons, and a third tanker squadron, No. 214, was reformed on this type on July 1, 1966. The Victor B.K.Mk.1A carries a Mk.20B refuelling pod beneath each wing with a Mk.17 hose drum unit faired into the rear of the original weapons bay. Up to 52,860 lb. of transferable fuel may be carried, and average refuelling time for a fighter is four minutes and for a bomber is ten minutes.

B.Mk.2: The 67th production Victor embodied a number of major changes as the first B.Mk.2. The installation of 17,250 lb.s.t. Conway R.Co.11 turbofans was accompanied by an increase in

wing span and gross area, these being raised from 110 ft. and 2,406 sq. ft. to 120 ft. and 2,597 sq. ft. respectively. The increases in span and area resulted from the insertion of stub-wing extensions inboard of the engines and slight extension of the wingtips. A Bristol Siddeley Artouste turbine was installed in the starboard wing root, and the air intakes were enlarged. The first Victor B.Mk.2 flew on February 20, 1959, but the first Squadron to receive this more advanced type, No. 139, did not begin conversion until three years later, in February 1962. Earlier, in August 1960, it had been announced that a substantial proportion of the orders previously placed for the Victor B.Mk.2 were to be cancelled, a decision largely motivated by changed operational considerations, and only one additional bomber unit, No. 100 Squadron, was to receive this type.

During production of the Victor B.Mk.2, several modifications were introduced. The 19,750 lb.s.t. Conway R.Co.17 supplanted the Conway R.Co.11, the increased power being devoted mainly to extending the cruising speed further toward the buffet boundary and increasing operating altitude; radar chaff-dispensers in the

GENERAL ARRANGEMENT DRAWING: *A Victor B.Mk.2 (XL513) of No. 139 (Jamaica) Squadron based at R.A.F. Wittering.*

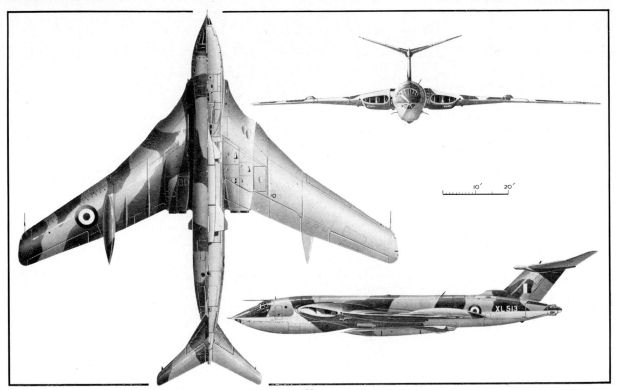

form of Whitcomb bodies were introduced on the upper wing surface trailing edges, and changes were made to the weapons bay to permit the Blue Steel Mk.1 rocket-driven supersonic stand-off missile to be carried. The Blue Steel, which is now the principal weapon of the Victor B.Mk.2, is mounted semi-externally, attached to a beam in the weapons bay and necessitating special cut-down weapon-bay doors. This weapon reduces the performance of the Victor by only 2–3 per cent, and may be launched from high or low altitudes. The Victor may be modified from Blue Steel-carrying form for free-falling nuclear or high-explosive bombs within 24–30 hours, the maximum conventional load being 35 1,000-lb. bombs, these being mounted on five internal carriers.

The Victor B.Mk.2 carries five crew members, pilot, co-pilot, navigator, radar operator and electronics officer. Fuel is housed in bag-type tanks in the wings and fuselage, and internal capacity may be augmented by two large-capacity underwing tanks.

B.(S.R.)Mk.2: A strategic reconnaissance version of the B.Mk.2 bomber, the Victor B.(S.R.)Mk.2 equips No. 543 Squadron at Wyton, the R.A.F.'s Central Reconnaissance Establishment. The main task of No. 543 Squadron is high-level maritime reconnaissance, providing overall ocean surveillance for R.A.F. Coastal Command and other maritime air and naval forces, this being combined with high altitude photo reconnaissance by day and night. Radar mapping is used in the primary maritime role, and

camera equipment is housed in packs which are housed in the weapons bay. These packs can accommodate a wide variety of camera combinations, the F.96Mk.2 camera being used for day reconnaissance, the F.89Mk.3 for night reconnaissance, and the F.94Mk.4 for aerial survey tasks. In addition to a camera pack, the weapons bay can house a maximum of three canisters containing a total of 108 photoflashes, or two photoflash canisters and an auxiliary fuel tank. Alternatively, a camera pack and two auxiliary tanks may be carried to provide a maximum fuel range substantially in excess of that of the B.Mk.2 bomber.

Power Plants: *Four Rolls-Royce Conway R.Co.17 Mk.201 turbofans each rated at 19,750 lb.s.t.*
Performance: *Max. speed, 630* m.p.h. at 36,000–50,000 ft. (Mach 0.95); max. cruise, 610* m.p.h. at 55,000 ft. (Mach 0.92); range cruise, 560* m.p.h. at 40,000 ft. (Mach 0.85); combat radius (with Blue Steel for hi-lo-lo-hi mission) 1,730 mls., (high altitude mission) 2,300 mls.; maximum range (with underwing tanks), 5,200* mls.; service ceiling, 55,000* ft.*
Weights: *Max. loaded, 200,000* lb.*
Dimensions: *Span, 120 ft. 0 in.; length, 114 ft. 11 in.; height, 30 ft. 1½ in.; wing area, 2,597 sq. ft.*
*APPROXIMATE

HAWKER SIDDELEY VULCAN

Equipping the bulk of R.A.F. Bomber Command squadrons, the Vulcan represents the ultimate in transonic medium bomber design, and is expected to remain in first-line service until the mid 'seventies, although from 1969–70 its primary role will be tactical. Development of the Vulcan was initiated in 1947, the first proto-type flying on August 30, 1952, and the first production example following on February 4, 1955, the initial model being designated Vulcan B.Mk.1. The first squadron to be formed on this type was No. 83 which began conversion in May 1957, but even prior to its service introduction, this version of the Vulcan was considered as

(*Above and below*) *A Vulcan B.Mk.2 (XM572) carrying the Blue Steel stand-off weapon. The B.Mk.2 equips seven R.A.F. squadrons.*

(Above) Vulcan B.Mk.2 (XM649) from R.A.F. Coningsby. The principal R.A.F. strategic bomber, the Vulcan B.Mk.2 was phased out of production late in 1964.

substantially reduced and, simultaneously, both span and area were increased from 99 ft. and 3,554 sq. ft. to 111 ft. and 3,964 sq. ft., and the new wing was introduced on the 46th and subsequent Vulcans on the assembly line which were duly designated as B.Mk. 2s. The first Vulcan B.Mk.2 flew on August 19, 1958 with 17,000 lb.s.t. Olympus 201 turbojets, deliveries to R.A.F. Bomber Command beginning on July 1, 1960. Later production B.Mk.2s adopted the 20,000 lb.s.t. Olympus 301, early production examples being progressively re-engined, and this version of the bomber is currently operated by Nos. 9, 12, 27, 35, 50, 83 and 617 Squadrons, all within R.A.F. Bomber Command's No. 1 Group. The primary weapon is the Blue Steel Mk.1 stand-off missile which, carried semi-externally, can be launched at both high and low level, and which reduces performance by only two per cent. Since 1964, the mission capability of the Vulcan B.Mk.2 has been extended to include low-level penetration. Production of the Vulcan was completed late in 1964.

an interim model, and only some 45 B.Mk.1s were built. These were successively fitted with the 11,000 lb.s.t. Olympus 101, 12,000 lb.s.t. Olympus 102, and 13,500 lb.s.t. Olympus 104, and were progressively up-dated as B.Mk.1As with later avionics and ECM equipment in the extreme rear fuselage, and with still further equipment changes as B.Mk.1Bs, these aircraft equipping Nos. 44 and 101 Squadrons of R.A.F. Bomber Command's No. 1 Group. The Vulcan B.Mk.1B carries the standard V-bomber crew complement of five members, and the internal weapons bay can accommodate a maximum of 21 1,000-lb. general-purpose bombs. Cruise performance includes Mach 0.92 at 45,000 ft. and a maximum cruising altitude of 50,000 ft., high-altitude tactical radius on internal fuel being of the order of 1,700 miles.

In order to take advantage of the substantial increases in power offered by new versions of the Olympus turbojet, the thickness/chord ratio over the outer portions of the Vulcan's wing was

Power Plants: *Four Bristol Siddeley Olympus B.Ol.21 Mk.301 turbojets each rated at 20,000 lb.s.t.*
Performance: *Max. speed, 645* m.p.h. at 40,000–45,000 ft. (Mach 0.98); max. cruise, 620* m.p.h. 40,000–55,000 ft. (Mach 0.94); tactical radius (for hi-lo-lo-hi sortie profile) 1,700* mls., (at 40,000–55,000 ft.) 2,300* mls.; max. range, 4,750* mls.; max. cruising altitude, 55,000* ft.*
Weights: *Loaded, 180,000–200,000* lb.*
Dimensions: *Span, 111 ft. 0 in.; length, 99 ft. 11 in.; height, 27 ft. 2 in.; wing area, 3,964 sq. ft.*
*APPROXIMATE

GENERAL ARRANGEMENT DRAWING: *A Vulcan B.Mk.2 (XM645) of No. 1 Group, R.A.F. Bomber Command, based at Coningsby.*

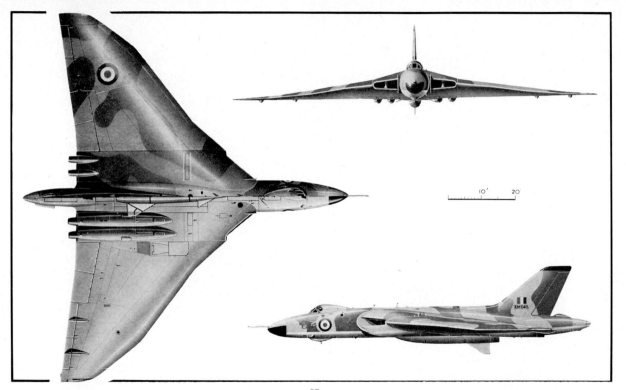

ILYUSHIN IL-28 (BEAGLE)

or 23-mm. cannon for flak suppression and for use against fixed and moving targets in the close support role, and two similar weapons manipulated by the radio operator in the extreme tail for rear defence and possibly for dispensing a mixture of tracer and 'chaff' to confuse the radar of intercepting fighters and the guidance systems of missiles. Some Il-28s have tandem radomes beneath the centre fuselage, one of these presumably housing countermeasures equipment, and an operational and pilot training version, the Il-28U, has the nose glazing deleted and a second cockpit with a full set of controls for the pupil pilot inserted ahead and below the standard cockpit. All versions of the Il-28 may be fitted with 200 Imp. gal. (240 U.S. gal.) auxiliary tanks at the wingtips.

Still serving in substantial numbers with the V.-V.S., despite its obsolescence, and with 14 other national air arms, the Il-28 three-seat light tactical bomber was designed to meet a V.-V.S. specification formulated in 1946, competitive designs being the Tupolev Tu-14 and Sukhoi Su-10, and prototype trials were initiated late in 1947. Production was begun in the following year and continued until 1960. Powered by progressive developments of the British centrifugal-type Nene turbojet evolved by the Klimov bureau, the Il-28 entered V.-V.S. service in 1949–50 with 4,960 lb.s.t. RD-45 engine, this being supplanted at an early production stage by the 5,952 lb.s.t. RD-45FA and, finally, by the improved VK-1 of 6,040 lb.s.t. A transonic successor to the Il-28 evolved by the Ilyushin bureau in the early 'fifties, the Il-54 (Blowlamp), failed to meet V.-V.S. requirements, the competitive Yak-28 being selected for further development, and in the interim, the Il-28, despite its ageing design, was retained in full production.

A relatively simple, straightforward design, the Il-28 can accommodate four 1,100-lb. or up to twelve 550-lb. bombs in its weapons bay, and gun armament comprises two fixed forward-firing 20-mm.

Power Plants: *Two Klimov VK-1 centrifugal-flow type turbojets each rated at 6,040 lb.s.t.*
Performance: *Max. speed, 580 m.p.h. at 15,000 ft. (Mach 0.81), 530 m.p.h. at 32,800 ft.; range cruise, 450 m.p.h. at 32,000–38,000 ft.; tactical radius, (with 4,400-lb. bomb load) 685 mls., (with two 200 Imp. gal./240 U.S. gal. wingtip tanks) 850 mls.; ferry range, 2,200 mls.; service ceiling, 41,000 ft.*
Weights: *Empty, 27,400 lb.; max. loaded, 44,000 lb.*
Dimensions: *Span, 68 ft. 2¼ in.; length, 62 ft. 0 in.; height, 21 ft. 11¾ in.*

GENERAL ARRANGEMENT DRAWING: *An Il-28 of the 8th Air Division of the Chinese Air Force of The People's Liberation Army.*

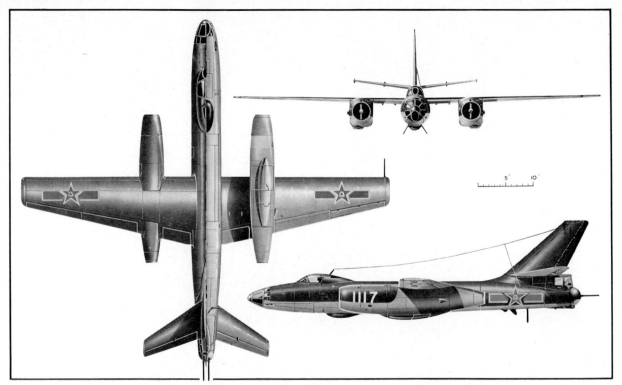

MARTIN B-57

No combat aircraft has experienced a more chequered career in U.S.A.F. service than the B-57 two-seat light tactical bomber. Added to the inventory in 1955, the principal production variant of this British-designed bomber, the B-57B, had, by the early 'sixties, been retired from active U.S.A.F. service, most examples being converted to reconnaissance configuration for use by the Air National Guard. In 1964, however, with the escalation of the war in Vietnam, the B-57 embarked on a new combat career, and since the arrival in August of that year of the two B-57B-equipped squadrons, the 8th and 13th, operating under the 405th Tactical Fighter Wing at Bien Hoa, it has been continuously in action, and aircraft converted for the reconnaissance task have been withdrawn from the A.N.G. and restored to tactical bomber configuration for U.S.A.F. use in South-East Asia.

The B-57 was, in its original form, patterned closely on the Canberra B.Mk.2, a manufacturing licence for which having been acquired by the Glenn L. Martin company on April 19, 1951. The first eight production aircraft, designated B-57A, differed from their progenitor solely in having engineering changes dictated by U.S. production techniques, the first example flying on July 20, 1953, but the following 67 aircraft housed cameras aft of the bomb-bay, and entered U.S.A.F. service late in 1954 as RB-57As, these subsequently being transferred to the A.N.G. with which they continue to serve. Extensive design modification to increase the aircraft's suitability for the tactical night intrusion role had, in the meantime, resulted in the B-57B, the first example of which flew on June 28, 1954.

B-57B: The B-57B introduced a new forward fuselage providing tandem seating for the two crew members, a rotary weapons-bay door, and eight 0.5-in. wing-mounted machine-guns. The B-57B entered service with the U.S.A.F. Tactical Air Command in January 1955, continuing in first-line T.A.C. service until 1959, and of the 202 examples of this model manufactured, some 30 were transferred to the Pakistan Air Force and, in 1965, an initial batch of four was passed to the Vietnamese Air Force. The B-57B, which has been the subject of a series of conversion programmes at Martin-Baltimore's Aircraft Modification Center

(Left) The B-57B, which was returned to U.S.A.F. service in 1964 for operation in S.E.Asia, has seen considerable service in Vietnam, and serves in small numbers with the Vietnamese Air Force.

GENERAL ARRANGEMENT DRAWING: *A Martin B-57B (53-3826) of the 8th Bomb Squadron, U.S. 13th Air Force.*

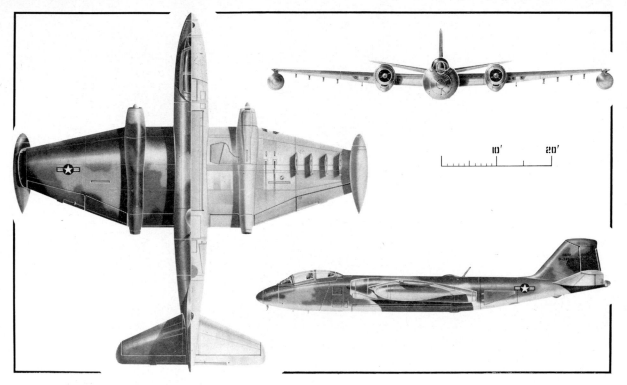

(Above) A B-57B tactical light bomber of the U.S.A.F.'s Pacific Air Forces.

over the past three years, bomb-bays being re-installed, avionics up-dated and counter-measures equipment introduced, carries a 5,000-lb. bomb load on the rotary door, and up to 3,000 lb. of additional ordnance may be carried on underwing pylons. In Vietnam, where one 13th Air Force B-57B squadron is deployed on a rotational basis from Clark Field in the Philippines, the B-57B has proved itself to possess excellent air-to-ground capabilities, and able to loiter in the combat zone for substantial periods.

B-57C: Essentially a dual-control version of the B-57B and retaining the basic model's tactical capabilities, the B-57C flew on December 30, 1954, and 38 aircraft of this type were built to serve alongside the B-57B, providing combat proficiency training capability.

B-57E: The final production version of the basic tactical bomber, the B-57E was a multi-purpose model easily converted for the reconnaissance, transitional training, or target-towing roles. A total of 68 B-57Es was built to bring total production (excluding the RB-57D which see pages 78–79) to 383.

Power Plants: *Two Wright J65-W-5 turbojets each rated at 7,220 lb.s.t.*
Performance: *Max. speed, 582 m.p.h. at 40,000 ft. (Mach 0.88), 534 m.p.h at sea level (Mach 0.74); tactical radius, 1,100 mls. at 480 m.p.h.; normal range (clean), 2,300 mls.*
Weights: *Loaded, 49,000 lb.; max., 55,000 lb.*
Dimensions: *Span, 63 ft. 11½ in.; length, 65 ft. 6 in.; height, 15 ft. 7 in.; wing area, 960 sq. ft.*

TUPOLEV TU-16 (BADGER)

Broadly comparable in both role and performance with the B-47 Stratojet now phased out of the U.S.A.F. active inventory, the Tu-16 strategic medium bomber entered service with the *Aviatsiya Dalnovo Deistviya* during 1954–55, prototypes having entered the test phase in 1952 under the design bureau designation Tu-88, these competing with prototypes of the Ilyushin Il-46 designed to fulfil the same specification. During its production life, the Tu-16 was fitted with progressively more powerful turbojets, the principal of which was the RD-3M (AM-3M) of 19,180 lb.s.t., and a considerable proportion of the aircraft of this type remaining in V.-V.S. service have been adapted for maritime reconnaissance and patrol with anti-shipping missiles on pylons beneath the outboard wing panels, and for strategic reconnaissance with both optical and non-optical systems.

The standard production model, dubbed *Badger-A* in the West,

has a defensive armament of a single 23-mm. cannon mounted in the starboard side of the fuselage, and twin 20-mm. or 23-mm. weapons in a semi-recessed dorsal barbette, an aft ventral barbette and a tail turret. A maximum bomb load of the order of 20,000 lb. may be housed internally, and some two dozen Tu-16s of this type have been supplied to the air arm of the United Arab Republic. Reconnaissance adaptations of the basic aircraft have cameras in their weapons bays, and some carry scanner pods on underwing pylons, these presumably shadowing naval forces by passive homing on their radar emissions and using the distance between the pods as a base for triangulation. A maritime reconnaissance and patrol adaptation (*Badger-B*) carries two *Kennel* anti-shipping missiles on underwing pylons, these being relatively simple turbojet-driven weapons with warheads of about 1,000 lb., a range of less than 100 miles, and radar homing for the terminal

(Right) A Tupolev Tu-16 Badger-B equipped with Kennel anti-shipping missiles on underwing pylons in service with the Indonesian air arm. Tu-16s of the Morskaya Aviatsiya, the Soviet Union's shore-based naval air arm, carry similar weapons for the anti-shipping task, as do those of the U.A.R. Air Force.

(Left) A Tu-16 adapted for the reconnaissance role photographed over the North Pacific. Several variants of the reconnaissance Tu-16 exist, that illustrated apparently being equipped primarily for photographic tasks.

attack phase. The *Badger-B* version of the Tu-16 has been used in some numbers by the *Morskaya Aviatsiya*, and equips Nos. 41 and 42 Squadrons of Indonesia's air arm.

A third development of the Tu-16, the *Badger-C* (illustrated on

(Below) This photograph of an Indonesian Tu-16 (Badger-B) illustrates clearly the position taken up by the Kennel anti-shipping missiles on the underwing pylons. The Tu-16 equips Indonesia's 41st and 42nd Squadrons.

the opposite page), has an extensively modified nose to accommodate an extremely large search radar. This variant is also employed in the strategic reconnaissance role, and a missile-carrying model has the forward portion of the weapons bay eliminated to accommodate a *Kipper* stand-off missile, an air-breathing weapon bearing a superficial resemblance to the AGM-28 Hound Dog. Between 1,500 and 2,000 Tu-16s are believed to have been built, although the major proportion of these are now no doubt held at maintenance units as a strategic reserve.

Power Plants: *Two Mikulin AM-3M turbojets each rated at 19,180 lb.s.t.*
Performance: *Max. speed, 620 m.p.h. at 10,000 ft. (Mach 0.85), 610 m.p.h. at 20,000 ft. (Mach 0.87); range cruise, 495 m.p.h. at 38,000 ft. (Mach 0.75); max. range, (with 7,000-lb. bomb load) 3,800 mls., (with 20,000-lb. bomb load) 2,500 mls.*
Weights: *Max. loaded, 170,000* lb.*
Dimensions: *Span, 110 ft. 0 in.*; length, 121 ft. 0 in.*; height, 36 ft. 0 in.*; wing area, 1,815* sq. ft.*
*APPROXIMATE

GENERAL ARRANGEMENT DRAWING: *A Tupolev Tu-16 (Badger-C) of the V.-V.S.'s Aviatsiya Dalnovo Deistviya.*

The Tupolev Tu-20 long-range strategic bomber and reconnaissance aircraft is the only turboprop-driven aircraft in its category to have attained service.

TUPOLEV TU-20 (BEAR)

Now largely relegated to the strategic reconnaissance role, the Tu-20 is unique in being the only turboprop-driven strategic bomber to have attained first-line service with any air arm, and in combining airscrews with a swept wing. Before its original task was assumed by the ICBM, the Tu-20 was undoubtedly the largest single factor justifying the North American continental defence system and, thus, an outstanding economic success from the Russian viewpoint as it necessitated a completely disproportionate counter effort on the part of the U.S.A.

Whereas little interest in the turboprop-driven strategic bomber was evinced in the West, the Soviet Union initiated investigation into the possibilities of a turboprop-powered successor to the piston-engined Tu-4 strategic heavy bomber shortly after the Kuznetsov engine design bureau, with the aid of a team of German and Austrian engineers led by Dipl. Ing. Ferdinand Brandner,

began the development of large turboprop power plants, and in 1949, the Tupolev bureau produced the prototype Tu-85 powered by four large VD-4K turboprops. A thoroughly orthodox, straight-winged strategic bomber dubbed *Barge* in the West, the Tu-85 evidently offered only a marginal performance improvement over the existing piston-engined Tu-4, as its development past the prototype stage was abandoned in the early 'fifties in favour of the appreciably more advanced Tu-95, which was to enter service with the V.-V.S.'s Long-range Air Force, the *Aviatsiya Dalnovo Deistviya* as the Tu-20. The prototype was demonstrated over Tushino in 1955, five examples being demonstrated a year later, and the Tu-20 was available in service quantities in 1957–58. GENERAL ARRANGEMENT DRAWING: *A Tupolev Tu-20 (Bear-B) of the Aviatsiya Dalnovo Deistviya equipped with Kangaroo stand-off weapon.*

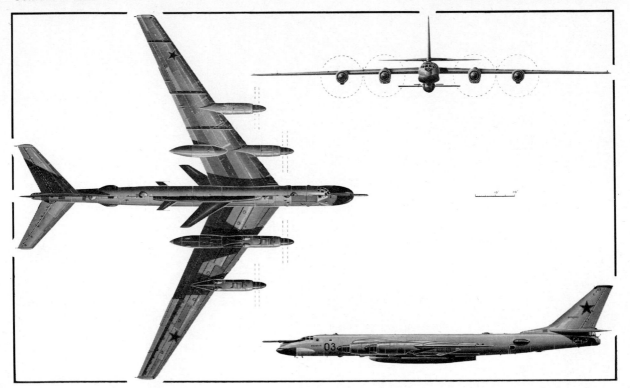

The Tupolev Tu-20 has now been largely relegated to the long-range reconnaissance role, being employed extensively for so-called "ferret" missions along the North American seaboard. The example illustrated (left) retains the original glazed bomb-aiming nose of the initial strategic bombing variant.

According to Dipl. Ing. Brandner, the Tu-20 was designed to attain 560 m.p.h. at 36,000 ft. (Mach 0.85) with the 16.4-ft. airscrews of its NK-12 turboprops turning at 750 r.p.m., corresponding to a tip speed of Mach 1.08. However, it was not stated that the Tu-20 had, in fact, attained this design speed, and the "over the target" speed of 500 m.p.h. at 41,000 ft. (Mach 0.76) ascribed to the aircraft by U.S.A.F. intelligence sources would seem to have been nearer to the bomber's true capability, this giving an airscrew tip speed of Mach 0.98. In the West, the Tu-20 has received the appellation of *Bear*, and two principal versions are currently in service, the *Bear-A* being the initial strategic bomber production form with a glazed bomb-aiming nose and now largely relegated to the strategic reconnaissance role, and the *Bear-B* representing an attempt to extend the operational life of the basic aircraft by adapting it as a carrier for a large stand-off weapon.

The initial Tu-20 possessed a defensive armament of one fixed forward-firing 20-mm. or 23-mm. cannon in the starboard side of the nose, and two weapons of similar calibre in each of a rear ventral barbette, a dorsal barbette and a tail turret. The large weapons bay reputedly accommodated a maximum of 25,000 lb. of free-falling conventional or nuclear weapons, and assuming that auxiliary fuel tanks occupy a considerable proportion of this bay for reconnaissance, tactical radius is likely to be increased from 3,900 to about 4,500 miles. The *Bear-B* version, first seen publicly over Tushino in 1961, features an extensively modified nose with a large duck-billed radome housing high-definition search radar, this being surmounted by an immense flight refuelling probe. The weapons bay has been modified to carry semi-externally the largest of Russia's known stand-off weapons, the turbojet-driven *Kangaroo* which, guided by the *Bear-B*'s radar, is likely to cruise over a range of some 250 miles at a speed of the order of Mach 1.3 with a multi-megaton warhead. A specialised reconnaissance version of the *Bear-B*, which has been employed extensively for

(Right) These close-up photographs of strategic reconnaissance Tu-20s illustrate clearly the differences between the nose sections of the so-called Bear-A (above) and Bear-B (below). The former retains the original glazed bomb-aiming nose, but the latter features a large duck-billed radome housing high-definition search radar, this being surmounted by an immense flight refuelling probe. A similar nose section is featured by the missile-carrying version of the Bear-B which carries a single Kangaroo stand-off weapon semi-externally. The missile-carrying variant is illustrated by the general arrangement drawing on page 67.

"ferret" missions, has a similar nose radome and is equipped with a wide array of both optical and non-optical sensors, electronics operators being housed in a pressurised compartment occupying the space previously taken up by the weapons bay.

Although the number of Tu-20s built is not known with certainty, it is believed that some 150 bombers of this type formed the backbone of the nuclear striking force of the *Aviatsiya Dalnovo Deistviya* in the late 'fifties, and production probably totalled some 300 aircraft.

Power Plants: *Four Kuznetsov NK-12M single-shaft turbo-props each rated at 14,750 e.s.h.p.*

Performance: *Max. speed, 550 m.p.h. at 36,000 ft. (Mach 0.83); max. cruise, 500 m.p.h. at 40,000 ft. (Mach 0.76); range cruise, 440 m.p.h. at 36,000 ft. (Mach 0.67); max. range (reconnaissance mission), 9,000* mls.; tactical radius (with single stand-off weapon), 3,000* mls.; service ceiling, 44,000 ft.*

Weights: *Normal loaded, 330,000–340,000* lb.; max. 370,000* lb.*

Dimensions: *Span, 163 ft. 0 in.*; length, 150 ft. 0 in.*; height, 40 ft. 0 in.*; wing area, 3,000* sq. ft.*

*APPROXIMATE

Roughly comparable with the B-58A Hustler, the "Blinder" employs a unique position for its twin turbojets above the aft fuselage.

TUPOLEV BLINDER

Although the origin of the medium bomber allocated the identification name *Blinder* by NATO is by no means certain, its design is generally ascribed to one of the design bureaux headed by A. N. Tupolev, although some sources have suggested that it is one of the progeny of V. M. Myasishchev. Displayed publicly at Tushino in June 1961, by which time it is believed to have attained pre-service status with the V.-V.S., the *Blinder* is, aerodynamically, one of the most sophisticated of Soviet warplanes so far revealed, and it is roughly comparable with the B-58A Hustler, although apparently possessing a somewhat lower dash performance than that of its American counterpart.

Presumed to have flown in prototype form in 1957–58, the Blinder appears to carry four crew members, and two versions have been seen; one being the standard reconnaissance-bomber with a short weapons bay positioned well aft and a sharply-pointed nose radome, and a missile-launching version with a broad nose radome, and a semi-retractable flight refuelling probe. The type of power plant employed by the *Blinder* is uncertain, but the current civil versions of the RD-3M turbojet employed by the Tu-16 are rated at 20,940–21,385 lb.s.t. in their AM-3M-500 form, and a military equivalent of these with afterburning to boost thrust by some 25–30 per cent should be adequate to provide the performance with which western intelligence experts endow this warplane.

Evidently intended as a successor to the Tu-16, the *Blinder* has several unusual design features, the most interesting of which being the unique position of the turbojets in relatively short pods

GENERAL ARRANGEMENT DRAWING: *A Tupolev Blinder with semi-externally housed air-to-surface missile.*

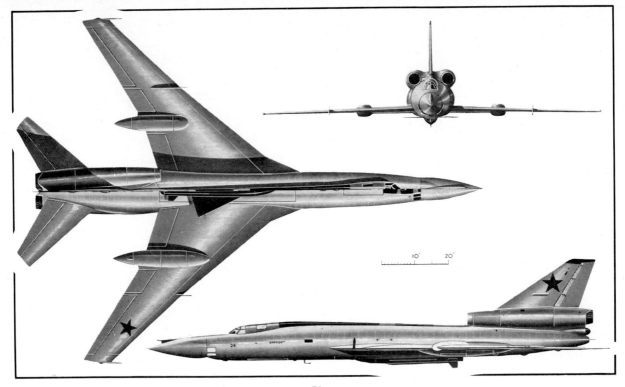

The so-called "Blinder" (left) is one of the most sophisticated combat aircraft designs so far revealed by the Soviet Union. Presumably the intended successor to the Tu-16, the "Blinder" embodies a number of unusual design features.

cameras. The tandem weapons bays appear to house up to 20 1,100-lb. bombs, and a single remotely-controlled cannon in the extreme tail presumably dispenses a mixture of chaff and tracer to confuse the radar of intercepting fighters and the guidance systems of missiles. Little is known about the ASM mounted semi-recessed in the lower fuselage of the *Blinder* illustrated

above the aft fuselage, these offering the minimum wetted area, keeping the intakes clear of wing wake, and leaving the fuselage free to carry a useful load. At high incidences it is likely that this engine positioning results in the engines ingesting some rough air-flow from vortices shed from the fuselage sides, but such effects are possibly limited to a brief period at unstick. The wing plan-form has compound taper, leading edge sweepback varying from 50° outboard to 70° at the root, and the four-wheel bogie main undercarriage members are housed in fairings projecting aft of the wing trailing edges.

The pilot and a second crew member sit in tandem beneath a canopy which features the bare minimum of transparency area, and the other crew members occupy positions lower in the cabin section. A strip of windows on either side of the bomb aiming position suggests an emphasis on reconnaissance with a series of

on the previous page, and the operational status of the missile-carrying variant is not known with certainty.

Power Plants: *Two axial-flow turbojets each rated at 19,200* lb.s.t. and 26,500* lb.s.t. with afterburning.*
Performance: *Max. speed, 925* m.p.h. at 40,000 ft. (Mach 1.4); max. cruise, 630 m.p.h. at 40,000 ft. (Mach 0.95); tactical radius (hi-lo-lo-hi mission profile with supersonic approach and escape), 1,400* mls.; service ceiling, 60,000* ft.*
Weights: *Max. loaded, 185,000* lb.*
Dimensions: *Span, 91 ft. 0 in.*; length, 133 ft. 0 in.*; height, 17 ft. 0 in.*; wing area, 2,030* sq. ft.*
*APPROXIMATE

RECONNAISSANCE AIRCRAFT DEVELOPMENT

RECONNAISSANCE information falls into two broad categories: tactical and strategic. The former provides up-to-the-minute data on the strength, disposition, and movements of units that are actually fighting, or may shortly be brought into action, together with background information on logistic and other facilities in the area. Because conditions in the vicinity of the battle can change very rapidly, this type of information is best provided by aerial surveillance (rather than by spies or from prisoner interrogation), and therefore tactical reconnaissance aircraft are used by both East and West, their designs being very frequently based on standard fighter-bombers.

Strategic reconnaissance, on the other hand, is concerned with relatively permanent targets deep inside hostile territory, and with the enemy's general war potential. It follows that this category of intelligence work is carried out in peacetime just as in war, and that traditional espionage methods may be employed as the time factor is less important. In this respect the East is at a considerable advantage, since anyone can travel freely around the Western countries picking up information, and indeed most data on their military, technical, and economic states are freely available through the press and trade journals. In contrast the Communist Bloc remains a closed book, due to severe restrictions on individual freedom, and the complete uselessness of their periodicals as intelligence sources. The West has therefore been obliged to resort to aerial surveillance in peacetime as the principal means of providing warning of any impending attack, and of assessing the Communists' progress with aircraft, missiles, and nuclear warheads.

The first generation of Soviet turbojet fighters was of rather modest performance, and (coupled with the limitations of their search and control radars) this enabled the West to make short incursions into Communist airspace, providing photographic coverage to a depth of perhaps a hundred miles. However, the situation changed completely in the late 'forties due to the introduction of the MiG-15, which was developed to reach an operational ceiling of 52,000 ft. and was faster than any operational aircraft but the F-86 Sabre. In 1949, American losses increased sharply, and it became obvious that overflights could only be continued if a reconnaissance aircraft capable of exceptionally high altitudes could be evolved. Rather than accept the delays associated with a completely new design, the U.S.A.F. produced the "featherweight B-36" from the massive six-engined bomber which had given Air Defense Command such a hard time in interception exercises. Stripped of all unnecessary equipment and presumably most of its remote-controlled barbettes, this aircraft managed to defy Soviet defences from 1950 to 1952, by which time the system of fighter control had been tightened up, and the first MiG-17s were being introduced.

The withdrawal of the B-36s left a very serious gap, and various desperate measures were tried to overcome the problem. Possibly the most unlikely of these techniques was the use of unmanned photographic balloons, launched from bases in West Germany whenever a suitable reversal of wind direction was forecast. It is hardly surprising that this method was abandoned just as soon as a specialised high-altitude aircraft could be developed.

The B-47 which replaced the B-36 in strategic bomber units was less suitable for adaptation to photographic reconnaissance, as its relatively high wing loading gave a mean cruise altitude of only 40,000 ft. Nevertheless, some 255 examples of the RB-47E were manufactured in the mid-1950s and used for short intrusions behind the Iron Curtain, providing tactical coverage and probing defences. More sophisticated versions were the EB-47H, which had a crew of five and was equipped for monitoring Soviet radio and radar transmissions, and the RB-47H, which had an extra crew member and was fitted for both electro-magnetic and photo-

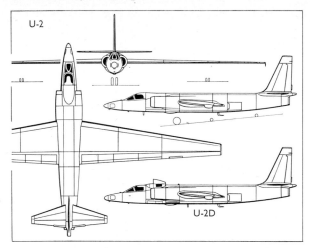

U-2

U-2D

graphic reconnaissance. These aircraft used the space provided by the empty bomb-bay to house a pressurised compartment in which the electronics operators were seated. The general method of operation in the so-called "ferret" mission has been to fly along Soviet boundaries, noting the characteristics of the various transmissions, and sometimes turning in toward the coast in an attempt to simulate an attack and thus encourage the use of secret fighter control radars and communications. At the same time further information can be provided by oblique photography and by the use of SLAR (sideways-looking radar), which provides a continuous map of the ground alongside the aircraft. Since the flight is normally made outside territorial limits, the country under surveillance has no legal right to take action against "ferret" aircraft, and indeed the U.S. has tolerated a considerable number of such flights by the Tu-16 and the Tu-20, particularly around Alaska, but on occasion the Soviet Union has proved markedly less lenient.

LOCKHEED U-2

In view of the difficulty of obtaining information on Russian activities by spy networks, and of the lack of strategic reconnaissance data following the withdrawal of the stripped B-36s,

(Left) One of five examples (56-6954) of the two-seat Lockheed U-2D, the remaining 50 U-2s built all being single-seaters. Like the U-2B and -2C, the U-2D is powered by the J75-P-13 turbojet, and is now employed primarily for such tasks as high altitude air sampling and monitoring missile launchings.

(Right) A pinion tank-fitted Lockheed U-2A strategic reconnaissance aircraft.

(Right) A pinion tank-fitted Lockheed U-2A strategic reconnaissance aircraft.

the CIA (Central Intelligence Agency) approached Lockheed with the idea of producing a completely new aircraft, which could cruise for long periods at heights unattainable by normal service machines. For security reasons this approach may well have been made either through the NASA or the U.S.A.F., with the special reconnaissance and navigation equipment fitted at a later stage by military personnel.

In order to achieve extreme altitude the aircraft required a large wing area and a long span, to provide support in the thin air of the stratosphere with the minimum of drag. In addition it necessitated unusually clean surface finish, and a powerful engine that would still provide a thrust of roughly one-twentieth of the aircraft weight at the desired cruise height. However, perhaps the most important point of all was to achieve a very low basic weight, which implied stressing for quite low airspeeds and low manoeuvre factors. Such a weak structure is usually very susceptible to gusts, so the Lockheed team produced an automatic system to sense the disturbance and deflect the flaps and ailerons accordingly, thus reducing gust loads. Tailwheel undercarriages are lighter than conventional nosewheel layouts, and the former line was thus adopted, with further weight saving by the use of a single main gear with jettisonable outriggers for lateral support on the ground. After take-off these "pogos" fall clear, and in landing the wings are protected by skids in the form of turned-down tips, which also provide a slight improvement in lift/drag ratio.

Early U-2As had a fuel capacity of only 785 U.S. gallons, which limited the range to 2,200 miles. Slipper tanks of 105 U.S. gallons boosted this to 2,600 miles, but this was still too short for overflights, and therefore a "wet wing" was introduced, giving a volume of 1,335 U.S. gallons. At this stage the Pratt & Whitney J57-P-37A of 11,200 lb. was adequate for cruising in the region of 55,000 ft., but far more power was essential if the U-2 was to survive for any length of time in the face of Mach 2.0 fighter developments. The J57 was therefore replaced by the J75-P-13 from the same manufacturer, giving a static rating of 17,000 lb. and a cruise altitude of 70,000 ft. or more. By this time the take-off weight had risen from 15,850 lb. to 19,750 lb., but the range was also up to 4,000 miles, making possible overflights covering much of the Soviet Union and China. Reconnaissance equipment consisted of a long-focus camera giving exceptionally clear photographs in spite of the immense altitudes, and arranged to operate through a series of windows in the belly of the U-2, thus covering the ground from horizon to horizon. In addition, electronic sensing devices picked up and recorded radio and radar transmissions.

The first U-2 commenced test flying in mid-1955, and by the start of the next year training of the CIA pilots had begun in Nevada. Aircraft were first sent overseas in May 1956 to Lakenheath and Wiesbaden, to be followed by operations from Turkey and Japan under the cloak of high-altitude atmospheric research. For the next four years the aircraft flew over hostile territory with impunity, Russian fighters stalling out well below its cruise height. However, even the U-2's success could not last for ever, and by 1960 the Soviet Union had developed the SA-2 Guideline surface-to-air missile and had deployed it to defend major centres of population and military targets. Overflights were then taking place on a monthly basis, and it was only a question of time before a U-2 was lost. On April 9, 1960 a U-2 penetrated as far as Kiev, and an attempt was made to shoot it down, but without success. On May 1st, reputedly acting on information that a major Russian space vehicle launching was to take place, pilot Gary Powers was instructed to carry out a mission from Peshawar in Pakistan to Bodo in Norway. His U-2B was brought down by a missile in the region of Sverdlovsk.

As a result of the international outcry that followed the Powers incident, the U.S. gave an assurance that no further flights would be made over the Soviet Union. This was no small price to pay, since the U-2 had already proved its value in obtaining information on Russian heavy bomber strength (enabling estimates of Mya-4 numbers to be considerably down-graded), and was urgently needed to continue the watch on ICBM build-up. However, the aircraft was still usable over other Communist countries, especially those with which the U.S. had no diplomatic links. In October, 1962, a tip-off was received in Washington from Oleg Penkovsky (a Colonel in Soviet intelligence, who was later sentenced to death for espionage) that Russian MRBMs were being supplied to the Castro regime in Cuba, and this report was confirmed on the 14th by a high-altitude reconnaissance mission flown by a U-2 from the 4080th Strategic Wing. Daily flights were then ordered for the period of the emergency, and appear to have continued on a less frequent basis since the Russians backed down and withdrew the missiles.

This aircraft has also been employed for mapping South Vietnam, the task being carried out in 1964 when U.S. military personnel were only in the country as "advisers", and turbine-powered aircraft were theoretically excluded under the terms of the armistice agreement. Further North, the U-2 was used for a considerable period (and may conceivably still be in use) by the Chinese Nationalists for surveillance of the mainland. Two were purchased in 1960, shortly after the Powers affair, but they were both lost in September 1962, one being shot down over China and the other crash-landing on Taiwan. Four replacements were then obtained, but at least one of these was lost in a training accident in the U.S.A., and two more had been brought down over China by mid-1964. At that time a total of at least eighteen of the fifty-five U-2s built had been lost, and it is clear that only a handful of the type remain in use at the present day. These aircraft are now employed almost exclusively in pure research, although no doubt they are also regarded as a useful reserve force in case it should prove necessary to carry out a discreet surveillance of some potential crisis spot. Among many tasks which might be classed as providing military information, the U-2 has been frequently employed in measuring radio-activity in the upper atmosphere (which provided some clues as to the nature of the Chinese bomb), and in measuring infra-red emission from missile launches and re-entry vehicles. Reports suggest that the U-2 has been used as an IR-picket off the Alaska coastline, searching for missile emissions.

IMITATION AND REPLACEMENT

One effect of the U-2 operations of 1956 was that the Soviet Union undertook the development of a similar high-altitude aircraft, but in this case the design was based upon an existing type—the Yak-25—rather than started from scratch. This approach

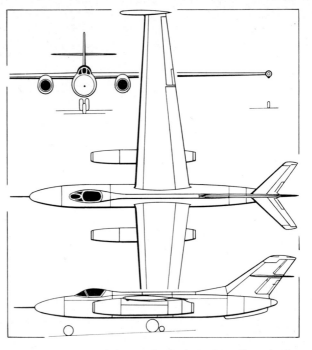

(*Above and right*) *A strategic reconnaissance derivative of the Yak-25 known in the West as the "Mandrake".*

naturally limited the weight-saving that could be achieved, and therefore the altitude that could be reached, although in the light of subsequent events this does not appear to have been a serious drawback. The Yakovlev team retained the rear fuselage, under-carriage, and tail assembly of the standard Yak-25, together with the two Klimov RD-9 turbojets of 7,200 lb. reheat thrust (as used also on the MiG-19). To this they added a straight wing of 75 ft. span, more than twice that of the normal wing, plus a new single-seat front fuselage. The resulting aircraft, dubbed Mandrake by NATO, is estimated to be slightly heavier than the U-2, grossing 22,000 lb. at take-off. Cruise height is in the region of 60,000 ft., although the absolute ceiling may approach 70,000 ft. These figures are consistent with the payload-height records achieved by the type designated "RV" by the Russians, which lifted 2,205 lb. to 67,113 ft., and 4,409 lb. to 66,188 ft. on July, 29 1959. Very little information has been released on the Mandrake, although it has been reported in Europe and in sightings over northern India. It is generally assumed to have entered service only shortly before the U-2 incident of 1960, and then to have been withdrawn from surveillance of the West in order to remove any possibility of counter-charges of spying. It was in 1960 that Russia stopped military aid to China, and it therefore seems very likely that the small batch of Mandrakes was switched to surveillance of those regions of China bordering on the Soviet Union. Since the best Chinese interceptor was until recently the MiG-19—although there is now evidence that the Sino-Communists have succeeded in

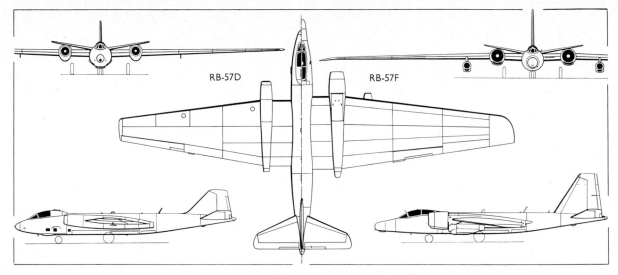

RB-57D　　　　　RB-57F

evolving Mach 2.0 interceptors based on the early MiG-21s received from the Soviet Union before Russian aid was withdrawn —which can only reach 55,000 ft., the Mandrake has been reasonably safe in this task, but it would be reasonable to suppose that further development is taking place with more powerful and economical engines, the latter being particularly important in view of its limited radius of 1,200 miles.

From the U.S. viewpoint, the cessation of the U-2 flights over Russia was a serious blow, although even in 1960, the U.S.A.F. had begun to recover film capsules jettisoned over the Pacific from reconnaissance satellites. The Samos family of orbital vehicles has since been in continual use, but their information is necessarily of lower quality than might be obtained by manned aircraft. Whether this will remain true for the surveillance capability of the MOL (manned orbital laboratory) remains to be seen. However, even at the time of the U-2 incident, plans were in hand for a successor, and indeed metal had already been cut for the first Lockheed A-11.

Whereas the U-2 had been designed purely for altitude without regard for speed (in fact it cruises at Mach 0.7), the A-11 was intended from the outset to achieve immunity from ground fire by a combination of high speed and extreme altitude, cruising in the region of Mach 3.0 and 75,000 ft. Design began following a contest held in 1958, the work proceeding under extreme secrecy until the existence of the programme was announced by President Johnson on February 29, 1964, when several examples of the aircraft were already flying. The initial batch of twelve aircraft is believed to have been funded by CIA, but there is no indication that the A-11 has been put to work in the manner of its predecessor, aside from feasibility demonstration over Cuba. One reason for this may be that the high performance cruise can only be obtained at considerable cost in range; despite the gross weight of 136,000 lb. the reconnaissance radius is believed to be only 1,500 miles. This is somewhat disappointing in view of the very sophisticated contours of the delta wing, with its extensions stretching forwards to spread the lift along the fuselage, and in view of the relatively poor airfield performance that has been accepted to achieve a high/ lift drag ratio in the cruise. Some increase in fuel capacity (and gross weight in consequence) has been provided in the slightly larger SR-71 version now entering service with the SAC, but really effective strategic ranges appear to depend on the use of flight refuelling, and this technique will doubtless be employed.

Some idea of the aircraft's performance may be gained from the record figures of the experimental interceptor version, the YF-12A, of 2,070 m.p.h. and 80,237 ft., and it is claimed that the SR-71 can bring under surveillance 60,000 sq. miles of the earth's surface in one hour.

Another aircraft which might be regarded as a replacement for the U-2 is the General Dynamics RB-57F, the most recent of a long line of high-altitude reconnaissance variants of the English Electric Canberra. On the British side, the P.R.Mks.3 and 7 were straightforward photographic versions of the B.Mks.2 and 6 (the P.R.Mk.7 and B.6 having fuel in the wings, and the 7,500 lb. Avon 109 in place of the 6,500 lb. Avon 101), but the later P.R.Mk. 9 aimed at much higher altitudes. Entering service in the late 'fifties, this variant had an increased chord inboard of the engines, a span enlarged from 64 ft. to 67 ft. 10 in., and Avon 206 turbojets of 10,050 lb. thrust, giving a cruise altitude of up to 55,000 ft.

The Martin RB-57D is somewhat better as a high-altitude performer, having J57-P-37As of 11,000 lb., and a span of 106 ft. Twenty of this model were produced, and two supplied to the Chinese Nationalists for surveillance of the mainland, but wing structural problems resulted in the RB-57D's grounding in 1963, and new wings for nine of these were being manufactured early in

(Right) A Martin RB-57D strategic reconnaissance aircraft (53-3973) at Wright-Patterson A.F.B. All RB-57Ds were grounded in 1963 as a result of wing structural problems, but nine were returned to service in 1966 after the manufacture of new wings.

(*Left*) *The General Dynamics RB-57F derivative of the B-57 (61-3503 being illustrated) may be fitted with a pair of auxiliary J60-P-9 turbojets beneath the wings as seen in these photographs. The extended fuselage nose accommodating electronic equipment increases overall length to 68 ft. 10 in.*

1966. However, the General Dynamics RB-57F version is even more potent, having two TF33-P-11 turbofans of 18,000 lb. supplemented by a pair of 3,300 lb. J60-P-9 turbojets in pods under the outboard wings. In addition this aircraft has an entirely new wing of 122 ft. span, with three spars and honeycomb skins, midspan ailerons and spoilers, but no flaps. The nose is extended to contain radar, the vertical tail area has been doubled, and the fuselage tanks eliminated to provide equipment space, all of the fuel being carried in integral tanks outboard of the engines, where it provides the maximum relief for bending loads. The RB-57F entered service with the Defense Atomic Support Agency in 1964, ostensibly to ensure that the provisions of the test ban treaty were carried out by sampling the upper atmosphere for radio activity. However, should it be needed for espionage, the cruise altitude is approximately 75,000 ft. and the range is over 4,000 miles.

Before leaving the subject of strategic reconnaissance, it may be noted that numerous types have been converted for this duty in small quantities because they offered long range, reasonable speed, and large stowage volume for special types of equipment. These aircraft include the Victor B.(S.R.)Mk.2 with so-called "camera crates" slung in the weapons bay, and radar mapping

(Right) Originally built for the strategic bombing role, the Myasishchev Mya-4 now performs the strategic reconnaissance task in small numbers. (Below, right) The GC-130A Hercules has served as a launching platform for Ryan Firebee reconnaissance drones (see page 116).

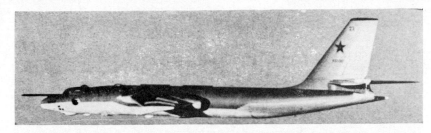

(Right) Originally built for the strategic bombing role, the Myasishchev Mya-4 now performs the strategic reconnaissance task in small numbers. (Below, right) The GC-130A Hercules has served as a launching platform for Ryan Firebee reconnaissance drones (see page 116).

equipment, the RC-135A Stratolifter, the B-52B with a two-man reconnaissance capsule in the bomb-bay, the RA-3B Skywarrior with up to twelve cameras, EA-3B and RB-66C for electronic surveillance, the RB-66B for day/night photo-reconnaissance (one was lost over East Germany in 1964), and the little-known U.S.A.F. RB-69A version of the U.S. Navy P-2. In addition, the RC-135B and RC-130A Hercules are used for mapping, one of the latter being shot down over Russia in 1958.

ENGLISH ELECTRIC CANBERRA P.R.MK.9

At an early stage in Canberra development (see pages 47–51) a requirement was formulated for a photographic reconnaissance version, and a prototype was flown on March 19, 1950, this differing from the B.Mk.2 bomber in having a 14-in. additional section in the forward fuselage for a camera bay, the size of the bomb-bay being reduced to the minimum needed to carry photoflash bombs, and fuel capacity being increased from 1,377 to 1,917 Imp. gal. (1,654 to 2,302 U.S. gal.), wingtip tanks adding 488 Imp. gal. (586 U.S. gal.) to the total. Carrying seven cameras, the photo-reconnaissance model entered production as the Canberra P.R.Mk.3, the first production example flying on July 31, 1952, and 36 examples subsequently being built. This model was succeeded by the P.R.Mk.7 which differed from its predecessor in having the 6,500 lb.s.t. Avon 101s replaced by 7,500 lb.s.t. Avon 109s, and similar integral wing tanks to those of the B.Mk.6 bomber, these providing a total internal capacity of 2,817 Imp. gal. (3,383 U.S. gal.) and increasing range without wingtip tanks from 3,585 miles to 4,340 miles. The camera installation was similar to that of the P.R.Mk.3, and the first production P.R.Mk.7 flew on October 28, 1953, a total of 74 aircraft of this type being built, and

(Left) Seen in service with No. 58 Squadron, the Canberra P.R.Mk.9, together with earlier photographic models, had to fulfil the R.A.F.'s entire strategic reconnaissance commitment between the premature withdrawal of the Valiant B.(P.R.)K.Mk.1 at the beginning of 1965 and the availability of the Victor B.(S.R.)Mk.2 in 1966.

eight of these being modified for use by the Indian Air Force as Canberra P.R.Mk.57s. The Canberra P.R.Mk.7 currently equips Nos. 17, 31, 80 and 81 Squadrons of the R.A.F., and serves alongside the later P.R.Mk.9 in Nos. 13 and 58 Squadrons.

The Canberra P.R.Mks.3 and 7 were essentially conversions of the B.Mks.2 and 6 bombers and, like their counterparts, their maximum operational altitude was limited to 48,000 ft. by the aircrew breathing equipment, but the appearance in service of the MiG-15 interceptor, capable of reaching altitudes well in excess of 50,000 ft., rendered the Canberra, which had previously enjoyed some immunity from interception at its maximum operational altitude, no longer suitable for so-called "ferret" missions along Soviet boundaries or for short incursions of Soviet territory, resulting in a demand for a photographic aircraft capable of operating at appreciably greater altitudes. Work was therefore initiated on the redesign of the basic Canberra specifically for the high-altitude photographic role, and the result was the Canberra

P.R.Mk.9 which differed appreciably from all earlier variants of this aircraft.

Intended for strategic reconnaissance missions at altitudes in excess of 50,000 ft., the Canberra P.R.Mk.9 embodied major wing redesign, the overall span being increased by 4 ft. and the chord on the sections inboard of the engines being extended, resulting in an increase in gross wing area of 84 sq. ft., this change being accompanied by the introduction of 11,250 lb.s.t. Avon 206 turbojets. The prototype P.R.Mk.9 was flown on July 8, 1955, this being a conversion of a P.R.Mk.7, but a substantial amount of additional redesign was subsequently undertaken by Short Brothers and Harland, which, together with equipment changes, resulted in three years elapsing before, on July 27, 1958, the first production aircraft flew. One decision necessitating extensive re-

GENERAL ARRANGEMENT DRAWING: *A Canberra P.R.Mk.9 (XH137) of No. 58 Squadron, No. 3 Group, R.A.F. Bomber Command.*

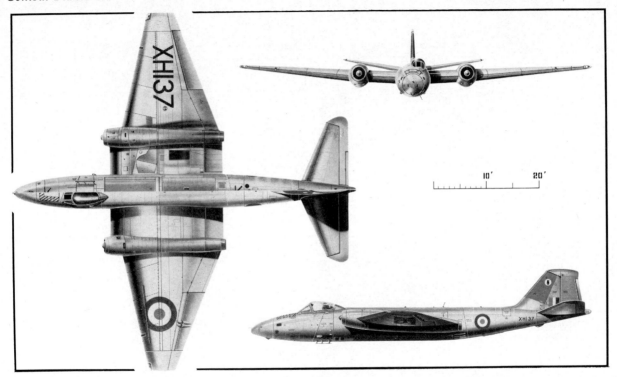

10'   20'

(Left) Manufactured in small numbers by Short Brothers and Harland, the Canberra P.R.Mk.9 raised the operational altitude of the reconnaissance Canberra from 48,000 ft. to 55,000 ft. Appreciably more powerful than its predecessors, the P.R.Mk.9 has a glass-fibre frangible hatch above the navigator's ejection seat in the nose.

design work was that concerning provision of an ejector seat for the navigator who, in the prototype, did not have this escape aid. The introduction of the ejector seat necessitated redistribution of all navigational and photographic control equipment, and the replacement of the prone photographic sighting position by a periscopic sight. As the original entrance door for the navigator could no longer be used, the entire nose of the aircraft, with much of its equipment, was hinged for ground entry and egress, and a glass-fibre frangible hatch was installed above the Martin-Baker Mk.4 ejector seat.

The first unit to receive the Canberra P.R.Mk.9 was No. 58 Squadron with No. 3 Group of R.A.F. Bomber Command, and it was subsequently issued to No. 39 Squadron with Air Headquarters Malta, and serves alongside the P.R.Mk.7 with No. 13 Squadron in the Near East Air Force. This Canberra variant was manufactured solely by Short Brothers and Harland, and 45 aircraft of this type had been built when production terminated in 1961.

Power Plants: *Two Rolls-Royce Avon 206 turbojets each rated at 11,250 lb.s.t.*
Performance: *Max. speed (at 35,000 lb.), 553 m.p.h. at 40,000 ft. (Mach 0.838); maximum range (drop tanks jettisoned when empty), 3,970 mls.; initial climb (at 35,000 lb.), 8,000 ft./min.; service ceiling (at 50,000 lb.), 48,000 ft., (at 35,000 lb.), 55,000 ft.*
Weights: *Empty, 29,000 lb.; max. loaded, 57,500 lb.*
Dimensions: *Span, 67 ft. 10 in.; length, 66 ft. 8 in.; height, 15 ft. 7 in.; wing area, 1,044 sq. ft.*

(Above) One of the sixteen SR-71s (61-7954) of the 9th Strategic Reconnaissance Wing based at Beale A.F.B., California.

LOCKHEED SR-71

Introduced into service with the U.S.A.F. Strategic Command's 9th Strategic Reconnaissance Wing in January 1966, the SR-71 is currently the most advanced strategic reconnaissance aircraft to have attained service status, and is claimed to be capable of bringing 60,000 square miles of the earth's surface under surveillance in one hour when flying at 80,000 ft. The SR-71 is the definitive reconnaissance derivative of the Lockheed A-11 which was the successful contender in a design contest held in 1958 for an aircraft combining the survival potential of sustained Mach 3.0 cruise at extreme altitudes with a range capability sufficient to permit deep penetrations of communist territory. Developed largely with funds provided via the Central Intelligence Agency, the first of twelve A-11s was flown late in 1961, three of these subsequently being modified to YF-12A experimental interceptor configuration (Vol. I page 58), and others being involved in the SR-71 development programme initiated in February 1963.

SR-71: Flown for the first time on December 22, 1964, the tandem two-seat SR-71 is essentially similar to the A-11 in overall configuration but substantially heavier, and the initial production contract calls for some 30 aircraft, including several examples of the training version. The pilot and reconnaissance systems operator are seated in conventional ejection seats under individual rearward-hinged canopies, and the wide variety of reconnaissance systems, ranging from simple battlefield surveillance equipment to multiple-sensor, high-performance systems for interdiction reconnaissance and to strategic systems for specialised surveillance, are housed internally. An astro-inertial navigation system, incorporating the inertial guidance platform originally developed for the cancelled GAM-87A Skybolt ASM, is the SR-71's primary navigational aid, this providing accurate navigation without reliance on external aids or detectable signal emissions. The structure of the SR-71, optimized for maximum performance at

(*Above*) *The SR-71B trainer* (61-7956) *and* (*below*) *the SR-71* (61-7950)

gal.) per hour, and take-off is presumably facilitated by starting with a nominal proportion of the 10,000–12,000 U.S. gal. (8,300–10,000 Imp. gal.) total fuel, the tanks subsequently being topped up to capacity in the air. The SR-71 operates at altitudes of 80,000–100,000 ft. at sustained cruising speeds of the order of Mach 3.0, acceleration to speeds in the vicinity of Mach 3.5 being reserved for specific penetrations and escape.

SR-71B: A training version of the SR-71, the SR-71B has an elevated and fully instrumentated cockpit for the pilot instructor, this occupying the position taken by the systems operator in the standard SR-71, the systems operator in the SR-71B being seated lower in the fuselage with ports on either side. Fixed ventral fins under each engine and similar to those featured by the original A-11 are provided to compensate for a decrease in high-speed yaw stability resulting from the introduction of the raised cockpit, and some sensing equipment has been eliminated.

Power Plants: *Two Pratt & Whitney J58 turbojets each rated at 34,000 lb.s.t. with afterburning.*
Performance: *Short-period max. speed,* 2,300* *m.p.h. at 80,000 ft.* (*Mach.* 3.5); *max. sustained cruise,* 1,980 *m.p.h.* (*Mach* 3.0); *endurance at continuous Mach 3.0 cruise,* 1.5 hr.*; *range at 70,000–90,000 ft.,* 3,000* *mls.*
Weights: *Loaded,* 140,000–145,000* *lb.; max.,* 170,000 *lb.*
Dimensions: *Span,* 55 *ft.* 7¼ *in.; length,* 107 *ft.* 4¾ *in.; height,* 18 *ft.* 6 *in.*
*APPROXIMATE

extreme altitudes, is relatively light, making extensive use of titanium alloys, and the 34,000 lb.s.t. J58 turbojets are canted downwards several degrees, enabling the forward fuselage to operate at a higher incidence than the main wing for maximum lift while allowing symmetrical ram air compression during cruise. The J58 single-spool engines employ exotic fuels, and for sustained Mach 3.0 cruise fuel consumption is 8,000 U.S. gal. (6,660 Imp.

GENERAL ARRANGEMENT DRAWING: *An SR-71* (61-7954) *of the* 9*th Strategic Reconnaissance Wing,* 14*th Strategic Aerospace Division, at Beale A.F.B., California.*

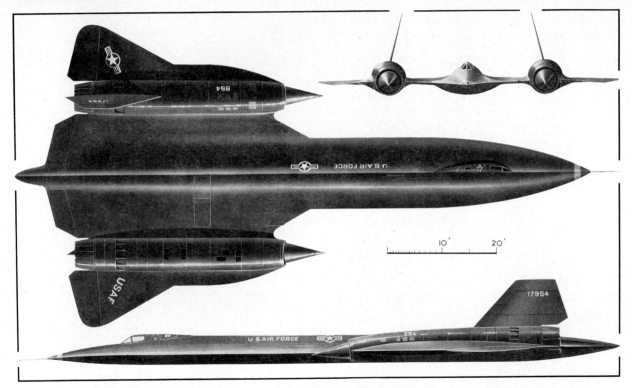

NORTH AMERICAN RA-5C VIGILANTE

Combining reconnaissance with the heavy attack role, the RA-5C is currently operated by the U.S. Navy's Reconnaissance Attack Squadrons (RVAH-) 1, 5, 9, 11, 12 and 13, supplanting both the A-3B Skywarrior and RF-8A Crusader. The RA-5C is essentially

(*Above and below*) *RA-5C Vigilante (Bu.No.150834) in the new camouflage applied in 1966 to some U.S. Navy aircraft in S.E. Asia.*

a reconnaissance aircraft with attack capability evolved from the A-5A medium-range shipboard attack bomber now withdrawn from first-line U.S. Navy service and operated only by RVAH-3 for the training of Vigilante flight and maintenance crews at Sanford Naval Air Station, Florida.

A-5A: The initial model of the Vigilante, the A-5A, was produced to meet a 1955 requirement for an advanced shipboard attack aircraft initially known as the NAGPAW (North American General-Purpose Attack Weapon), the first of two prototypes of which flew on August 31, 1958. Among advanced features embodied by the design were variable-geometry air intakes, 'blown' inboard flaps —the only movable wing trailing edge surfaces—for low-speed control, a 'taileron' for control about all three axes in conjunction with wing-mounted spoiler-deflectors and a single slab vertical surface, and a linear weapons bay—a tunnel running lengthwise in the aft fuselage between the engines—from which stores were ejected rearwards. Production was initiated as the A-5A, and the type was deployed aboard the U.S.S. *Enterprise* with VAH-7 in August 1962. However, the A-5A suffered protracted teething troubles which were associated primarily with the revolutionary method of launching internally-housed stores—the linear bay was fitted with rails and a catapult and was intended to permit a wide variety of delivery manoeuvres for the nuclear store—and these, coupled with the U.S. Navy's belief that strategic bombing should not be part of the service's assignment, curtailed procurement, and only 55 A-5As were delivered, the majority of these having since been converted to the RA-5C configuration.

A-5B: The first of two growth versions of the Vigilante with increased range and load-carrying capabilities, the A-5B was flown on April 29, 1962, and, intended primarily for the attack role,

GENERAL ARRANGEMENT DRAWING: *An RA-5C Vigilante (Bu.No. 149306) of Reconnaissance Attack Squadron (RVAH-) 5, the 'Savage Sons of Sanford', from the U.S.S.* Ranger.

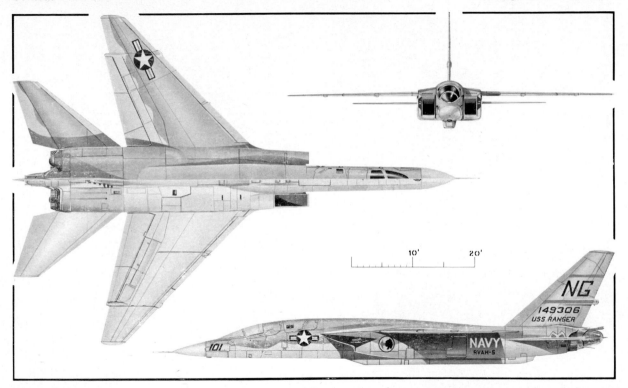

This photograph of an RA-5C (Bu.No.151622) of RVAH-1 from the U.S.S. Independence *shows clearly the ventral fairing in which side-looking airborne radar and a variety of cameras may be mounted in removable modules. Only two of the permissible four underwing pylons are seen fitted, and these may carry such items as chaff-dispensing or strobe-type flasher pods, or fuel tanks.*

featured enlarged flaps, an extension of the boundary layer control system to blow air over the top surfaces of the wing from front to rear, raised dorsal fuselage contours, and the provision of two additional underwing stores pylons. Only prototypes of the A-5B were completed, production examples on the assembly line being modified to RA-5C standards with the change in accent from attack to reconnaissance capabilities.

RA-5C: Embodying the aerodynamic changes introduced in the A-5B and retaining the REINS (Radar Equipped Inertial Navigation System) equipment of the A-5A, the RA-5C carries an extremely

sophisticated reconnaissance system which feeds information back to the Integrated Operational Intelligence Centre for processing and rapid evaluation. Carrying two crew members seated in tandem, the RA-5C includes in its reconnaissance equipment vertical, oblique and split-image cameras, and SLAR (Side-Looking Airborne Radar) is mounted in removable modules in a long ventral fairing. It possesses both active and passive electronic countermeasures capability with sensors in radio and infra-red regions, and the associated equipment is packaged in the linear bay. Two high-intensity strobe-type flasher pods are mounted on the underwing pylons to illuminate the ground beneath the aircraft. Each of the four pylons can lift a 400 U.S. gal. (330 Imp. gal.) fuel tank or a 2,500-lb. load of offensive stores, including 1,000-lb. Mk.83 or 2,000-lb. Mk.84 bombs, or AGM-12 Bullpup ASMs.

The prototype RA-5C flew on June 30, 1962, and the first squadron to convert to this type was RVAH-5 whose aircraft were deployed aboard the U.S.S. *Ranger* in June 1964. Production of the RA-5C had been completed by the beginning of 1966 at which time the conversion of A-5As to RA-5C standards was continuing.

Power Plants: *Two General Electric J79-GE-8 turbojets each rated at 10,900 lb.s.t. and 17,000 lb.s.t. with afterburning.*
Performance: *Max. speed, 1,385 m.p.h. at 40,000 ft. (Mach 2.1); max. stabilised speed (clean condition), 1,254 m.p.h. (Mach 1.9); max. low-level cruise, 633 m.p.h. (Mach 0.83); range cruise, 560 m.p.h. at 40,000 ft. (Mach 0.85); max. range, 2,995 mls.; operational ceiling, 64,000 ft.*
Weights: *Loaded, 61,730 lb.*
Dimensions: *Span, 53 ft. 0 in.; length, 73 ft. 2½ in.; height, 19 ft. 4¾ in.; wing area, 725* sq. ft.*
*APPROXIMATE

TACTICAL RECONNAISSANCE

The essential features of a tactical reconnaissance aircraft are good stability at high speeds and low level, coupled with long fatigue life and effective defensive armament. In addition, lateral intakes simplify the installation of cameras. The F-86F Sabre has admittedly been converted for photo-reconnaissance, but the nose-intake layout requires more extensive structural modifications, and probably gives less accessibility. Of the subsonic fighter conversions, the most successful have been the Hunter F.R.Mk.10 (a three-camera aircraft based on the five-camera private venture) and the RF-84F Thunderflash which can accommodate up to six cameras in the nose. On the Russian side, tactical reconnaissance is largely carried out by the two-seat Yak-28 (Flashlight-D), the glazed nasal position clearly giving superior visual surveillance capability. An aircraft that has proved its use in Vietnam is the electronic-reconnaissance EA-4E Skyhawk, which detects the illumination radars of the SA-2 Guideline sites, and directs strikes by F-100s and F-105s.

Turning to supersonic types, most of this work is still carried out

by the RF-8A Crusader and RF-101C Voodoo. The U.S. Navy RF-8A, of which 144 were built, has a squared-off centre fuselage containing three CAX-12 trimetrogon cameras and two vertical K-17s. One of these unarmed aircraft was shot down while flying reconnaissance over Laos in mid-1964, and the type has seen considerable active service in low level missions over Cuban missile bases in 1962, and more recently in Vietnam. Tactical Air Command's RF-101C has a basic fit of one 12-inch KA-2 forward oblique and a fan of three KA-2s or KA-18s giving horizon-to-horizon cover. Optional extras include a pair of 36-inch KA-1s fitted just behind the cockpit to give precision mapping from altitude, and a Fairchild KA-52 panoramic camera using a rotating prism to produce a 180-degree scan at each exposure. The RF-101C has likewise been employed over Cuba and Vietnam, and the type acquired some degree of notoriety on April 16, 1965, when a TAC aircraft on a training flight made four unauthorised photographic runs over the secret French nuclear complex at Pierrelatte, hotly pursued by a Vautour IIN!

Continued on page 116—

A small number of F-86F Sabre fighter-bombers were converted for the tactical reconnaissance role as RF-86Fs, one K-17 and two K-22 cameras being installed in a special bay beneath the cockpit. Mitsubishi produced 18 such conversions, and these (right) currently equip the Japanese Air Self-Defence Force's No. 501 Reconnaissance Squadron.

(*Left*) *Mirage IIIR tactical reconnaissance aircraft of Escadron 3/33 "Moselle".*

DASSAULT MIRAGE IIIR

Intended for low- and medium-altitude day and night reconnaissance and armed reconnaissance missions, the Mirage IIIR is essentially a derivative of the Mirage IIIE strike fighter (Vol. I, pages 76–78), and equips the two operational *escadrons*, 2/33 'Savoie' and 3/33 'Moselle', of the *Armée de l'Air*'s only tactical reconnaissance wing, the 33e *Escadre de Reconnaissance Tactique*. The airframe and power plant of the Mirage IIIR are basically similar to those of the IIIE, but the redesigned and lengthened nose replaces the Cyrano II radar of the strike fighter with an array of OMERA Type 31 cameras. The forward compartment in the extreme nose can accommodate an F100 vertical or F200 forward oblique camera, and alternative arrangements in the main compartment include a mix of up to four side oblique F100, F200 and F600 cameras for day missions, or one vertical and two oblique F200 or F600 cameras and a photo-electric cell for nocturnal missions, a CSF radar altimeter automatically adjusting the camera repetition rate in relation to altitude. A removable flare launcher for 80 7.62-cm. photo-flash cartridges which may be fired singly, continuously or in salvo, is fitted for night missions.

GENERAL ARRANGEMENT DRAWING: *A Mirage IIIR (No. 305) of Escadron 3/33 'Moselle' of the 33e Escadre de Reconnaissance Tactique, Armée de l'Air, based at Strasbourg-Entzheim.*

0   5'   10'

For the armed reconnaissance mission a removable mounting with twin 30-mm. DEFA 5-52 cannon and 250 rounds of ammunition may be installed in the forward fuselage bay, and similar underwing loads to those of the Mirage IIIE may be carried, the pilot being provided with a SFOM reflector sight and a CSF LABS (Low Altitude Bombing System). Fuel is housed in two 108 Imp. gal. (130 U.S. gal.) and one 80 Imp. gal. (96 U.S. gal.)

fuselage tanks, and two 114 Imp. gal. (137 U.S. gal.) wing tanks. For extended missions, these tanks may be supplemented by an auxiliary tank of 70 Imp. gal. (84 U.S. gal.) in the forward fuselage bay in place of the cannon pack, and two 137 or 286 Imp. gal. (164 or 343 U.S. gal.) underwing drop tanks.

The first of 80 Mirage IIIR tactical reconnaissance aircraft for the *Armée de l'Air* flew on February 1, 1963, and an essentially similar aircraft for Switzerland's *Flugwaffe* is designated Mirage IIIRS. A prototype of the Mirage IIIRS was built and tested by the parent company in mid-1965, and a further 17 aircraft of this type are to be manufactured in Switzerland with deliveries to the *Flugwaffe* from mid-1968 to mid-1969. The Mirage IIIRS is being fitted with the TARAN-1RS, this consisting of the basic navigation element of the complete TARAN fire-control radar of the Mirage IIIS interceptor. Its map display is driven by the inertial platform, but the IIIRS carries no radar. It is normally flown with two flush-fitting, non-jettisonable underwing tanks of 110 Imp. gal. (132 U.S. gal.) capacity.

Power Plant: *One SNECMA Atar 9C3 turbojet rated at 9,436 lb.s.t. and 13,624 lb.s.t. with afterburning.*
Performance: *Max. speed, 1,420 m.p.h. at 39,370 ft. (Mach 2.15), 925 m.p.h. at sea level (Mach 1.21); max. stabilised speed, 1,188 m.p.h. at 60,000 ft. (Mach 1.8); range (max. external fuel), 1,290 mls. at 595 m.p.h. (Mach 0.9) at 36,000 ft.; tactical radius (clean), 180 mls. at sea level, (with max. fuel), 350 mls.; max. endurance, 2 hr. 10 min.; time to 36,000 ft., 6 min.*
Weights: *Empty, 14,330 lb.; loaded, 19,840 lb.; max., 27,116 lb.*
Dimensions: *Span, 26 ft. 11½ in.; length, 46 ft. 5 in. (including probe), 50 ft. 10½ in.; height, 13 ft. 9⅛ in.; wing area, 365.973 sq. ft.*

GRUMMAN OV-1 MOHAWK

Grumman's Model G-134 frontline tactical observation and reconnaissance aircraft was originally conceived under a joint U.S. Army-Marine Corps programme, being subsequently developed solely for the Army with which it currently serves as the OV-1 Mohawk. Operated in Vietnam since July 1962, the OV-1 has proved particularly successful in the surveillance and target acquisition role with the result that procurement, which was stopped in Fiscal 1964, has been resumed by the U.S. Army which is purchasing some 15 in Fiscal 1966 and 30 in Fiscal 1967. Three basic versions of the OV-1 have been manufactured for the U.S. Army: the OV-1A for visual and photographic reconnaissance; the OV-1B for electronic surveillance of large areas, and the OV-1C with infra-red surveillance equipment for the detection of enemy concentrations in tactical-size areas. The OV-1A arrived in Vietnam with the 23rd Special Warfare Aviation Detachment shortly after its début in U.S. Army service, and in the autumn of 1964 was joined by the 4th Aerial Surveillance and Target Acquisition Detachment equipped with the OV-1B and -1C. These two units were combined to form the 73rd Aerial Surveillance Company in January 1965, and this unit, operating primarily from Vung Tao, is equipped with a mixture of all Mohawk versions.

The first of an initial evaluation and development batch of nine YOV-1A Mohawks flew on April 14, 1959, the design providing from the outset for the installation of camera, infra-red and radar reconnaissance and surveillance systems without major structural modifications. The two crew members were seated in side-by-side ejection seats, armour protection being provided for both pilot and observer, and design accents were placed on rough-field and STOL capabilities and a high degree of manoeuvrability, leading-edge slats and large-span flaps enabling the basic Mohawk without external stores to take-off and clear a 50-ft. obstacle within 880 ft., and minimum constant-altitude turning radius at sea level is 355 ft. with 1.6 g.

OV-1A: The initial version which entered service with the U.S. Army in 1962, the OV-1A for visual and photo reconnaissance has an internally-mounted KA-30 camera for oblique and vertical photography in mid-fuselage, some examples also having a Fairchild KA-60 panoramic camera mounted in the nose. Fifty-two flares for night photography may be carried by two removable upward-firing pods mounted above the wing roots, and there are two external stores stations under the wing which may each carry a 150 U.S. gal. (125 Imp. gal.) or 300 U.S. gal. (250 Imp. gal.) fuel tank. Standard fuel is housed by a single 276 U.S. gal. (230 Imp. gal.) tank located in the fuselage over the wing. The aircraft is stressed to withstand a positive load factor of 5 g, and hydraulically-operated air brakes are attached to the fuselage sides, maximum diving speed being equivalent to 450 m.p.h.

JOV-1A: Employed by the 73rd A.S.C. for armed reconnaissance missions, the JOV-1A ('J' indicating special test) is a survivor of the U.S. Army's incursion into the field of armed fixed-wing aircraft terminated in the spring of 1965 by the Defense Department. Originally operated by the 11th Air Assault Division, the JOV-1A is essentially similar to the standard OV-1A but has a gunsight and is equipped for conventional ordnance delivery, two additional pylons being added outboard of the standard stores station beneath each wing (the hard points for the additional pylons being incorporated in the structure of all Mohawks), each station having a 500-lb. capacity. These pylons usually carry a mixture of 2.75-in. rocket pods and 0.5-in. machine-gun pods.

OV-1B: The electronic surveillance OV-1B differs from the -1A in a number of respects. Carrying APS-94 SLAR (Side-Looking Airborne Radar) in an 18-ft. fibreglass pod slung asymmetrically beneath the starboard fuselage side, equipped with APN-129 Doppler, and retaining the KA-30 camera, the OV-1B does not feature the dual controls of the -1A, and is crewed by a pilot and

(Left) The Grummam OV-1B Mohawk electric surveillance aircraft, seen in the camouflage applied for service in S.E. Asia, has enjoyed considerable success in Vietnam.

the KA-30 camera, the OV-1C has a UAS-4 infra-red sensor mounted in the underside of the aft fuselage, and single pilot controls with the systems operator seated to starboard. The first of 31 OV-1C Mohawks modified by the introduction of later infra-red equipment, real-time data link capability, and uprated engines was delivered to the U.S. Army mid-1966.

Power Plants: *Two Lycoming T53-L-3 (-7) turboprops each rated at 1,005 (1,150) e.s.h.p.*
Performance: *Max. speed, 308 (297) m.p.h. at 5,000 ft.; max. cruise, 304 (275) m.p.h.; econ. cruise, 251 (257) m.p.h.; range at 230 m.p.h. at 5,000 ft., 437 (414) mls., with two 150 U.S. gal./125 Imp. gal. auxiliary tanks, 906 (872) mls.; initial climb, 2,950 (2,350) ft./min.; service ceiling, 25,000 ft.*
Weights: *Empty, 10,000 (10,975) lb.; loaded, 12,672 (13,650) lb.; max., 15,031 (15,983) lb.*
Dimensions: *Span, 42 ft. 0 in. (47 ft. 10¾ in.); length, 41 ft. 0 in. (43 ft. 7¾ in.); height, 12 ft. 8 in.; wing area, 330 (360.59) sq. ft.*
Note: *Specification relates to OV-1A, figures in parentheses applying to the OV-1B.*

SLAR operator, the latter being seated to starboard. An autopilot is provided, and airframe changes include the removal of the air brakes and an increase in wing-span from 42 ft. 0 in. to 47 ft. 10¾ in. The increased weights of 10,975 lb. empty equipped and 13,650 lb. in normal loaded condition, or 15,983 lb. with two 150 U.S. gal. auxiliary tanks, are catered for by the replacement of the -1A's 1,005 e.s.h.p. T53-L-3 turboprops by 1,150 e.s.h.p. T53-L-7s.

OV-1C: Physically the same aircraft as the OV-1A and retaining

GENERAL ARRANGEMENT DRAWING: *An OV-1B Mohawk (25888) serving with the U.S. 7th Army in Germany.*

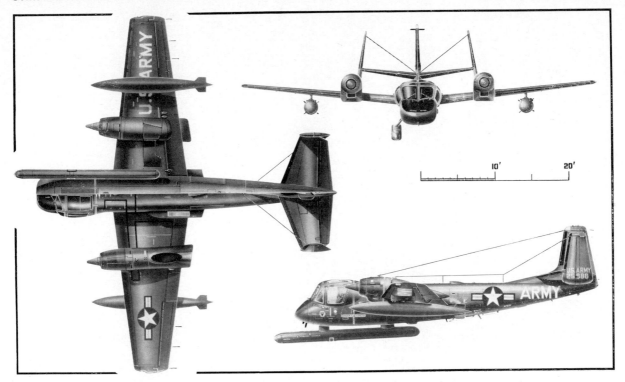

(Left) An RF-8G Crusader of VFP-63, the first U.S. Navy unit to operate this re-manufactured version of the original RF-8A. Changes include the introduction of a "hard harness" wiring system, modified camera stations, new avionics and provision for underwing sensor pods.

LING-TEMCO-VOUGHT RF-8 CRUSADER

The RF-8 Crusader, which achieved some prominence during the Cuban Crisis in 1962 when the U.S. Navy's Light Photographic Squadron 62 (VFP-62) undertook daily low-level aerial surveillance flights over the island with aircraft of this type, was evolved in parallel with the F-8 shipboard interceptor (page 107, Vol. I), and in its remanufactured RF-8G version equips both U.S. Navy Light Photographic Squadrons, VFP-62 and -63 which deploy detachments to the various Carrier Air Wings.

The conversion of the basic F-8 interceptor to RF-8 unarmed reconnaissance standards involved the replacement of the cannon and fire control equipment by a camera bay of squared-off section, this accommodating three CAX-12 trimetrogen cameras and two K-17 vertical cameras. To compensate for the increased cross-sectional area resulting from the introduction of this bay, the upper contour of the fuselage was area-ruled to result in a slightly humped-back profile. Provision was made for internally-stowed photo-flash bombs, and powered by a similar J57-P-4A turbojet to that of the F-8A interceptor, the first photo-reconnaissance model, the RF-8A, was flown on December 17, 1956. A total of 144 RF-8A Crusaders was subsequently built, and in addition to

being issued to VFP-62 and -63, they served with the Marine Corps Composite Reconnaissance Squadrons (VMCJ) 1, 2 and 3 in which, during 1966, they were in process of replacement by the RF-4B Phantom II. Twin ventral fins for improved directional stability, particularly at high speeds, were added retrospectively to some RF-8As, and in January 1965 Ling-Temco-Vought was awarded a contract for the remanufacture of 53 U.S. Navy RF-8As.

The remanufactured model, which has received the designation RF-8G, switches from the J57-P-4A turbojet to the -22; adopts a "hard harness" type wiring system similar to that embodied in the later interceptor models of the Crusader; introduces modified camera stations with KA-45, KA-46, KA-53 and KA-58 cameras, although the ability to mount the CAX-12 trimetrogen camera arrangement is retained, and navigational capability is improved by the addition of the APN-153B Doppler radar and an ASN-41

GENERAL ARRANGEMENT DRAWING: *An RF-8G Crusader (Bu. No. 146871) of U.S. Navy Light Photographic Squadron (VFP-) 63 based at Naval Air Station Miramar, California.*

computer. The J57-P-22 turbojet is rated at 10,200 lb.s.t. and 16,000 lb. with afterburning, but as installed in the RF-8G it delivers 8,130 lb.s.t. and 12,434 lb. with afterburning. Ventral fins have been standardised for the RF-8G, and a stronger wing spar is incorporated during the process of remanufacture, permitting provision of a strong point in each wing for electronic reconnaissance sensor pods. No provision is made for drop tanks.

The first RF-8G was flown on August 31, 1965, and the first of two U.S. Navy Light Photographic Squadrons to convert from the RF-8A to the RF-8G, VFP-63 at NAS Miramar, received the first example of the remanufactured aircraft on October 4, 1965, subsequently deploying the RF-8G with detachments aboard carriers of the Pacific Fleet.

Power Plant: *One Pratt & Whitney J57-P-22 turbojet rated at 10,200 lb.s.t. and 16,000 lb.s.t. with afterburning.*
Performance: *Max. speed (clean),* 1,076 *m.p.h. at 40,000 ft. (Mach 1.63); range cruise (with external sensor pods),* 574 *m.p.h. at 36,000 ft. (Mach 0.87); tactical radius,* 600 *mls.; max. unrefuelled range,* 1,300 *mls.; time to 55,000 ft.,* 6.2 *min.; service ceiling,* 55,000 *ft.*
Weights: *Empty,* 18,500 *lb.; Loaded,* 29,000 *lb.; max. loaded,* 32,000* *lb.*
Dimensions: *Span,* 35 *ft.* 2 *in.; length,* 54 *ft.* 3 *in.; height,* 15 *ft.* 9 *in.; wing area,* 350* *sq. ft.*
*APPROXIMATE

McDONNELL RF-4 PHANTOM II

The development of multiple-sensor reconnaissance versions of the F-4 Phantom II fighter (see page 115, Vol. I) for the U.S.A.F. and U.S. Marine Corps was initiated in 1962, emphasis being initially placed on the model for the former service, the RF-4C which is currently supplanting the RF-101C and RB-66C with the Tactical

Reconnaissance Wings of the U.S.A.F.'s Tactical Air Command, and which had been deployed operationally over Vietnam by the beginning of 1966 when one of the 363rd Tactical Reconnaissance Wing's squadrons joined the 460th TRW's RF-101C Voodoos.

RF-4C: Identical to the F-4C in all its major structural, control and power plant elements, except for the forward fuselage which has been lengthened and re-contoured to accommodate a complete complement of cameras, an optical viewfinder, and other reconnaissance equipment, the RF-4C has been assigned to the 10th, 26th, 67th 363rd and 460th Tactical Reconnaissance Wings, the production example having flown on May 18, 1964. This was preceded by two YRF-4C prototypes converted on the assembly line from U.S. Navy F-4Bs for development and evaluation purposes, the first of these having flown on August 20, 1963. The

The YRF-4C (below), originally a modified U.S. Navy F-4B, was modified late in 1965 to serve as a prototype for the proposed TSF (Tactical Strike Fighter) version of the Phantom II.

GENERAL ARRANGEMENT DRAWING: *An RF-4C Phantom II* (65-0855) *of the 22nd Tactical Reconnaissance Squadron of the 26th TRW.*

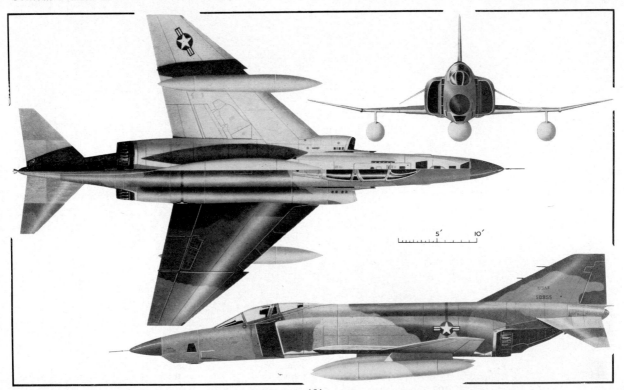

5′   10′

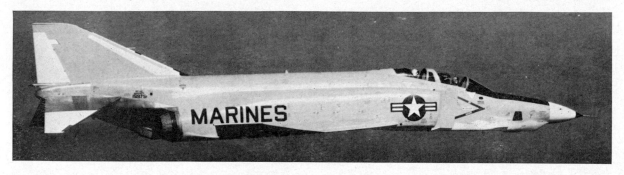

(Above) The first RF-4B Phantom II (Bu. No. 151975) for the U.S. Marine Corps, and (below) an RF-4C of the 22nd Tactical Reconnaissance Squadron of the 26th T.R.W. The RF-4B lacks the dual controls featured by the RF-4C, and retains the probe-type flight refuelling system and smaller wheels of the shipboard F-4B. Other changes include provision of rotatable camera mounts and the deletion of some avionics.

RF-4C embodies all the changes introduced by the U.S.A.F.'s F-4C, but the missile control radar and provision for Sparrow missiles have been deleted, the missile well space being utilized for infra-red and radar reconnaissance equipment. The aft fuselage has been modified for photo flash ejectors for night target illumination and long-range HF communications equipment, the antenna for which is mounted in the leading edge of the vertical tail surfaces.

Capable of all-weather, high-low, day-night selective reconnaissance, the RF-4C carries a Hycon KS-72A forward oblique framing camera, and Fairchild KA-56 low- and high-altitude panoramic cameras in the nose bay. The KA-56 cameras employ rotating prisms and incorporate equipment for rapid in-flight processing and an ejection device for dropping film casettes to intelligence posts for immediate use. An alternative tri-camera array of twin 6-in. side oblique cameras and one 3-in. vertical camera may be installed between the low- and high-altitude panoramic cameras. The nose bay also houses the forward-looking radar, this being smaller than that of the F-4C and, enclosed by an upward-folding radome, results in a 37 per cent weight reduction in the nose section. A SLAR (Side-Looking Aircraft Radar) antenna is mounted beneath the forward cockpit, the computer and recorder control being housed in the equipment bay occupying part of the space of the No. 1 fuselage fuel cell of the F-4C; the forward-looking radar is primarily for terrain avoidance but is scope-monitored and has limited reconnaissance capability; the Litton ASN-48 inertial system differs from that of the F-4C in having a reconnaissance adapter unit stabilizing the various sensors in flight, and the systems operator who occupies the second cockpit is provided with full dual controls permitting him to act as second pilot on long endurance missions.

RF-4B: Configured for the U.S. Marine Corps, the RF-4B features the extended nose and reconnaissance sensor installations of the RF-4C mated to the F-4B airframe with probe-type in-flight refuelling system and the smaller mainwheels of its fighter equivalent. Other changes include the addition of rotatable camera mounts, the deletion of certain electronic reconnaissance equipment and unduplicated flight controls, and the RF-4B has no armament capability. The first RF-4B was flown on March 12, 1965.

(Right) An RF-4C (64-1019) of the 10th Tactical Reconnaissance Wing, U.S.A.F.E., landing at Alconbury with one 600 U.S. gal. (500 Imp. gal.) and two 370 U.S. gal. (308 Imp. gal.) long-range tanks. Two RF-4C wings were included in U.S.A.F.E. strength, one based in the U.K. and the other in France, until the summer of 1966 when one squadron of the French-based 26th T.R.W. was transferred to the U.K., the other squadron being repatriated.

Power Plants: *Two General Electric J79-GE-15 turbojets each rated at 10,900 lb.s.t. and 17,000 lb.s.t. with afterburning.*
Performance: *Max. speed (clean), 1,485 m.p.h. at 48,000 ft. (Mach 2.25), 950 m.p.h. at 1,000 ft. (Mach 1.2); low level tactical radius (with 600 U.S. gal./500 Imp. gal. drop tank), 600* mls. at 510 m.p.h.; high altitude tactical radius (clean), 800* mls.; ferry range (with one 600 U.S. gal./500 Imp. gal. and two 370 U.S. gal./308 Imp. gal. drop tanks), 2,300 mls. at 575 m.p.h. at 40,000 ft.; initial climb, 27,000–28,000* ft./min.; operational ceiling, 62,000 ft.*
Weights: *Empty, 30,000* lb.; loaded (clean), 46,500* lb.*
Dimensions: *Span, 38 ft. 4¾ in.; length, 62 ft. 10½ in.; height, 16 ft. 6 in.; wing area, 530 sq. ft.*
*APPROXIMATE
Note: *Specification applies specifically to RF-4C but is generally applicable to RF-4B.*

103

McDONNELL RF-101 VOODOO

The RF-101, which has borne the brunt of the U.S.A.F.'s tactical reconnaissance commitment in Vietnam, operating from Tan Son Nhut with Pac.A.F. and other squadrons assigned to the 7th. A.F., has outlived in operational service the single-seat tactical strike fighter from which it was derived. To meet a Tactical Air Command requirement for a photographic aircraft with high supersonic speed capability, the RF-101 was an adaptation of the F-101 strike fighter which had first flown on September 29, 1954. Twenty-nine pre-production and 50 production F-101As were followed by 47 F-101Cs, the later model embodying some structural strengthening

to improve its low-level capabilities, and the strike fighter served with one T.A.C. unit, the 81st Tactical Fighter Wing which finally relinquished its Voodoos in 1965. The first of two photo-reconnaissance prototypes, designated YRF-101A, was flown on May 10, 1956, this differing from the F-101A in having the cannon armament deleted, the fuselage nose extended, and facilities provided for six electronically-controlled high-speed framing cameras. The first three production aircraft (RF-101A-20) had similar fuel tankage to the F-101A, but subsequent aircraft (RF-101A-25, -35, -40, etc.) had the 2,126 U.S. gal (1,773 Imp. gal.) fuselage tank capacity supplemented by a 90 U.S. gal. (75 Imp. gal.) tank in each wing.

RF-101C: Only 35 production RF-101As had been completed when similar structural strengthening to that applied to the F-101C strike fighter resulted in the RF-101C being introduced on the assembly line, the first example of this variant flying on July 12, 1957, and 166 subsequently being manufactured. Cameras normally comprised a long focal length Fairchild KA-1 framing camera, one vertical and two side oblique KA-2 framing cameras, and one CAI KA-18 strip camera, but during 1964, a modernisation

(Left) An RF-101C Voodoo (56-0201) o the 66th Tactical Reconnaissance Wing, a component of the U.S.A.F.E.

GENERAL ARRANGEMENT DRAWING: *An RF-101C-55 Voodoo of the 66th Tactical Reconnaissance Wing, U.S.A.F.E., based at Upper Heyford, Oxfordshire.*

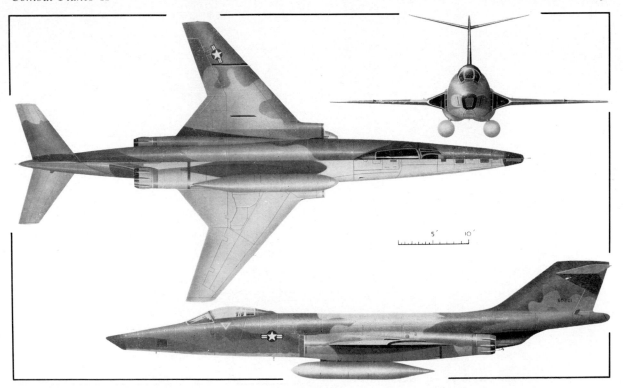

5′   10′

The RF-101 Voodoo has borne much of the brunt of the U.S.A.F.'s tactical reconnaissance commitment in Vietnam, its designated successor being the RF-4C Phantom II. RF-101 units operating in S.E. Asia have suffered a relatively high attrition rate, and the two RF-101C-55 Voodoos illustrated above are part of a Pac.A.F. unit.

programme resulted in Hycon KS-72A cameras replacing the KA-2s and faster KA-45s which had been installed in some RF-101Cs during the previous year. The F-101A and C Voodoos relinquished by the 81st T.F.W. have been modified to RF-101 configuration originally to re-equip the A.N.G.'s 123rd Tactical Reconnaissance Wing assigned to the Tactical Air Command, and 25 RF-101C Voodoos have been supplied to the Chinese Nationalist Air Force. RF-101C squadrons operating in Vietnam have suffered a high rate of attrition—one squadron losing 70 per cent of its original aircraft in nine months—and the Voodoo is being supplemented and will eventually be replaced by the RF-4C

Phantom II, but is likely to remain in the U.S.A.F.'s inventory until 1968.

Power Plants: *Two Pratt & Whitney J57-P-13 turbojets each rated at 10,100 lb.s.t. and 14,880 lb.s.t. with afterburning.*
Performance: *Max. speed, 1,040 m.p.h. at 38,000 ft. (Mach 1.58), 716 m.p.h. at sea level (Mach 0.94); range cruise (clean), 575 m.p.h. at 36,000 ft. (Mach 0.87); max. range, 1,700 mls., (with two 450 U.S. gal./375 Imp. gal. drop tanks) 2,200 mls.; initial climb rate, 14,000 ft./min.; service ceiling, 52,000 ft.*
Weights: *Normal loaded, 42,550 lb.; max., 48,720 lb.*
Dimensions: *Span, 39 ft. 8 in.; length, 69 ft. 3 in.; height, 18 ft. 0 in.; wing area, 368 sq. ft.*

REPUBLIC RF-84F THUNDERFLASH

Evolved in parallel with the F-84F Thunderstreak specifically for the tactical reconnaissance role, the RF-84F possesses an essentially similar airframe to that of the fighter-bomber, but the introduction of wing root air intake duct location in order to permit the installation of a camera bay in the nose drastically changes the external appearance of the aircraft. Phased out of service with the U.S.A.F., the RF-84F is currently operated by the 42*ème Escadrille* by the *Force Aérienne Belge*, the No. 729 *Eskadrille* of the R.Dan.A.F., a squadron of the Royal Hellenic Air Force, the 18° and 132° *Gruppi* of the *Aeronautica Militare Italiano*, Nr. 717 *Skvadron* of the R.No.A.F., and a squadron of the Turkish Air Force's 1st Tactical Air Force, 386 of the 715 RF-84Fs manufactured having been acquired for supply to foreign air forces under Mutual Defence programmes.

The prototype Thunderflash, the YRF-84F, was flown in February 1952, this being, in fact, the first pre-production machine, and deliveries to S.A.C. and T.A.C. reconnaissance units began in

March 1954, the 715th and last production example being completed in January 1958. The first production RF-84Fs were powered by the 7,200 lb.s.t. Wright J65-W-3 turbojet, but later aircraft received the uprated J65-W-7. The camera bay in the nose accommodates up to six cameras in forward-facing, trimetrogen and individual oblique and vertical installations. The vertical

(Above, right) An RF-84F Thunderflash (52-7394) of the Aeronautica Militare Italiano, and (right) an RF-84F of Belgium's 42ème Escadrille. The RF-84F remains in first-line service and provides the primary tactical reconnaissance capability with six air arms.

(*Above*) *RF-84F Thunderflash aircraft of the Danish No.729 Squadron.*

camera bay has hydraulically-operated retractable doors, and behind these there is an aperture for a vertical viewfinder with periscopic presentation on the cockpit panel. The RF-84F may also be used for nocturnal photographic-reconnaissance missions, photoflash ejectors being carried in underwing tanks.

The wing root intakes are slightly less efficient than the nose intake of the F-48F Thunderstreak (Vol. I, page 158), but the performance handicap is marginal, the RF-84F being redlined at Mach 1.175 as compared with Mach 1.18 for the fighter-bomber. Total fuel capacity, including two 450 U.S. gal. (375 Imp. gal.) drop tanks is of the order of 1,500 U.S. gal. (1,250 Imp. gal.), and an armament of four 0.5-in. M-3 machine guns are installed in the outer intake walls. Later production RF-84Fs introduced spoilers on the upper surface of each wing to boost the maximum rate of roll to 300° per second, mainly to cater for asymmetric "hang-ups" of underwing tanks.

Power Plant: *One Wright J65-W-7 turbojet rated at 7,800 lb.s.t.*
Performance: *Max. speed (clean), 679 m.p.h. at sea level (Mach 0.89), 607 m.p.h. at 35,000 ft. (Mach 0.92); tactical radius (clean), 420* mls. at 36,000–40,000 ft.; maximum range (with two 450 U.S. gal./375 Imp. gal drop tanks), 2,000* mls.; initial climb (clean), 7,900 ft./min.; service ceiling, 46,000 ft.*
Weights: *Loaded (with two 450 U.S. gal./375 Imp. gal. drop tanks), 26,800 lb.*
Dimensions: *Span, 33 ft. 7¼ in.; length, 47 ft. 7¾ in.; height, 15 ft. 0 in.; wing area, 330* sq. ft.*
*APPROXIMATE

GENERAL ARRANGEMENT DRAWING: *An RF-84F Thunderflash (FR-15) of the 42ème Escadrille de Reconnaissance-Photographique of the Force Aérienne Belge based at Bierset.*

(Above) An S35E Draken tactical reconnaissance aircraft of the Flygvapnet's F21, and (left) the array of seven OMERA cameras carried by the S35E in the nose bay and wing housings. Up to four drop tanks may be carried for extended-range missions.

SAAB 35E DRAKEN

A tactical reconnaissance derivative of the J35D fighter embodying some features introduced by the J35F, such as a redesigned and raised cockpit canopy and the Saab zero-zero ejection seat, the Saab 35E flew in prototype form on June 27, 1963, and as the S35E entered service with one *Division* of F11 at Nyköping in the autumn of 1965, the first aircraft being delivered to the wing on August 17th of that year. A second *Division* of F11 converted to the S35E during the course of 1966 when deliveries also began to F21 at Luleå in northern Sweden.

Structurally similar to the J35D, the S35E is not intended as a

GENERAL ARRANGEMENT DRAWING: *An S35E Draken of F21, the Norrbottens Flygbaskår, at Kallax, Luleå*

During 1966, the S35E began to supplant the obsolete S29C with F21 at Luleå, an S35E from this wing, sporting the new camouflage adopted by Flygvapnet for all tactical aircraft during 1966, being illustrated (left).

multiple-sensor aircraft, and has no radar reconnaissance capability, its reconnaissance equipment being restricted to a battery of OMERA cameras comprising two SKa 24-600 vertical cameras in the wing bay occupied by cannon in the J35D, and one SKa16B forward oblique, one SKa24-600, one SKa24-44 vertical and two SKa24-100 side oblique cameras in the redesigned nose. The pilot, who has a Jungner optical camera sight, can select either high or low altitude mission alternatives without changing cameras or film magazines, and to permit quick access to and extraction of camera magazines the nose cone slides forward on rails. A Saab FH 5 flight control system is provided, and equipment includes PN-59/A and PN-793/A navaids, and Fr17 VHF with Fr16 stand-by. Internal fuel tankage of 630 Imp. gal. (757 U.S. gal.) may be supplemented by 50 Imp. gal. in auxiliary tanks in the wing camera bays, and for long-range or ferry missions two or four 113 Imp. gal. (135 U.S. gal.) drop tanks may be carried beneath the wings and fuselage.

Powered by a similar RM6C engine to the J35F interceptor, the S35E is 937 lb. lighter than the F-model in clean loaded condition, climb rate and ceiling being marginally higher. It is scheduled to remain in *Flygvapnet's* active inventory throughout most of the 'seventies, and will share the reconnaissance task with the S37 Viggen, which will have both camera and non-optical reconnaissance systems.

Power Plant: *One Svenska Flygmotor RM6C (Rolls-Royce RB.146 Mk.60 Avon) rated at 12,710 lb.s.t. and 17,260 lb.s.t. with afterburning.*

Performance: *Max. speed (clean), 1,255–1,320* m.p.h. at 36,000–40,000 ft. (Mach 1.9–2.0), 875* m.p.h. at sea level (Mach 1.15); range cruise (max. external fuel), 560* m.p.h. at 40,000 ft. (Mach 0.85); tactical radius (internal fuel), 350 mls.; ferry range (with four 113 Imp. gal./135 U.S. gal. drop tanks), 900–1,000* mls.; initial climb, 39,500 ft./min.; service ceiling, 55,000 ft.*

Weights: *Empty, 16,118 lb.; loaded (clean), 21,892 lb.; max. loaded, 26,000 lb.*

Dimensions: *Span, 30 ft. 10¾ in.; length (including probe), 50 ft. 4 in., (excluding probe) 46 ft. 10¼ in.; height, 12 ft. 8⅛ in.; wing area, 529.8 sq. ft.*

*APPROXIMATE

YAKOVLEV YAK-28 (FLASHLIGHT-D)

A second generation derivative of the Yak-25 (*Flashlight-A*) tandem two-seat night and all-weather interceptor now obsolescent but retained in V.-V.S. service, the Yak-28 was evolved by the Yakovlev design bureau in competition with the Il-54 from the Ilyushin design bureau during the early 'fifties as a low-level tactical strike and reconnaissance two-seater. The original prototype, which allegedly flew in 1955 and was demonstrated at Tushino in the following year, differed from the Yak-25 primarily in having a redesigned forward fuselage in which the rear cockpit was deleted and a position provided for the second crew member in a sharply-pointed glazed nose. Afterburners were added to the RD-9 turbojets, and a highly swept extension was introduced on the inboard wing leading edge, raising the critical Mach number slightly. At a later stage the wingtips were extended, similar modifications being applied to a tandem two-seat all-weather and night fighter (*Flashlight-C*) evolved in parallel and subsequently

(*Below*) *The Yak-28, although evolved initially for the low-level tactical strike role with secondary reconnaissance capability, is now serving primarily in the latter role.*

One of the principal tactical reconnaissance aircraft of the V.-V.S.'s Frontovaia Aviatsiya, the Yak-28 is a "second generation" derivative of the Yak-25 interceptor (see Vol. I, pages 178–180). Primarily employed in the photographic role, the Yak-28 reportedly includes in its equipment sensors in the radio and infra-red regions.

abandoned, presumably owing to the marginal performance increase offered over the Yak-25 and its short time lead over later all-weather interceptors.

Further aerodynamic improvements were introduced before the Yak-28 attained production status, drooping leading-edge extensions being added to the outer wing panels and the vertical tail

surfaces being revised, and the type entered service with the V.-V.S.'s *Frontovaya Aviatsiya* in the late 'fifties. Dubbed *Flashlight-D* in the West, the Yak-28 has no direct western counterpart, its role being performed by more straightforward conversions of fighters, such as the Hunter F.R.Mk.10 and the McDonnell RF-101 Voodoo. For the tactical reconnaissance role, the Yak-28 has cameras installed in the extreme nose, and its equipment is believed to include sensors in radio and infra-red regions. A 30-mm. cannon is mounted semi-externally in the starboard side of the forward fuselage, and for the attack role four jettisonable weapons pylons may be mounted underwing, one between the engine nacelle and fuselage and the other immediately outboard of the engine nacelle on each side. These pylons, the loads suspended from which project extremely far forward of the wing leading edges, carry 1,100-lb. conventional bombs, ASMs, 210-mm. HVARs, 55-mm. FFAR pods, or drop tanks.

Power Plants: *Two Klimov RD-9 (VK-9) turbojets each rated at 6,170 lb.s.t. and 7,850 lb.s.t. with afterburning.*
Performance: *Max. speed, 686 m.p.h. at sea level (Mach 0·9), 627 m.p.h. at 40,000 ft. (Mach 0.95); low-level cruise, 570 m.p.h. (Mach 0.75); tactical radius (clean), 200 mls. at 1,000 ft., 500 mls. at 36,000 ft.; initial climb, 16,000–18,000 ft./min.; service ceiling, 15,000 ft.*
Weights: *Normal loaded, 25,000 lb.; max., 30,000 lb.*
Dimensions: *Span, 38 ft. 6 in.; length, 53 ft. 6 in.; height, 12 ft. 6 in.; wing area, 342 sq. ft.*
Note: *Performance, weights and dimensions are estimated and should be considered as provisional.*

GENERAL ARRANGEMENT DRAWING: *A Yak-28 (Flashlight-D) of the V.-V.S.'s Frontovaya Aviatsiya.*

10'   20'

━━━━━━━━━━━*Continued from page 91*

More recent designs include the Saab 35E and Mirage IIIR, both of which use OMERA 31 cameras, and the CF-104, which can mount an under-fuselage Vicom pod of four Vinten cameras. Probably the most sophisticated of all fighter conversions is the RF-4C, which is equipped with a forward oblique Hycon KS-72A, plus Fairchild KA-56 panoramic cameras for both high- and low-altitude, an infra-red linescan device, and SLAR. A photo-flash cartridge ejector is situated in the rear fuselage for night reconnaissance, and the low-altitude panoramic camera has in-flight processing and provision for cassette ejection to speed reconnaissance data to the ground controller.

Aside from time delays, the major deficiency in the reconnaissance field is still in obtaining information at night or in bad weather. Even as late as the Cuban crisis, it was admitted that on some days it was impossible to reconnoitre because of cloud. The

The RB-66C Destroyer (54-478) is one of several reconnaissance derivatives of the land-based counterpart of the U.S. Navy's A-3 Skywarrior. The RB-66C was intended primarily for all-weather electronics reconnaissance, 30 being manufactured.

limitations of flash cartridges are now being overcome by the use of strobe lights on the aircraft, and all-weather reconnaissance is being tackled by SLAR, infra-red, and low-light TV with synthetic image improvement. However, electronic reconnaissance will never replace the use of cameras under good conditions, and there are similarly many situations where there is no substitute for "pure eyeball". For visual reconnaissance one of the most useful designs is the U.S. Army's 200-m.p.h.-plus Mohawk, although the capability of later models has been further improved by electronic sensors. The OV-1B version with APS-94 SLAR, and the OV-1C with UAS-4 infra-red surveillance equipment are both operated in Vietnam, where they have been particularly successful in detecting sampan movements at night (the IR set homing on to the outboard engines fitted to these craft). In fact, the U.S. Army which stopped procurement of the OV-1C in 1964, has resumed procurement in 1966.

Another technique developed as a result of the fighting in Vietnam has been use of Ryan Firebee reconnaissance drones, launched from C-130A Hercules operating from Bien Hoa in South Vietnam, and recovered by parachute descent on pre-selected beaches. The drone is based on the BQM-34A target, which has a Continental J69 turbojet of 1,300 lb. thrust, and reaches an absolute ceiling of 55,000 ft. Range and altitude have been increased by extending the wing span from 12.9 ft. to nearly 20 ft., and the fuselage has been lengthened to rectify the balance and accommodate more fuel. These drones have been primarily employed in surveillance of southern China, where at least eight have been shot down. Looking to the future, it is possible that an improved version will be developed from the supersonic XBQM-34E now under construction, which will boost the maximum speed from 0.9 to 1.8 Mach, and produce a ceiling of 62,000 ft. However, it is widely held that the reconnaissance role of the high-flying aircraft will ultimately be taken over by manned orbital vehicles, and the emphasis may therefore swing toward high-speed, low level drones.

MARITIME PATROL AND ANTI-SUBMARINE WARFARE AIRCRAFT DEVELOPMENT

In addition to carrying out the strategic and tactical missions already discussed, reconnaissance aircraft have been developed for the specialised task of maritime patrol. This role places great emphasis on endurance for convoy escort and for shadowing enemy naval units, and on generous cabin space for the various electronic sensors and associated operators, and for the operations room where all the search information is co-ordinated and attacks on submarines are planned and directed. Speed and defensive armament have generally been of lesser importance in view of the small risk of encountering air opposition, but some air forces are now calling for improved dash capability in order to reach search areas with the minimum of delay.

First and foremost in time of conventional war aerial surveillance is required to study the patterns of enemy ship movements and to watch for new types of vessels as they come into service. But in the past 20 years one of the primary objectives has been to develop methods of watching, tracking and catching the new and formidable types of submarines. This dangerous underwater weapon which nearly brought the allies to their knees in two world wars has undergone radical changes in hull design and methods of propulsion in the past 20 years. These vessels can now dive to great depths—the U.S. nuclear submarine *Thresher* is believed to have broken up by accident at least 1,000 ft. down but this depth has probably now been exceeded in normal operations.

In addition the modern submarines can move under water at speeds greater than most normal surface ships and they are not slowed down by rough weather. The *George Washington* class of U.S. nuclear-powered Polaris submarine has a quoted under-water speed of 35 knots. Adding still further to their tactical advantages today's submarines can remain submerged for long periods, up to several weeks. Their philosophy of attack is to remain concealed at all times, releasing weapons against an enemy

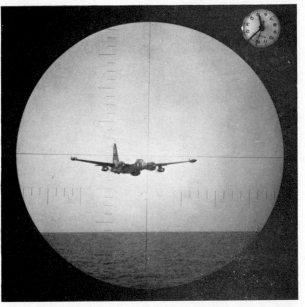

A periscope's view of a Lockheed SP-2H Neptune maritime aircraft.

they never see. Normally this will be against ships or shore installations but the development of the hunter-killer submarine means that one will fight another in the dark sea depths.

The nuclear submarine is a formidable weapon against which there is still no counter because it is almost impossible to find.

It can stay down and run with its own surface ships or move swiftly away to intercept enemy vessels. It can lie quietly on the bottom for weeks without trace and then, at a command, fire its missiles and move stealthily off station to return for more weapons. The task of reconnaissance at sea is, therefore, a difficult one. It involves the co-operative use of aircraft, ships and fixed undersea installations with perhaps in the future hydrofoils and hovercraft.

The primary purpose of maritime reconnaissance is to keep track of the movement of submarines at all times and to locate areas where they might lie undetected. A secondary task of the dual purpose maritime patrol aircraft is to force a submarine to deflect from its programme or to destroy it. But the chances of an effective airborne attack against a high speed underwater enemy are slender. Surface vessels and helicopters can deal more effectively with the enemy once its position has been established by reconnaissance.

PATROL AND ASW EQUIPMENT

There is a marked reluctance among manufacturers to discuss their part in marine surveillance, largely because the steps forward are so small in relation to the enormous effort required to produce them. Every change is, therefore, a closely guarded secret.

The methodical search for a submarine begins with two general assumptions. First it must pass through defined areas to reach its operational zone. Second its task and weapon range will limit the area in which it will operate. It is the role of reconnaissance aircraft to define the target, fix its position and if possible destroy it.

The current generation of maritime patrol aircraft have four well-established methods of detection and tracking:

Radar to watch for any part of the boat which shows above the surface—the snort tube, radar mast or radio aerial.

Underwater sound listening devices and echo ranging equipment. These are the sonobuoys originally developed in World War II and since greatly improved in range and reliability.

Magnetic detection equipment which shows if the earth's magnetic field has been distorted by the presence of metal objects. This form of detection is widely used in aerial prospecting for metals.

Electronic countermeasures such as DF equipment and jamming transmitters.

Much of the equipment carried today was designed to detect the presence of the conventional air breathing submarine. Although the U.S.A., for example, now has 50 nuclear submarines which do not need large quantities of air for their engines, there are still large fleets of conventional boats in service with the navies of major world powers.

Modern surveillance or search radar can be used to produce pictures of photographic quality and minute detail in high-flying aircraft. It covers very large areas of sea and is mainly useful for keeping track of ships. In the large area covered by search radar the presence of a snort tube or periscope would not be detected. Funds have, therefore, been made available in the U.S.A. for the production of special radar to detect small objects of this type. Radar capable of doing this would also be useful for keeping track of sonobuoy patterns, but the development of this high-resolution radar capable of peering through sea clutter and detecting an exposed periscope, presents an extremely difficult task demanding a breakthrough in the state-of-the-art. Facilities exist in modern radar to change from a fixed-aircraft, moving-surface presentation to a ground stabilised display. Sometimes called "true motion" radar, the aircraft movement and movement of other objects is related to a stationary surface.

A fixed-wing aircraft uses as a link between its medium (air) and the medium of the submarine (water) floating radio transmitters which are first dropped into the sea in a pattern. A helicopter can lower a portable sound listening device into the sea and then move from point to point in the area. A sonobuoy pattern once dropped from a fixed-wing aircraft cannot be altered, however.

(Right) The Beriev Be-6 was the last Soviet piston-engined maritime patrol flying boat, and remains in service in some numbers. The Be-6 has two 2,000 h.p. Shvetsov ASh-73 air-cooled radial engines, and weighing 51,588 lb. loaded, has a maximum speed of 258 m.p.h. at 7,875 ft., a cruising speed ranging from 210 to 225 m.p.h., and a maximum range of 3,045 mls.

There are two main types of sonobuoys. A passive one which floats in the sea collecting all the sea sounds around it and transmitting them back to the aircraft, and an active one which acts as an echo ranging device. Small charges are exploded in the active sonobuoy pattern and echoes returned by any large object in the sea are picked up and transmitted. Returned sound can be computed in the aircraft and displayed as a target position. The chief disadvantage of explosive echo ranging in the early stages of a search is that it instantly gives away to the submarine commander the fact that a hunt has been mounted. The American AQA-3 Jezebel passive long-range acoustic search equipment used by most U.S. Navy patrol and ASW aircraft has given good results, but target localization is another matter, and attempts are being made to replace the associated Julie active (explosive) sonobuoys with a passive detection system known as DIFAR (Directional Finding and Ranging). The proposal is that one DIFAR would be dropped by the aircraft, this returning a directional indication of the target. A second would then be dropped and the correlation of the information provided by the two DIFARs would isolate the target's location. DIFAR phase studies are currently being undertaken in the U.S.A.

Measurement of distortion of the earth's magnetic field is possible with a magnetometer. They are frequently used to locate the position of ore bodies below the surface of the earth. A submarine will change the normal pattern of natural magnetism by its mass of steel and this alteration can be detected by sensitive magnetic anomaly detectors (MAD). Although it has serious limitations, MAD is positive in its identification of a metal object in the water. This is important because a school of fish or a whale can give echo responses similar to a submarine on Sonar (sound navigation and ranging).

There are several limitations to MAD as a primary means of detection. Its range is very small which means that an aircraft has to fly almost directly over the target to get a response. It requires a stable platform, no easy matter when aircraft are flying low in rough conditions. MAD can only detect a submarine when it is close to the surface. Finally it has to be kept well clear of magnetic parts of the aircraft. It is for this reason that the detector is usually at the end of a long boom in the tail.

But for the investigation of stationary submerged objects MAD is invaluable. Steel wrecks off the North American coastline have been plotted and a record of their magnetic pattern made. This will limit their use by submarines, which could otherwise lie along-side the wreck safe from detection by MAD equipment.

Another form of anomaly has been found when a submarine is close to the surface. It has an effect on the field strength of radar or radio signals returned from an area above the submerged vessel. Because the range of radio signals is severely limited in water a submarine must still, from time to time, put an aerial above the surface to send or receive messages. Airborne direction finders will then give a bearing of the submarine even with modern sending techniques which compress a message into a fraction of a second. Aircraft also carry jamming equipment to deny the enemy his communications link.

Other equipment which can be used to detect the presence of air breathing submarines is ASH or "sniffer". This rapidly separates from air samples the ionised exhaust gases left by a diesel engine. Its limitation is that it can only say that a diesel engine has been in that part of the ocean and cannot differentiate between a motor ship and a submarine.

FUTURE EQUIPMENT

As the older type of submarine is phased-out of service leaving only the continuously submerged nuclear type, new methods of ocean search have to be found. A number of possibilities are being explored and include such seemingly unlikely avenues as detecting the "bump" in the ocean caused by a submarine running close to the surface. The magnitude of this small change of height depends on the depth of the submarine, its speed and size. But one of the promising future reconnaissance systems is the measurement and recording of black-heat or infra-red energy. A propeller turning in the water will raise its temperature suffi-ciently for it to be measured with sensitive infra-red detectors. Claim to have recorded by infra-red measurable quantities of heat in the water up to several hours after a submarine has passed has been made in the U.S.A.

Scanning detectors are now becoming available which give a

heat plan on film or paper of the surface under the aircraft. With them it should be possible to record the propeller and hull heat of a submerged vessel as the warmed water reaches the surface.

But in spite of the increasing sophistication of reconnaissance equipment the clues left by a submerged vessel are tiny compared with the enormous volume of water in which it lies hidden. Its tell-tales are so small that they may be missed altogether in the agglomeration of signals which the reconnaissance crew receives from its various sensors. To help the aircrew, various small computers which in the past handled one aspect of reconnaissances are being replaced by a single central digital-type, capable of filtering and processing incoming data from a dozen different sources and giving in return a clear picture to an airborne tactical commander.

These airborne computers make extensive use of micro-minia-ture techniques and for their size they will handle prodigious amounts of data. One of their tasks for example will be to filter out unwanted noise received by sonobuoys and help to identify significant sounds. A computerized systems integration approach towards co-ordination and evaluation information derived from the ASW sensors of the aircraft has been given the code name "Project A-New" by the U.S. Navy. A prototype system has been flying in a P-3A Orion since 1965, and during 1968 a start will be made in retrofitting all Orions with the "A-New" system at a cost of $1,000,000 (£357,000) per aircraft, and a version of the "A-New" will be carried by the VSX shipboard ASW aircraft to suc-ceed the S-2 in the 'seventies.

But if all this makes the job of reconnaissance at sea sound simple it is worth putting the task into perspective. The *Santa Maria*, a large ocean liner, was taken over by force in mid-ocean. In spite of a huge air and surface search the ship was not detected for several days and then visually by a Dutch freighter which came across it by accident. Contrast this with the problem of trying to locate a submerged, fast submarine fitted with equipment that tells its Commander when detection equipment is being used against it and which is deliberately trying to avoid contact. Then the problem of ocean surveillance begins to assume its true size. At the present time, approximately 60 of the Soviet Navy's 400 submarines are nuclear-powered vessels, and production of nuclear submarines in the Soviet Union is currently approximately 10 per year, conventionally-powered submarines being retired from service at a similar rate. By 1970, the Soviet Navy will thus have some 100 nuclear-powered submarines in service, assuming no major increase in production in the interim, and it is safe to prophesy that many years and a lot of money will be spent before the problem of countering these potent vessels can be said with safety to have been beaten.

THE AIRCRAFT — MARITIME PATROL

In the early days of maritime reconnaissance many countries favoured the use of flying boats, since their ability to operate from the open sea under reasonably calm conditions gave them a significant advantage in rescue duties, and more flexibility in choice of bases. The latter point was demonstrated by the Catalinas and Mariners of World War II in the island-hopping campaigns of the Pacific, but in other respects the flying boat proved a disappointment, particularly in regard to the excessive time taken in refuelling, rearming, maintenance and overhaul. The performance penalty incurred by the hull further detracted from the flying boat concept, and with the advent of jet engines it was felt by many experts that the aerodynamic drag of the planing hull was no longer compatible with the speeds then attainable.

In Britain the flying boat was abandoned for military purposes shortly after the end of the war, but in the United States an attempt was made to produce a very advanced design which could not only achieve high subsonic speeds, but could also operate in the open sea for 90 per cent of the time, its design allowing for waves of up to 6 ft. This aircraft, the Martin SeaMaster, first flew in 1955 and had several novel features, including a hull of unusually high length/beam ratio, a rotatable weapon bay (which

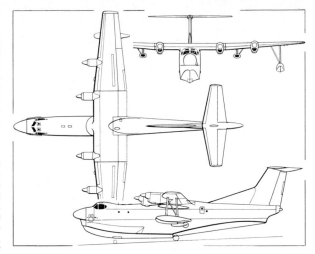

Currently under construction by Shin Meiwa, the PX-S maritime patrol flying boat powered by four 2,850 e.s.h.p. General Electric T64-IHI-10 turboprops will have empty and normal loaded weights of 50,700 lb. and 72,750 lb. respectively, overload gross weight being 88,200 lb. Estimated performance includes a maximum speed of 345 m.p.h. and a range cruising speed of 230 m.p.h., normal range being of the order of 1,380 miles, and maximum range being 2,300 miles. Both span and length will be approximately 108 ft. 3 in., and overall height will be 29 ft. 6 in. Current plans call for the manufacture of 22 PX-S flying boats for the Japanese Maritime Self-Defence for delivery between 1971 and 1973, and the first of two prototypes is scheduled to commence flight trials during the summer of 1967.

was loaded through a hatch in the top of the fuselage), and special water flaps for braking and manoeuvring. Unfortunately two SeaMaster prototypes experienced catastrophic structural failures in flight, and the programme was dropped. However, one medium-range flying boat has remained in service to the present day with the U.S. Navy: the Martin P-5 Marlin. Progressively developed from the XP5M-1 which flew in 1948, the Marlin is a direct descendant of the wartime Mariner, and has recently been used in patrol and rescue operations off Vietnam. Although piston-engined, the aircraft has been fitted with very advanced search equipment, including ASQ-8 MAD (Magnetic Anomaly Detection) gear and the Julie explosive echo-sounding and Jezebel passive acoustic systems, and under a retrofit programme the Marlin is now being equipped with a single General Electric J85-GE-2 turbojet in the rear of the hull to reduce take-off time and distance at high gross weights. An unusual design feature of the Marlin is the use of enlarged engine nacelles to house a pair of torpedoes or 1,000 lb. bombs, in addition to its eight underwing bomb stations.

Japan has retained interest in the flying boat for maritime patrol, and a research programme initiated by Shin Meiwa some six years ago with the aim of developing a medium-range flying boat with STOL capabilities will bear fruit in mid-1967 with the flight of the first prototype of the PX-S which, if successful, will be manufactured for the Japanese Maritime Self-Defence Force which service envisages acquiring 22 flying boats of this type between 1971 and 1973. Powered by four 2,850 e.s.h.p. General Electric T64-IHI-10 turboprops, the PX-S will employ boundary layer control for high lift and STOL characteristics, this being supplemented by an airscrew slipstream-deflection system, and it is claimed that the high length-to-beam ratio will endow the PX-S with outstanding seaworthiness, a groove-type spray suppressor evolved by Dr. S. Kikuhara aiding operation in rough seas. In view of the relatively high performance of the PX-S, the retention of fixed, braced stabilising floats is surprising, and offensive stores,

such as two homing torpedoes, will be housed in underwing pods between the engine nacelles.

Russia has also continued to make use of flying boats in maritime patrol work, although really long range operations are left to the land-based Tu-16, Tu-20, and Mya-4. The Beriev Be-6 has two piston engines, like the Marlin, but is a somewhat lighter design, weighing little over 50,000 lb. compared with almost 77,000 lb. for the P-5B. The Be-6 is reputed to have flown in 1945 as the LL-143, and may have now been superseded by the Be-10 which was first seen in 1961. Latest in the Beriev line, the swept-wing Be-10 is the only turbojet flying boat in service anywhere in the world. With a take-off weight in the 100,000 lb. class, the Be-10 is estimated to achieve a radius in the region of 1,300 miles and an endurance of 6-8 hours. Search radar is assumed to be carried in the underside of the nose, and stores are probably released from the sides of the fuselage, Sunderland-fashion.

The first land-based patrol aircraft were adaptations of bombers such as the Liberator and Lancaster, but the Lockheed P-2 Neptune was designed from the outset for this role and achieved remarkable success, more than 1,000 being produced over a 19-year run. Since the first prototype flew in 1945, the Neptune has steadily acquired more sophisticated equipment, increasing its gross weight from 54,500 lb. to almost 80,000 lb., and necessitating a pair of Westinghouse J34 turbojets to augment the thrust of its Wright turbo-compound radials. However, this aircraft has proved basically too small for present-day ASW (Anti-Submarine Warfare) gear, somewhat short on range and speed, and lacking in the crew comfort required to maintain peak efficiency over long periods of operation.

Despite the Neptune's limited internal capacity and the fact that the parent company discontinued production several years ago, Kawasaki, the Japanese Neptune licensee, has continued development of the basic design to produce the GK-210 (alias P2V-Kai), an up-dated turboprop-powered derivative of the P-2H Neptune. The prototype GK-210 began its flight test programme in the summer of 1966, and the Japanese Maritime Self-Defence Force anticipates acquiring 68 aircraft of this type to replace its present P-2H Neptunes. Apart from having 2,850 e.s.h.p. T64-IHI-10 turboprops in place of the Wright turbo-compound radials, and indigenous J-3-IHI-7C auxiliary turbojets of 3,086 lb.s.t. which supplant the Westinghouse J34-WE-36s, the GK-210 differs from the P-2H in having a 45-in. section inserted in the fuselage between the wing leading edge and flight deck to provide space for an additional crew member, a tactical co-ordinator, as well as further avionics; the APS-20 search radar is replaced by X-band APS-80A resulting in a smaller ventral radome; the main undercarriage members have been redesigned and are now of twin-wheel type, and vertical tail surface area has been increased. By comparison with the P-2H, empty weight of the GK-210 is some 10,000 lb. lower, and take-off gross weight is 8,000 lb. lower. The first production model is scheduled to fly early in 1969.

R.A.F. Coastal Command operated the Neptune in the early 1950s, but this aircraft was withdrawn in 1956 in favour of the later marks of Avro Shackleton, a four-engined design based on the Lincoln bomber. Although noisy and unpressurised like the Neptune, the Shackleton is somewhat larger, grossing around 100,000 lb. and offering an unusually capacious weapon bay, a large retractable search radar, and a limited ability to carry troops in emergency operations. The latest modification to this series is the addition of two 2,500 lb. Viper turbojets to the outboard nacelles in order to relieve the work load on the ageing Griffon piston engines. However, this change cannot overcome the fundamental problem of airframe fatigue life, and it is therefore planned to replace the earlier R.A.F. Shackletons with a maritime reconnaissance derivative of the Comet. Powered by four Rolls-Royce Spey turbofans, this HS.801 project will combine large cabin volume and excellent dash performance at modest development cost, the only major airframe change being the addition of a second "bubble" below the pressure cabin to house the offensive warload. This aircraft may not rival the endurance of the latest

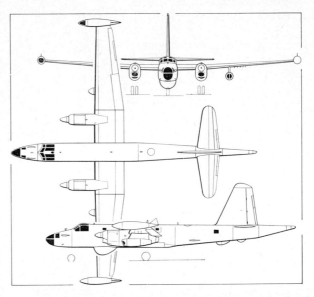

A progressive development of the 22-year-old Lockheed Neptune design, the Kawasaki GK-210, or P2V-Kai, illustrated above and on page 125, is a turboprop-powered derivative of the P-2H version of the Neptune which currently serves with the Japanese Maritime Self-Defence Force. Power is provided by two 2,850 e.s.h.p. T64-IHI-10 turboprops and two auxiliary J-3-IHI-7C turbojets to supplement take-off power and boost dash and over-target performance. Current proposals call for the manufacture of 68 GK-210 maritime patrol aircraft with deliveries commencing in 1969.

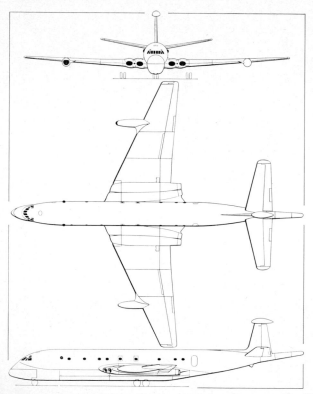

The Hawker Siddeley HS.801 maritime patrol aircraft (left) has been evolved from the commercial Comet 4C transport as a successor to the piston-engined Shackleton M.R.Mk.2C from 1969, 38 HS. 801s having been ordered with prototype trials scheduled to commence in 1967. Powered by four Rolls-Royce RB.168 Spey turbofans, the HS.801 will provide an on-station patrol time of more than six hours at a range of 1,150 miles from base. Offering considerable cubic capacity for ASW systems and offensive stores, the HS.801 will be the first pure jet maritime patrol aircraft intended for land-based operations to be evolved for this task from the outset. Approximate overall dimensions include a span of 115 ft., a length of 127 ft., and a height of 30 ft.

turboprop proposals, with its on-station patrol capability of some six hours at a distance of 1,150 miles from base, but its usefulness in the secondary trooping role (carrying perhaps sixty fully-armed men in place of the Shackleton's twenty-nine) is probably unequalled. One of the two HS.801 prototypes that are being produced by the adaptation of original Comet airframes will be Avon-powered and used for the development of special maritime equipment, and the other, Spey-powered, will be used for aerodynamic development.

The R.C.A.F. still operates Neptunes, but since the late 1950s these have been supplemented by three squadrons of the Canadair Argus for long-range patrol duties. Grossing 148,000 lb., this is the heaviest maritime reconnaissance aircraft used by the West, although development costs were kept within reason by utilising the wings, tail surfaces, undercarriage, and flight control systems of the Britannia commercial transport, together with four piston engines similar to those of the Neptune, the fuselage being a new Canadair design. The Argus might be criticised for its fixed search radome and maximum speed of only 315 m.p.h., but its endurance of up to twenty-four hours is unlikely to be surpassed for many years.

In seeking a replacement for the Neptune, the U.S. Navy chose to adapt the Lockheed Electra turboprop airliner. The resulting

(Right) The prototype Kawasaki GK-210, or P2V-Kai, an updated version of the Lockheed P-2H Neptune for the Japanese Maritime Self-Defence Force, began flight trials on July 21, 1966 (see page 123 for general arrangement drawing). Carrying up to 12 crew members, it has empty and normal loaded weights of 45,300 lb. and 75,500 lb. respectively, its long-range cruising speed being 230 m.p.h.

P-3 Orion, which has also been ordered for the R.A.A.F. and the R.N.Z.A.F., incorporates many design alterations, including a shortened front fuselage, a weapon bay ahead of the wing torsion box, and a MAD "sting" at the tail. Equipped with the latest search devices, the Orion has been claimed to be the most effective ASW system currently in operation, and performance has been progressively improved with the introduction of more powerful Allison T56 turboprop engines.

Notwithstanding the technical merits of the Shackleton, Argus, and Orion, the existence of these aircraft does represent a general failure of NATO countries to formulate common requirements and agree on an aircraft which can be produced in worthwhile quantity. The Breguet Atlantic was selected as meeting the NATO specification for a maritime reconnaissance aircraft, and production was shared between France, Federal Germany, Belgium, the Netherlands, and the U.S.A., but only the first two countries have so far ordered the type. Its pair of Tyne turboprops enable it to attain speeds up to 390 m.p.h., and an endurance of eighteen hours. Like the Shackleton, its search radome is retractable, but the Atlantic's weapon bay is of far more advanced design, with doors sliding over the outside of the fuselage to present a cleaner

(Below) A mock-up of the PX-S maritime patrol flying boat currently under construction for the Japanese Maritime Self-Defence Force.

Gannet A.S.Mk.4s are currently being phased out of service with Germany's Marinefliegergeschwader 3 (in the service of which the Gannet A.S.Mk.4 is seen above) in favour of the Breguet Atlantic. Sixteen Fairey Gannet A.S.Mk.4 anti-submarine aircraft, together with two Gannet T.Mk.5 trainers were supplied to the Indonesian Navy which is one of the last services to include the A.S.Mk.4 version of this aircraft (illustrated below) in its first line strength. The Gannet A.S.Mk.4 is powered by a Bristol Siddeley Double Mamba 101 coupled turboprop rated at 3,035 e.h.p., attains a maximum speed of 299 m.p.h. at sea level, and has a patrol endurance of 4.9 hrs.

shape to the airflow, and thus permit release at much higher speeds. This aircraft is only now entering service, but it has already been suggested that NATO should start thinking of an eventual replacement, using turbofans of high bypass ratio to produce the same endurance at even higher speeds.

THE AIRCRAFT — ANTI-SUBMARINE

The general requirements of good endurance and generous cabin space demanded by the maritime patrol task apply equally to the fixed-wing shipboard anti-submarine warfare aircraft, if somewhat scaled down by carrier operating demands. In Royal Navy service, the fixed-wing Fairey Gannet has now given place to the helicopter for the ASW role, but France's *Aéronavale* continues to operate the Breguet Alizé from the carriers *Clémenceau* and *Foch*, and despite the service's leadership in the development of ASW helicopters, the U.S. Navy continues to operate the fixed-wing Grumman Tracker which has now been in continuous production for 14 years, this type being deployed aboard the U.S. Navy's eight ASW carriers and serving from shore bases with the U.S. Navy Reserve. The Tracker has also been supplied to a number of foreign air arms, and its successor, yet another fixed-wing type currently dubbed the VSX and now in the planning stages, is unlikely to be available in quantity until the early 'seventies, and had not, at the time of closing for press, received formal U.S. Defense Department approval. Several contractors, including Douglas, Grumman, Lockheed and McDonnell, have received VSX study contracts, and as currently envisaged this aircraft will have two turbofans, have a gross weight of less than 40,000 lb., and its range will exceed 1,000 miles. The VSX is to incorporate the "Project A-New" computerised systems integration scheduled for installation in P-3C Orions, this co-ordinating and evaluating all information obtained by the aircraft's sensors. The Soviet Union's only known specialized fixed-wing shore-based ASW aircraft, the Gannet-sized TU-91 *Tarzan* of 1955, dubbed "Boot" in the West, did not attain production.

AVRO SHACKLETON

The R.A.F.'s sole maritime patrol aircraft for more than a decade, and expected, in its M.R.Mk.3 form, to continue in service well into the 'seventies when it will share Coastal Command's reconnaissance task with the HS.801, the Shackleton traces its ancestry back to the wartime Lancaster bomber, and the first of three prototypes flew on March 9, 1949. The initial production model, the Shackleton M.R.Mk.1, flew on October 24, 1950, and a total of 77 M.R.Mk.1s and 1As was built before this model was succeeded by the M.R.Mk.2 which currently equips Nos. 37, 38, 42, 205 and 224 Squadrons, and which is scheduled to be phased out and replaced by the HS.801 from 1969.

M.R.Mk.2: By comparison with the initial production model, the M.R.Mk.2 had the primary radar moved from the nose to the aft fuselage, the fuselage nose itself being redesigned, and the tail turret with its twin 0.5-in. machine guns gave place to a tapered observation cone. A new retractable ventral radome permitted an uninterrupted 360° scan, and the four 2,450 h.p. Griffon 57A engines enabled a maximum speed of 272 m.p.h. to be attained at

10,000 ft., maximum and economical cruising speeds being 255 and 200 m.p.h. respectively. Ten crew members were carried, and from 1961, all aircraft of this type were modernised as M.R.Mk.2Cs, their avionics and ASW systems being brought up to the standard of the later M.R.Mk.3. A total of 69 Shackleton M.R.Mk.2s was built before, in 1956, it was finally supplanted on the assembly line by the M.R.Mk.3.

M.R.Mk.3: Introducing a nosewheel undercarriage for the first time, the Shackleton M.R.Mk.3 also featured a rearranged flight

(Right) Shackleton M.R.Mk.3 (XF701) after completion of Phase 3 modifications, including Viper B.S.V.11 turbojets in the rear of the outboard engine nacelles, improved crew comfort, and a revised fuel system. All M.R.Mk.3s are being progressively brought up to similar standards.

*(Left) A Shackleton MR.Mk.2C of No.
42 Squadron, R.A.F. Coastal Command.
Currently equipping five squadrons, the
M.R.Mk.2C will be progressively phased
out in favour of the turbofan-powered
HS.801 from 1969.*

deck, revised outboard wing panels, and a modified fuel system which, embodying fixed wingtip tanks, had a total capacity of 4,248 Imp. gal. (5,102 U.S. gal.). Other modifications included a frameless flight deck canopy and provision of a sound-proofed wardroom. The nosewheel undercarriage was incorporated at some minor expense of weapons-bay capacity. For example, a typical offensive load for tactical operations consisted of 12 1,000-lb. bombs as compared with 15 carried by the M.R.Mk.2.

The first Shackleton M.R.Mk.3 flew on September 2, 1955, and deliveries began 18 months later, in 1957, 42 being manufactured of which eight were supplied to the *Suid-Afrikaanse Lugmag*, these equipping No. 35 Squadron of that service's Maritime Group. In R.A.F. Coastal Command service, the Shackleton M.R.Mk.3 equips Nos. 120, 201 and 206 Squadrons whose aircraft are being progressively up-dated by the installation of a 2,500 lb.s.t. Bristol Siddeley Viper B.S.V.11 turbojet in the rear of each outboard engine nacelle to provide supplementary take-off power. Simultaneously, provision is being made for the emergency jettisoning of all fuel. A typical ASW stores load comprises three Mk.30 acoustic homing torpedoes, nine Mk.11 depth charges, 12 Mk.2 marine markers, and 12 sonobuoys. For the emergency transport role, the M.R.Mk.3 can carry 29 troops with their equipment stowed in special weapons-bay panniers. The ASW systems have

been constantly updated during its long service career, such items as the Autolycus ionization-detecting system for tracking snorkeling submarines having been added.

Power Plants: *Four Rolls-Royce Griffon 57A 12-cylinder liquid-cooled engines each rated at 2,450 h.p. and augmented for take-off by two 2,500 lb.s.t. Bristol Siddeley Viper B.S.V.11 turbojets.*
Performance: *Max. speed (at 85,000 lb.), 302 m.p.h. at 12,000 ft.; max. cruise, 253 m.p.h. at 10,000 ft.; range cruise, 200 m.p.h. at 1,500 ft.; normal range, 3,660 mls.; max. range, 4,215 mls.; initial climb (at 100,000 lb.), 850 ft./min.; service ceiling, 19,200 ft.*
Weights: *Empty, 57,800 lb.; normal loaded, 85,000 lb.; max., 100,000 lb.*
Dimensions: *Span, 119 ft. 10 in.; length, 92 ft. 6 in.; height, 23 ft. 4 in.; wing area, 1,458 sq. ft.*
Note: *Specification applies to M.R.Mk.3.*

GENERAL ARRANGEMENT DRAWING: *A Shackleton M.R.Mk.3 (XF 707) of No. 201 Squadron, R.A.F. Coastal Command.*

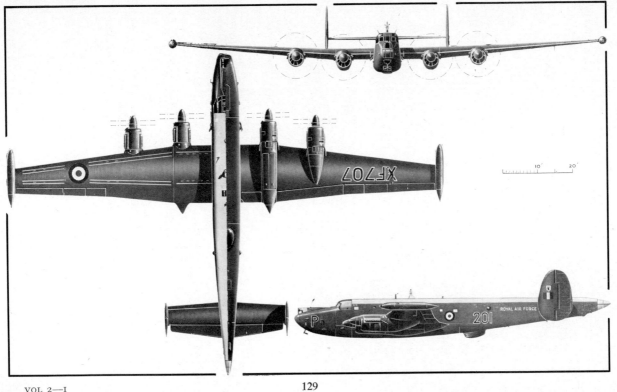

(*Left*) *Currently the fastest flying boat in operational service, the Be-10 is believed to be powered by turbofans, and has established a number of F.A.I.-recognised records for water-borne aircraft. It is reportedly serving with the Morskaya Aviatsiya in only limited numbers.*

BERIEV BE-10 (MALLOW)

Georgi M. Beriev has been the leading proponent of flying boats in the Soviet Union for more than 30 years, and, since the end of the Second World War, his design bureau has been responsible for all maritime patrol and reconnaissance flying boats operated by Russia's Naval Aviation, or *Morskaya Aviatsiya*. Beriev's first post-war maritime reconnaissance flying boat, the Be-6, which first appeared in 1945 under the design bureau designation LL-143, provided the backbone of the *Morskaya Aviatsiya* patrol force throughout the 'fifties, and in the same year that the Be-6 made its service début, 1949, the Beriev design bureau produced its first pure jet flying boat, the Be-R1, powered by two RD-45 centrifugal-flow turbojets. The Be-R1 was not developed past the prototype stage, but experience gained with this project undoubtedly contributed to the development of the appreciably larger and more advanced Be-10 (also known as the M-10) which appeared in prototype form in the late 'fifties, and is currently the only turbo-jet-driven flying boat in service anywhere in the world.

Designed to combine reasonable endurance with high subsonic dash capability, and limited capacity for operation in open waters, the Be-10 allegedly entered *Morskaya Aviatsiya* service in 1960, and possibly possesses the distinction of having been the first turbofan-powered military aircraft to attain operational status. Information supplied to the F.A.I. in 1961, when the Be-10 established an impressive series of international records for water-borne aircraft, referred to the engines by the designation AL-7PB and stated their thrust to be 14,330 lb., but the size of their intakes suggest that these engines are turbofans rather than turbojets, and as the Soloviev design bureau has led turbofan design in the Soviet Union, the AL-7PB possibly originated with this team. The original prototype featured appreciably longer engine nacelles than the production model, these extending to the raised flight deck and possibly housing RD-3 turbojets.

GENERAL ARRANGEMENT DRAWING: *A Beriev Be-10 maritime reconnaissance flying boat of the Morskaya Aviatsiya.*

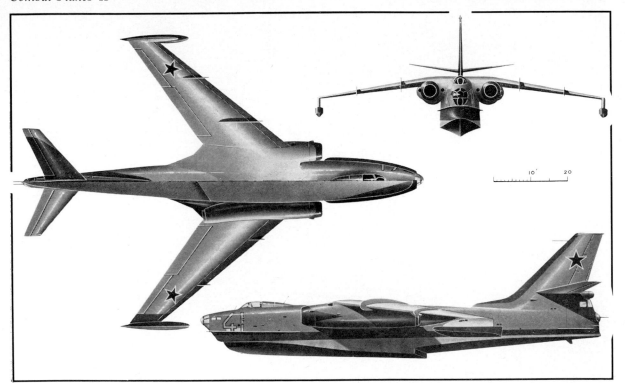

(Above and below) The Be-10 is currently the only pure jet flying boat in service, and a few are reportedly operated by Aeroflot.

The F.A.I.-recognised records offer some indication of the performance of the Be-10, these including a 566.69 m.p.h. speed record over a straight course, a 544.2 m.p.h. speed record with an

11,023-lb. payload over a 621-mile closed-circuit course, and altitude records of 49,088 ft. without payload, 46,135 ft. with 11,023 lb., and 39,360 ft. with 33,069 lb.

The Be-10 has a relatively long and narrow planing bottom to reduce hydrodynamic and aerodynamic drag, and to permit operation in rough water by cushioning the landing loads. The wing is shoulder-mounted on the tall hull, and the pronounced anhedral of the wing enables the wingtip stabilising floats to be attached to short pylons, thus eliminating the need for retraction gear. The capacious hull provides ample space for a large search radar dish which is presumably located in the forward portion, and defensive armament apparently comprises two fixed forward-firing 20-mm. or 23-mm. cannon in the nose and two similar weapons in a tail turret over which there is mounted gun-laying radar. The offensive load may be confined to small sub-kiloton depth charges, and such stores may be mounted on racks extending from the sides of the hull during an attack, as there is no indication of a rotary weapons door in the hull, the multi-spar wing structure cannot house stores, and there is no provision in the engine nacelles for weapons bays.

Power Plants: *Two Type AL-7PB turbojets (fans ?) each rated 14,330 lb.s.t.*
Performance: *Max. speed, 560* m.p.h. at 5,000 ft. (Mach 0.75), 500* m.p.h. at 36,000 ft.; range cruise, 350–400* m.p.h.; tactical radius (with nominal load), 1,300* mls.; patrol endurance, 6–8 hr.; service ceiling, 40,000* ft.*
Weights: *Empty, 53,000* lb.; loaded, 90,000* lb.; max., 100,000* lb.*
Dimensions: *Span, 73 ft. 0 in.*; length, 102 ft. 0 in.*; height, 33 ft. 0 in.*; wing area, 1,200* sq. ft.*
*APPROXIMATE

BREGUET 1150 ATLANTIC

In process of entering service with *Marinefliegergeschwader* 3 of Federal Germany's naval air arm at Nordholz, and with *Flottille* 21F of France's *Aéronavale*, the Br.1150 Atlantic maritime reconnaissance and patrol aircraft stems from a specification drawn up under the auspices of the NATO Armaments Committee, and is being manufactured by a consortium of French, Belgian and Dutch companies, the parent company acting as team leader and undertaking final assembly. The first of three prototypes, the Br.1150-01, was flown on October 21, 1961. The third prototype, which embodied a 3.28-ft. increase in forward fuselage length, flew on February 25, 1963, and the fourth aircraft, which was considered as a pre-production machine, joined the test programme on September 10, 1964. Initial contracts call for 40 Atlantics for the *Aéronavale* and 20 for the *Marineflieger*, and the first of these flew on July 19, 1965, the programmed production rate of three aircraft per month being attained early in 1966.

(Above and below) Br.1150 *Atlantic maritime patrol aircraft of the Federal German Navy's Marinefliegergeschwader 3 at Nordholz.*

Carrying 12 crew members, seven of which are accommodated in the central operations compartment, the Atlantic is equipped with *Arome* and *Arar* radars, the CSF search radar being mounted in a retractable radome under the forward fuselage, Marconi Doppler radar, and General Precision's VARS (Vertical and Azimuth Reference System), and CSF magnetic anomaly detection gear is mounted in the tail extension, but most of the ASW systems are essentially similar to those of the P-2H Neptune. The three-section weapons bay has an overall length of 29.52 ft. and is located in the unpressurised lower lobe of the fuselage, its doors being external to the

(Left) A Federal German Br.1150 Atlantic with weapons bay doors open and CSF DR-AA-2B search radar extended, and (below, left) the Br.1150-03 Atlantic prototype which flew for the first time on February 25, 1963. Thirty Atlantics were scheduled to be completed by the beginning of 1967.

avoided. The bay accommodates all NATO standard bombs, 386-lb. U.S. or French depth charges, and electric acoustic homing torpedoes of the Mk.43 Brush or L.K.4 types. The internal offensive load is supplemented by HVARs, French ASW rockets, or Nord AS.12 ASMs on two underwing pylons.

Integral fuel tanks between the front and rear wing spars plus wingtip tanks provide a total fuel capacity of some 4,400 Imp. gal. (5,285 U.S. gal.), approximating to 37.5 per cent of the normal gross take-off weight, and this is sufficient to permit the Atlantic to loiter for some 12 hours at a radius of 625 miles.

Power Plants: *Two Hispano-Suiza-built Rolls-Royce Tyne R.Ty.20 Mk.21 turboprops each rated at 6,105 e.h.p.*
Performance: *Max. speed, 363 m.p.h. at 19,685 ft.; max. cruise, 342 m.p.h. at 26,250 ft.; range cruise (at 95,900 lb.), 311 m.p.h. at 26,250 ft.; max. endurance cruise, 199 m.p.h. below 1,000 ft.; loiter endurance (to and from patrol area at 311 m.p.h.), 12 hrs. at 195 m.p.h. at range of 620 mls.; ferry range (standard max. internal fuel), 4,150 mls.; initial climb, 2,450 ft./min.; service ceiling, 32,800 ft.*
Weights: *Normal loaded, 95,900 lb.*
Dimensions: *Span, 119 ft. 1¼ in.; length, 104 ft. 1½ in.; height, 37 ft. 1¾ in.; wing area, 1,291.67 sq. ft.*

aircraft contours, and opening by sliding around four tracks, the centre section doors overlapping during retraction, and much of the drag and buffeting of orthodox weapons bay doors thus being

GENERAL ARRANGEMENT DRAWING: *A Br.1150 Atlantic of Marine-fliegergeschwader 3 of Federal Germany's Marineflieger der Bundeswehr*

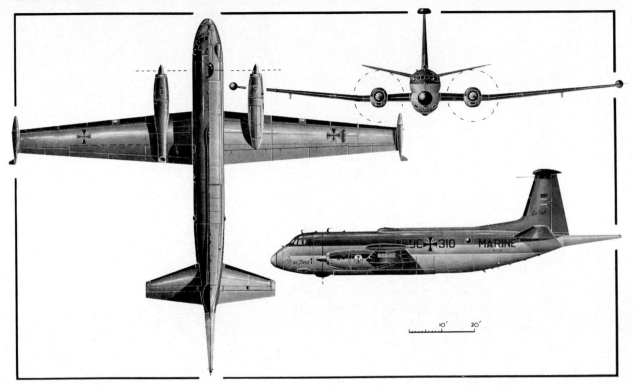

Apart from the few Gannets remaining in service with Australia, the Alizé is now the only fixed-wing turboprop-powered shipboard ASW aircraft in first-line service. It is currently expected to remain in Aéronavale service until at least 1970.

BREGUET 1050 ALIZÉ

The only turboprop-powered shipboard ASW aircraft in operational service apart from the few Fairey Gannets remaining with the Royal Australian Navy, the Br.1050 Alizé equips Flottilles 4F, 6F and 9F of France's *Aéronavale*, and No. 310 Squadron of the Indian Navy. In the immediate post-war years, the small turbo-prop-powered ASW aircraft combining hunter and killer roles in a single machine, appeared to hold considerable promise. The greater flexibility of ASW helicopters resulted in the Gannet, developed in the United Kingdom, enjoying only a brief career in operational service, and the Tu-91 *Tarzan* being abandoned in the Soviet Union, but the Alizé, developed somewhat later than its British equivalent, has now seen some six years of *Aéronavale* service, and will continue to be deployed aboard the carriers *Clémenceau* and *Foch* for several more years.

The Alizé (Tradewind) was evolved from the experimental Br.960 Vultur shipboard strike aircraft, and the first true prototype was flown on October 6, 1956. Three prototypes and two "pre-series" aircraft were followed by the first of 75 production Alizés for the *Aéronavale* on March 26, 1959. Carrying three crew members—

the pilot seated to port with one systems operator to starboard and the other to the rear—the Alizé can undertake low-altitude patrols of more than 3.5 hours' duration, as well as anti-shipping strike tasks, and the internal weapons bay can accommodate three 353-lb depth charges or one torpedo, plus two depth charges and six 5-in. HVARs or two Nord AS.12 ASMs underwing. The CSF search radar is housed in a retractable ventral radome, and omni-directional sonobuoys are accommodated in storage bays in the forward sections of the mainwheel housings. Internal fuel capacity totals 462 Imp. gal. (555 U.S. gal.), but provision is made in the weapons bay for the installation of a 105 or 171 Imp. gal. (126 or 205 U.S. gal.) ferry tank.

The first of 12 Alizés for the Indian Navy was accepted on January 7, 1961, and these aircraft are now deployed aboard the I.N.S. *Vikrant* by No. 310 Squadron. A small number of Alizés serve in target-towing and general duties roles with Escadrille 2S at Lann-Bihoué.

Power Plant: *One Rolls-Royce Dart R.Da. 7 Mk.21 turboprop rated at 2,020 e.s.h.p.*
Performance: *Max. speed, 285 m.p.h. at sea level, 290 m.p.h. at 3,000 ft., 292 m.p.h. at 10,000 ft.; patrol speed (radome extended), 144 m.p.h. at 1,500 ft.; patrol endurance (standard tankage), 5 hr. 12 min. at 1,500 ft.; max. endurance (radome extended and 270 Imp .gal./324 U.S. gal. auxiliary fuel), 7 hr. 40 min. at 15,000 ft.; ferry range, 1,785 mls.; initial climb, 1,380 ft./min.; service ceiling, 20,500 ft.*
Weights: *Empty, 12,566 lb.; loaded, 18,100 lb.*
Dimensions: *Span, 51 ft. 2 in.; length, 45 ft. 6 in.; height, 15 ft. 7 in.; wing area, 387.5 sq. ft.*

GENERAL ARRANGEMENT DRAWING: *A Br.1050 Alizé of Flottille 6F based at the Base Aéro Navale of Nimes-Garons*

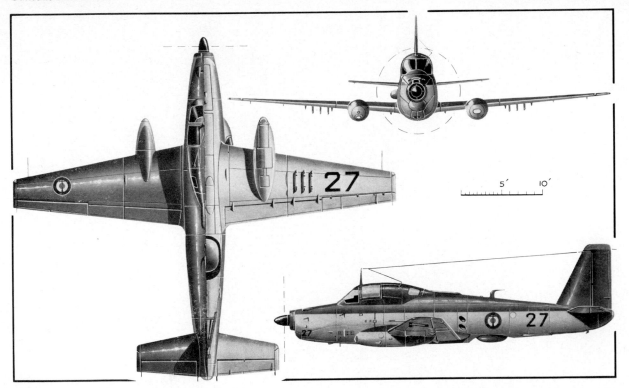

(Left) The third production Argus Mk.2 (20725).

and the wings, tail surfaces, flight controls and undercarriage of the Britannia transport. Expected to remain in service until the mid-'seventies, when piston-engine logistic problems are likely to render its further operation difficult, the Argus was flown for the first time on March 28, 1957, the initial aircraft performing prototype trials but being, in fact, the first production example. This, and the next 12 aircraft were designated Argus Mk.1 when the 14th aircraft introduced sufficient changes to warrant a Mk.2 designation. Twenty examples of the Argus Mk.2 were manufactured, the last of these being completed on July 13, 1960, and the principal differences between the two models were to be found in the differing dispositions of the navigational, communications and tactical avionics, external differences being provided by the smaller "chin" radome and ECM antennae above the fuselage of the definitive production version.

CANADAIR CL-28 ARGUS

The heaviest western maritime reconnaissance aircraft, the Argus, which officially entered service on May 1, 1958, equips the R.C.A.F. Maritime Air Command's three maritime reconnaissance squadrons on the eastern seaboard, Nos. 404 and 405 at Greenwood, Nova Scotia, and No. 415 at Summerside, Prince Edward Island. While perhaps open to criticism on the score of its relatively low maximum speed, the Argus is unsurpassed if judged by the maritime patrol aircraft's three most important parameters – range, endurance and internal capacity. Indeed, usefully long patrols over the Pacific can be mounted by the Argus directly from Atlantic coast bases, and this aircraft type has remained airborne for as long as 31 hours, while 24-hour patrols are considered normal by Argus-equipped squadrons. Designated CP-107 by the R.C.A.F., the CL-28 Argus is a unique hybrid in that it marries a fuselage of Canadian design with U.S. engines,

The Argus carries a crew of 15 – three pilots, three navigators, two flight engineers and seven electronics operators – and total internal fuel capacity of 8,200 U.S. gal. (6,828 Imp. gal.) may be supplemented by 600 U.S. gal. (500 Imp. gal.) in auxiliary weapons bay tanks. The search radar is housed by the fixed "chin" radome, and equipment includes Jezebel passive long-range acoustic search and Julie active echo ranging gear, ASH ionization-detection for

GENERAL ARRANGEMENT DRAWING: *A CP-107 Argus Mk.2 (20736) of No. 415 Squadron, R.C.A.F. Maritime Air Command at Summerside, Prince Edward Island*

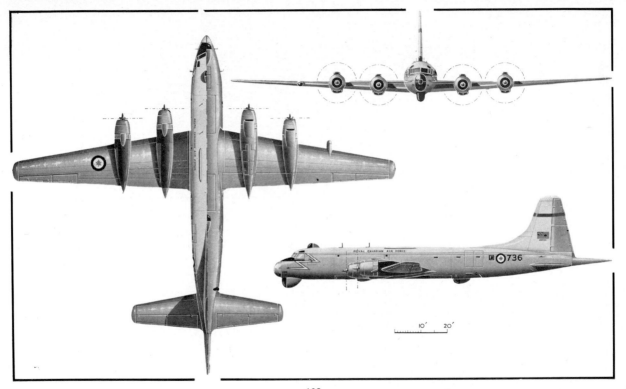

tracking the exhaust of snorkeling submarines, and MAD (Magnetic Anomaly Detector) gear. There are six air-operated sono-buoy chutes immediately aft of the tactical compartment, and each of the two weapons bays in the centre fuselage has a length of 18 ft. 6 in. and a 4,000-lb. weapons capacity, and this internal load of offensive stores, which can include depth bombs and homing torpedoes, may be supplemented by a further 3,800 lb of ordnance on each of two underwing pylons. Outside the ASW spectrum, the Argus can perform the mine-laying, long-range convoy escort and anti-shipping strike tasks. For maritime search and rescue the Argus carries at all times MA-1 rescue gear – two 20-man dinghies and survival packs, and for the transport role, a partial conversion accomplished in three hours and leaving all ASW equipment in position permits 55 passengers and 6,000 lb. of freight, or 10 passengers and 18,000 lb of freight to be ferried over 3,340 miles. A full conversion to the transport role with ASW equipment removed enables 80 passengers or 22,000 lb. of freight to be ferried over a similar range.

Power Plants: *Four Wright R-3350 Type 981 Turbo-Compound 18-cylinder radial air-cooled engines each rated at 3,400 h.p. for take-off and 3,700 h.p. with water injection.*
Performance: *Max. speed, 315 m.p.h. at 20,000 ft., 288 m.p.h. at sea level; max. cruise, 230 m.p.h. at sea level; normal cruise, 223 m.p.h. at 5,000 ft.; patrol speed, 190 m.p.h. below 1,000 ft.; patrol endurance (at range of 830 mls.), 12 hr., (at range of 1,210 mls.) 8 hr., (at range of 1,590 mls.) 4 hr.; ferry range (with two 500 Imp. gal./600 U.S. gal. auxiliary weapons bay tanks), 5,900 mls.; initial climb, 1,700 ft./min.*
Weights: *Empty, 81,000 lb.; normal loaded, 148,000 lb.*
Dimensions: *Span, 142 ft. 3½ in.; length, 128 ft. 3 in.; height, 36 ft. 8½ in.; wing area, 2,075 sq. ft.*

GRUMMAN S-2 TRACKER

In continuous production for the U.S. Navy for 14 years, during which it has been progressively updated, and scheduled to remain in production at least through Fiscal 1967, the Tracker currently equips 18 shipboard ASW squadrons, two of which are deployed aboard each of the eight U.S. Navy anti-submarine warfare carriers – four in the Atlantic and four in the Pacific, and eight U.S. Navy Reserve ASW squadrons for deployment aboard the four anti-submarine warfare carriers in the Reserve Fleet. With production approaching 1,000 aircraft, the Tracker is also widely used by foreign air forces and naval air arms, and enjoys the distinction of having been the first carrier-based aircraft capable of performing all the phases of the ASW mission – detection, classification and destruction – as a self-contained system.

Designated G-89 by its manufacturer, the Tracker was awarded a prototype contract on June 30, 1950, the prototype flying as the XS2F-1 on December 4, 1952, and production began in the following year as the S2F-1, subsequently changed to S-2A, some 500 Trackers of this model being produced by the parent company, both for the U.S. Navy and for export, and a further 100 being manufactured under licence in Canada as the CS2F-1. Apart from U.S. Navy replacement and air reserve training units, the S-2A currently serves with Patrol Squadron I of Argentina's *Aviación Naval* aboard the carrier *Independencia*; alongside the CS2F-1 in the 1° *Grupo de Aviacão Embarcada* of the *Fôrça Aérea Brasileira* aboard the carrier *Minas Gerais*; with the 86°, 87° and 88° *Gruppi Antisommergibill* of Italy's *Marinavia*; with the 11th, 12th, 13th and 14th Squadrons of the Japanese Maritime Self-Defence Force, and with the Netherlands *Marine Luchtvaartdienst* which possesses 12 S–2As in each of Nos. 2 and 4 Squadrons for service aboard the carrier *Karel Doorman*, and CS2F-1As equipping No. 1 Squadron which operates from Curaçao in the Netherlands West Indies. Fourteen S-2As are to be delivered to the Royal Australian Navy to re-equip No. 816 Squadron aboard H.M.A.S. *Melbourne*, and the Trackers equipping the Royal Canadian Navy's sole fixed-wing operational squadron, VS 880 aboard H.M.C.S. *Bonaventure*, now have updated systems and are redesignated CS2F-2s.

S-2A: The initial production version of the Tracker, the S-2A, the first example of which was delivered to the U.S. Navy in February 1954, normally carries four crew members – pilot, co-pilot/navigator, and two radar operators – and has APS-38 search radar in a retractable ventral radome; an ASQ-10 Magnetic Anomaly Detection boom retracting into the rear fuselage; ALD-3 electronic countermeasures DF to pinpoint radar or radio signals emanating from underwater craft; a 70-million candlepower searchlight mounted in the leading edge of the starboard wing, and other equipment includes TACAN, Doppler navigation radar, etc. The rear of the engine nacelles each house eight sonobuoys, and the weapons bay can accommodate two electric acoustic homing torpedoes, two Mk.101 depth bombs, or four 385-lb. depth charges. There are six underwing attachment points for 5-in. HVARs or 250-lb. bombs, and total internal fuel capacity is 270 U.S. gal. (225 Imp. gal.) which is sufficient for orbiting on station for some five hours at a range of 230 miles. Some S-2A Trackers have been modified for the ASW training mission as TS-2As, and with AQA-3 Jezebel passive long-range acoustic search equipment and a fuselage dispenser for 60 underwater sounding charges for echo ranging with the automatic target computing and plotting of the Julie localization equipment, the designation is changed to S-2B. An interim development, the S-2C intended to carry larger homing torpedoes in a weapons bay featuring an asymmetric extension on the port side, is no longer in operational service, only 60 having been built.

S-2D: Major changes in the basic Tracker design were introduced by the S-2D model which flew on May 21, 1959. Physically, the overall dimensions were increased, an 18-in. extension of the forward fuselage accompanied by a $3\frac{1}{4}$-in. widening, permitting

enlarging of the crew accommodation, and the overall wing span being increased. Internal fuel capacity was raised to 325 U.S. gal. (270.5 Imp. gal.), a modified engine nacelle configuration permitted

(Below) Canadian-built CS2F-2 Trackers of VS 880, the Royal Canadian Navy's sole fixed-wing operational squadron which is normally deployed aboard H.M.C.S. Bonaventure.

an increase in sonobuoy stowage from eight to 16 per nacelle bay, and ECM antennae were mounted in the wingtips. A Ground Track Plotter eliminated the computing and plotting duties previously required of the crew, and provided the pilot with an instantaneous picture of the tactical situation, the retractable MAD gear boom was lengthened, and an 85-million candlepower searchlight replaced the 70-million candlepower light of the S-2A. Other equipment introduced included the Sniffer passive submarine exhaust trail detector and instantaneous ECM direction finder with automatic cockpit read-out.

S-2E: S-2D Trackers have been progressively updated to current S-2E production standards with AQA-3 Jezebel long-range acoustic search equipment and its associated Julie active echo ranging, and the S-2E has now almost completely supplanted earlier versions of the Tracker with ASW Squadrons (VS-) 21, 22, 23, 24, 25, 26, 27, 28, 29, 31, 32, 33, 34, 35, 36, 37, 38 and 39, deliveries

---

Power Plants: *Two Wright R-1820-82WA nine-cylinder radial air-cooled engines each rated at 1,525 h.p.*

Performance: *Max. speed, 287 (280) m.p.h. at sea level; range cruise, 172 (166) m.p.h. at 5,000 ft.; patrol speed with MAD boom and radome extended, 150 m.p.h. at 1,500 ft.; max. range with standard tankage, 900 (1,352) mls.; initial climb, 1,920 ft./min.; service ceiling, 23,000 (22,000) ft.*

Weights: *Empty, 17,357 (18,315) lb.; loaded for carrier operation, 24,500 lb.; max., 26,300 (26,147) lb.*

Dimensions: *Span, 69 ft. 8 in. (72 ft. 7 in.); length, 42 ft. 0 in. (43 ft. 6 in.); height, 16 ft. 3½ in. (17 ft. 6 in.); wing area, 485 (499) sq. ft.*

Note: *Specification applies to S-2A, figures in parentheses relating to S-2E.*

of this model having begun in October 1962. During 1966, consideration was being given by the U.S. Navy to modifying the Tracker to carry a 165-lb. Nord AS.12 ASM beneath each wing to provide some stand-off capability.

(Left) S-2B Trackers of VS-876 operating off the coast of Oahu, Hawaii.

GENERAL ARRANGEMENT DRAWING: *An S-2E Tracker (Bu. No. 147537) of Anti-Submarine Squadron VS-26 aboard U.S.S. Randolph (CVS-15)*

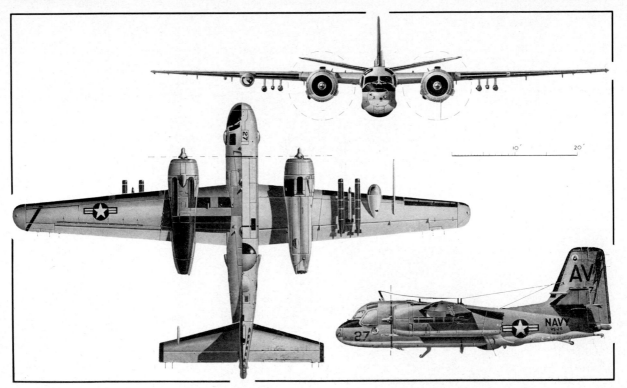

(Left) A P-2H Neptune (Bu.No.146431) of France's Aéronavale. Three Aéronavale Flottilles, 23F, 24F and 25F, currently operate maritime patrol aircraft of this type, examples of the earlier P-2F serving with Flottille 22F and the Section P2V-6 du Pacifique.

LOCKHEED SP-2H NEPTUNE

Although the replacement of the Neptune in the U.S. Navy's patrol force by the P-3 Orion began in 1962, this long-lived maritime reconnaissance aircraft still equips approximately half of the 27 land-based Patrol Squadrons in its SP-2E and SP-2H forms, and, manufactured continuously for 19 years, the Neptune equips patrol squadrons of eight foreign air arms, no fewer than 1,099 having been produced by the parent company, and a further 48 in Japan where development of the basic design is continuing. During the Neptune's 19-year production life there was a tremendous increase in the quantity and complexity of electronic devices designed to locate and kill submarines, but this remarkable aircraft succeeded in accommodating each new development in this field.

Although design of the Neptune was commenced in September 1941, concentrated development did not begin until the placing on April 4, 1944 of a U.S. Navy contract for two prototypes and 15 production aircraft, the first prototype flying on May 17, 1945. The initial model, the P2V-1, was powered by 2,300 h.p. R-3350-8 engines, and the 15 examples of this version were followed by 81

P2V-2s with R-3350-24W engines offering 2,500 h.p. dry and 2,800 h.p. with water injection, and modified defensive armament. More elaborate ASW systems and R-3350-27W engines rated at 2,700 h.p. dry and 3,200 h.p. with water injection were introduced by the 83 P2V-3s and -3Ws, while the 52 P2V-4s had R-3350-30W Turbo-Compound engines accompanied by a substantial increase in fuel capacity achieved by the provision of fixed wingtip tanks. When, in 1962, the designations of many U.S. Navy aircraft were revised, and the P2V-4 became the P-2D, this, together with all earlier versions of the Neptune had long since been supplanted in U.S. Navy service by later variants of the aircraft commencing with the P-2E which, first flown on December 29, 1950, was manufactured under the impetus of the Korean War in larger numbers than any other Neptune model, the last of 424 aircraft of this type being delivered in September 1954.

P-2E: In its original form, the P-2E featured an Emerson ball turret with twin 20-mm. cannon in the fuselage nose, the fixed nose guns of earlier models being deleted, and enlarged wingtip tanks raised total fuel capacity to 4,700 U.S. gal. (3,913 Imp. gal.), maximum gross weight being 76,152 lb. With R-3350-30W engines offering 3,250 h.p. with water injection for take-off, the P-2E attained a maximum speed of 341 m.p.h. at 9,500 ft. and had a maximum range of 4,750 mls. In addition to the nose turret, defensive armament comprised two 0.5-in. guns in a dorsal turret and twin 20-mm. cannon in the tail, maximum weapons load being 8,000 lb. The P-2E was progressively modified during its production life, the most noteworthy changes being the deletion of the nose turret which was supplanted by an elongated glazed observation position, and the provision of a MAD (Magnetic Anomaly Detection) tail extension. Post-production modification programmes included the up-dating of ASW systems, the deletion of the dorsal turret, and the fitting of two 3,400 lb.s.t. Westinghouse J-34-WE-34 turbojets in underwing pods to supplement take-off power and boost dash and over-target performance. Yet a further modification programme covering the installation of Julie active explosive echo-sounding and the complementary Jezebel passive detector system resulted in a change of designation to SP-2E, this version now being used primarily by the patrol squadrons of the U.S. Naval Reserve. Thirty-six P-2Es were supplied to the R.A.F. in 1952, and 12 of these eventually found their way to the *Forca Aérea Portuguesa* with which they still serve; six were transferred to Argentina's *Aviación Naval*, currently equipping Patrol Squadron I, and 14 entered service with the *Fôrça Aérea Brasileira* and equip the 7° *Grupo de Aviação*.

P-2F: Differing from its predecessor in being equipped for mine-laying and in having modified electronic equipment, the P-2F introduced stainless-steel engine nacelles, together with pressure fuelling and reduced-capacity wingtip tanks. The first P-2F flew on October 16, 1952, a total of 83 examples of this model being built the only remaining examples in first-line service being those serving with the French *Aéronavale*'s *Flottille* 22F and the *Section P2V-6*

(*Above*) *The P-2H Neptunes delivered to the R.Neth.N.A.S. originally featured unglazed noses housing cannon armament. Standard P-2H noses were progressively introduced, the rear aircraft in the above photo still retaining its unmodified nose.*

du Pacifique which operates this type from New Caledonia. With auxiliary J34-WE-36 jet pods the designation was changed to P-2G, but none of this version remains in service.

P-2H: Equipping the U.S. Navy's Patrol Squadrons (VP-) 1, 2, 9, 11, 17, 18, 23, 24, 31 and 56 as the SP-2H with Julie/Jezebel equipment, the P-2H was the final production variant of the Neptune, and the 359 examples produced by the parent company brought total Neptune production to 1,099 of which 838 were

(Left) A P-2H Neptune of No. 407 Squadron of the R.C.A.F. Maritime Air Command. A total of 25 P-2Hs was supplied to Canada, these supplementing the Canadian-built Argus maritime patrol aircraft.

delivered against U.S. Navy contracts, the remainder being manufactured against foreign and MAP contracts. The prototype of the P-2H, the YP-2H, was flown on April 26, 1954, this model having auxiliary turbojets from the outset and introducing the more powerful R-3350-32W engine. Other changes included a bulged cockpit canopy, revised crew accommodation, simplified multi-function control systems, a modified nosewheel unit and redesigned wingtip tanks. Initial production aircraft retained the twin 0.5-in. gun dorsal turret, but this was supplanted at an early production stage by a new Emerson turret with twin 20-mm. weapons and, eventually, dorsal armament was omitted entirely. Seven crew members are normally carried, comprising pilot, co-pilot, navigator-bombardier, radar/MAD operator, radio operator, sonobuoy-operator, and ordnanceman; normal fuel capacity is 2,200 U.S. gal. (1,832 Imp. gal.), although there is provision for a 700 U.S. gal. (583 Imp. gal.) ferry tank in the weapons bay. Internal armament can comprise two 2,165-lb. torpedoes, two 2,000-lb. mines, eight 1,000-lb. mines or bombs, or 12 325-lb. depth charges.

Sixteen P-2H Neptunes were supplied to the Japanese Maritime Self-Defence Force, and in 1958 the Japanese Kawasaki company received a contract for the licence manufacture of a further 42 P-2H Neptunes, this being supplemented by a contract for another six in 1962, and these currently equip the 1st, 2nd, 3rd and 4th Squadrons of the J.M.S.D.F. Further development of the basic Neptune design is being undertaken in Japan under the designation Kawasaki GK-210 (see pages 123 and 125).

Twenty-five P-2Hs were delivered to the R.C.A.F., and the type equips No. 407 Squadron of the Maritime Air Command at Comox; 12 were delivered to the R.A.A.F., these being operated by No. 10 Squadron at Townsville; a substantial number were delivered to France's *Aéronavale* under the MAP, and are operated by *Flottilles* 23F, 24F and 25F, and the last fifteen P-2H Neptunes built by the parent company were built for Holland's *Koninklijke*

GENERAL ARRANGEMENT DRAWING: *An SP-2H Neptune of U.S. Navy Patrol Squadron (VP-) 18 based at N.A.S. Jacksonville, Florida*

NAVY

LG

145914

NAVY

7

(Above) A P-2E Neptune (A89-304) of No. 11 Squadron, R.A.A.F., is seen flying past Diamond Head, Hawaii, in company with a P-3A Orion of the U.S. Navy's VP-28. The P-3B version of the Orion will shortly begin to supplant the R.A.A.F.'s P-2E Neptunes.

Marine Luchtvaartdienst and serve with No. 320 Squadron in the NATO Channel Command. The Dutch P-2Hs were originally delivered with an unglazed nose housing four 20-mm. cannon, but these weapons were later removed from most aircraft, a glazed observation position being reintroduced and the aircraft brought up to SP-2H standards. Subsequent modifications included provision to carry Nord AS.12 ASMs underwing, and the U.S. Navy was expected to modify its SP-2H Neptunes in a similar fashion mid-1966, two AS.12s beneath each wing endowing the aircraft with a stand-off capability of some four miles. The SP-2H Neptune is expected to remain in first-line U.S. Navy service until 1968–69 when the P-3C Orion will be standard with all patrol squadrons.

Power Plants: *Two Wright R-3350-32W Turbo-Compound 18-cylinder radial air-cooled engines each rated at 3,500 h.p. (for take-off with water injection) and two Westinghouse J34-WE-36 turbojets each rated at 3,400 lb.s.t.*
Performance: *Max. speed (all engines), 345 m.p.h. at 10,000 ft., (piston engines only), 298 m.p.h. at 8,500 ft., 260 m.p.h. at sea level; range cruise, 207 m.p.h. at 8,500 ft.; patrol speed, 173 m.p.h. at 1,000 ft.; maximum range (at normal cruise), 2,200 mls., (with 700 U.S. gal./583 Imp. gal. ferry tank), 2,860 mls.; service ceiling, 22,000 ft.*
Weights: *Empty, 49,935 lb.; loaded, 79,895 lb.*
Dimensions: *Span, 103 ft. 10 in.; length, 91 ft. 8 in.; height, 29 ft. 4 in.; wing area, 1,000 sq. ft.*
Note: *This specification applies specifically to the SP-2H.*

LOCKHEED P-3 ORION

Now the backbone of the patrol component of the U.S. Navy's Fleet Air Wings, having supplanted the ageing P-2 Neptune in more than a dozen of the 30 patrol squadrons, the P-3 is to be procured throughout Fiscal 1967, the first production contract having been placed on October 25, 1960. As the Model 185, the P-3 was the winner of a contest to fulfil the requirements of Type Specification 146 which, issued in August 1957, called for a land-based maritime reconnaissance aircraft based on an existing production airframe. The Model 185 was essentially an adaptation of the airframe of the commercial Electra transport, and with the award of a research and development contract, the third Electra prototype was modified to serve as an aerodynamic test-bed, flying in this form on August 19, 1958. Subsequently, a further Electra was converted, flying as the Y/P3V-1 (eventually redesignated YP-3A) on November 25, 1959, and sixteen months later, on April 15, 1961, the first pre-production P-3A was flown.

P-3A: Normally carrying a crew of 12, the P-3A offers some 60 per cent increase in ferry range and almost twice the speed of its predecessor, the P-2, coupled with improved versatility both within and outside the basic maritime roles. The up-dating of its avionic equipment during production has progressively enhanced its search and kill capabilities, and the so-called Deltic installation introduced with the 110th aircraft and including more sensitive ASW detection devices and improved tactical display equipment, is currently the most advanced system of its kind in operational service. The P-3A has a completely 'wet' wing which contains 71 per cent of the total of 9,200 U.S. gal. (7,660 Imp. gal.), of usable fuel, the remainder being divided between the combined centre section tank and fuselage bladder cell normally utilised only for extra-long flights, and cruising at 397–403 m.p.h., fuel consumption is 615 U.S. gal. (512 Imp. gal.) per hour.

The weapons bay is situated ahead of the wing centre section

(Right) The second of five P-3B Orion maritime patrol aircraft for the R.N.Z.A.F.(NZ4202). Delivery of the P-3B to New Zealand, the first foreign recipient of the Orion, began in August 1966. Ten similar aircraft are to serve with the R.A.A.F. from 1968.

A P-3A (Bu.No.152165) of VP-47 firing HVAR missiles.

P-3B: The initial model of the Orion has T56-A-10W turboprops rated at 4,050 e.s.h.p. for take-off and 4,500 e.s.h.p. for 1.5 min. with water-alcohol injection, but the P-3B has T56-A-14s offering 4,910 e.s.h.p. for take-off dry, and military rated power of 4,680 e.s.h.p., resulting in a substantial improvement in flight safety in the critical take-off and climb regime. The retrofit of all P-3As with the higher-powered engine is planned to ensure engine commonality throughout U.S. Navy patrol squadrons, and commencing in Fiscal 1968 all P-3As and P-3Bs will be retrofitted with a still more advanced avionics system to P-3C standards.

P-3C: The designation P-3C has been allocated to the definitive production Orion with the "A-New" avionics system. All Orions will eventually be brought up to this standard.

and can accommodate two Mk.101 nuclear depth bombs and four Mk.43, 44 or 46 torpedoes, or eight Mk.54 bombs. For the minelaying task the bay can house one 2,000-lb., three 1,000-lb., or six 500-lb. mines, and is supplemented by ten underwing pylons intended to carry and release mines. The extreme outboard pair of pylons can each carry a 500-lb. mine, the centre pair of pylons under the outer wing panels can each carry a 1,000-lb. mine, and the inboard pair plus the four beneath the centre section may each carry a 2,000-lb. mine. Alternatively, all ten pylons may carry torpedoes for ferry purposes, and rockets may be mounted singly or in pods on the two outboard pylons on each wing. The maximum external stores load is 13,713 lb. Internally-housed ASW search stores comprise 87 sonobuoys, 100 Mk.50 underwater sound signals, and 60 marine markers.

The first Patrol Squadron to receive its full complement of 12 P-3As was VP-8 of Fleet Air Wing 5 which attained its statutory strength at the end of 1962, and more than 150 Orions were in service by the middle of 1966 when deliveries of the improved P-3B had begun.

Power Plants: *Four Allison T56-A-14 turboprops each rated at 4,910 e.s.h.p. (4,591 s.h.p.) for take-off.*
Performance: *Max. speed (at 105,000 lb.), 476 m.p.h. at 15,000 ft.; cruise (at 105,000 lb.), 397 m.p.h. at 25,000 ft.; loiter speed, 230 m.p.h. at 1,500 ft.; loiter endurance at 1,500 ft. (four engines), 12.9 hr., (two engines) 17 hr.; max. mission radius, 2,533 mls., (3 hr. on station at 1,500 ft.), 1,934 mls.; initial climb (at Military Rated Power and 105,000 lb.), 3,270 ft./min., (at normal rated at 127,200 lb. from 1,500 ft.), 2,175 ft./min.; time to 25,000 ft. (at 127,200 lb.), 25 min.*
Weights: *Max. loaded, 127,200 lb.*
Dimensions: *Span, 99 ft. 8 in.; length, 116 ft. 10 in.; height, 33 ft. 8½ in.; wing area, 1,300 sq. ft.*

GENERAL ARRANGEMENT DRAWING: *A P-3A Orion (Bu.No.150605) of Patrol Squadron VP-49, Fleet Air Wing 5, based at Patuxent River Naval Air Station, Maryland.*

The last U.S. Navy maritime patrol flying boat, the SP-5B equips three squadrons, VP-40, -48, and -50.

MARTIN SP-5B MARLIN

The ancient mariner among U.S. Navy patrol aircraft and the service's last operational flying boat, the SP-5B Marlin currently equips three Patrol Squadrons, and has seen extensive use with VP-40 on surveillance patrols along the South Vietnamese coastline. With a design history dating back to July 1946, when preliminary studies were initiated for a successor to the wartime Mariner, the Marlin was first flown on May 4, 1948 as the XP5M-1. The first example of the initial production model, the P5M-1, flew on June 22, 1951, the first U.S. Navy Patrol Squadron to be equipped with the flying boat, VP-44, becoming operational on April 23, 1952. The P5M-1 was phased out of production in favour of the P5M-2 in 1954 after the completion of 114 aircraft, and the later model, which has been progressively up-dated during its service life, is now the only version serving with the U.S. Navy, its current designation being SP-5B.

Embodying considerable redesign over its predecessor, and flown (as the P5M-2) on April 29, 1954, the flying boat remained in production until December 20, 1960, and in its current SP-5B form is equipped with Julie active explosive echo-sounding and complementary Jezebel passive detector system. Internal tankage is provided for 2,025 U.S. gal. (1,686 Imp. gal.) of fuel, which, with jettisonable 805 U.S. gal. (670 Imp. gal.) tanks in each weapons bay, provides a total tankage for 3,635 U.S. gal. (3,026 Imp. gal.) of fuel. The weapons bays in the engine nacelles can accommodate four 2,165-lb. torpedoes, four 2,000-lb. bombs, four 2,000-lb. Mk.55 mines, eight 1,000-lb. Mk.52 mines, 16 500-lb. bombs or 16 325-lb. depth charges, and eight 1,000-lb. bombs or mines may be carried on underwing racks. One SP-5B was tested in 1964 with a Pratt & Whitney J60 turbojet mounted in the extreme rear of the hull, this reducing take-off by 20 seconds and 2,400 ft. at a gross weight of 80,000 lb., and this modification is being adopted for service introduction, the chosen turbojet being the General Electric J85-GE-2.

Power Plants: Two Wright R-3350-32W Turbo-Compound 18-cylinder radial air-cooled engines each rated at 3,450 h.p. for take-off and 3,700 h.p. with water injection.
Performance: Max. speed, 251 m.p.h. at sea level; patrol speed, 150–180 m.p.h. at 1,000–5,000 ft.; normal range (ASW patrol mission), 2,050 mls.; ferry range (with an 805 U.S. gal./670 Imp. gal. tank in each weapons bay), 3,100 mls.; initial climb, 1,200 ft./min.; service ceiling, 24,000 ft.
Weights: Empty, 50,485 lb.; loaded (ASW patrol), 76,635 lb.; max. overload, 85,000 lb.
Dimensions: Span, 118 ft. 2¼ in.; length, 100 ft. 7¼ in.; height, 32 ft. 8½ in.; wing area, 1,406.33 sq. ft.

GENERAL ARRANGEMENT DRAWING: *An SP-5B Marlin (Bu. No. 140147) of the U.S. Navy Patrol Squadron VP-40 based at Naval Air Station, Sangley Point, Philippine Islands.*

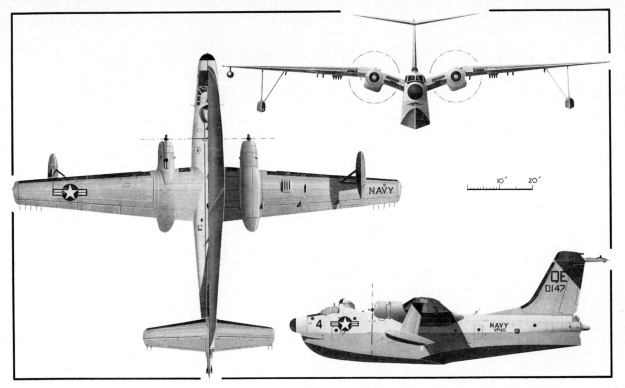

COUNTER-INSURGENCY AIRCRAFT

COUNTER-INSURGENCY, or COIN, is common currency today to describe aircraft and operations having a time-honoured place in aeronautical history. The COIN concept owes much to the R.A.F., which began developing air power for policing roles throughout the widespread territories of the British Empire immediately after the First World War, although the resulting general-purpose aircraft differed little at that time from first-line home-based equipment. From the European Continent, too, the colonial-type warplane emerged as a potent force for "keeping the natives' heads down". The elderly and picturesque British, French and Italian designs, which were capable of any duty ranging from V.I.P. and troop transportation to bombing and ground strafing, helped define the classic characteristics still relevant for today's COIN-type aircraft.

COIN-aircraft characteristics are shaped primarily by the fact that the requirements that they fulfil envisage the application of air power in conditions of complete air superiority, unchallenged by opposing fighters, and normally facing only weak and unsophisticated ground defences. This means that the usual priorities of all-out performance demanded for most combat aircraft can be overridden by load-carrying and short-field capabilities. The resulting COIN aircraft is obsolescent according to the values of total war, and is possibly vulnerable to sudden improvements in enemy ground defence sophistication, but for the uneasy peace of the Cold War, and for internal security duties, counter-insurgency types are as successful now as were the ancient general-purpose biplanes of the R.A.F. in policing the North-West Frontier of India, and Iraq, forty or so years ago.

Because of their low speed performance, COIN aircraft have a much lower rate of obsolescence than their more spectacular counterparts in the heavy strike roles, and tend to lead long operational lives. This is illustrated by the fact that the most successful COIN types to date have remained piston-engined and are of World War II or immediate post-war vintage. The Douglas B-26

Although the T-28D counter-insurgency derivative of the T-28A is no longer employed operationally by the Vietnamese Air Force, in whose markings it is illustrated (left), it serves with the air arms of Laos, Thailand, Bolivia and the Congo. The T-28D-5 differs from the initial T-28D-1 in having in-wing ammunition storage for the 0.5-in. underwing gun pods. The T-28D attains a maximum speed of 352 m.p.h. at 18,000 ft. and 298 m.p.h. at sea level. Initial climb rate is 3,780 ft./min., range is 1,184 miles at 203 m.p.h., and maximum loaded weight is 8,495 lb.

Invader, in fact, saw operational service before the end of the war and has only just been retired from combat by the U.S.A.F. As the most effective COIN aircraft of all time, the Douglas A-1 Skyraider dates from the immediate post-war period, but has made its mark in all the major limited conflicts since that time—in Korea, Algeria, and currently Vietnam. It is as operationally effective today as it was in 1950, and relatively recently there was even talk of resuming production of this lumbering load-carrier, deliveries of which terminated ten years ago and which is still affectionately deprecated by its pilots as the "Spad".

Another advantage of COIN-type aircraft is that they represent a breakaway from the fantastic cost spiral of sophisticated nuclear strike weapons systems, and their low price approach makes them saleable items among the smaller nations as well as the major powers. In many ways, the newly emergent countries have even greater requirements for COIN-type equipment because of their initial political instability and susceptibility to extra-national interference. A simple strike aircraft becomes practical from the procurement point of view through the small demands it makes on initial budgeting, pilot training and maintenance.

Although its historical precedents are mainly of European origin, the current COIN concept was shaped in the U.S.A. largely through political pressures. Since the nuclear stalemate has minimised the possibility of total war, there has been an increasing tendency towards limited conflicts which resulted in a reassessment by the U.S. defence planners of their close support requirements and the equipment available to meet them. This examination was intensified by American involvement in South Vietnam and adjacent areas, as part of its SEATO commitments, and also by the general U.S. policy of Communist containment in S.E. Asia by economic and military (counter-insurgency) action.

Spelt out in basic terms, the COIN concept calls for a simple, relatively lightweight, low-cost strike aircraft for the close support of ground forces in unsophisticated tactical warfare. One of its main purposes, according to U.S. Defense Department officials, is to arrest future Vietnam-type wars before they have a chance to grow in size to the point where larger and more expensive strike weapons must be introduced. COIN thus has a preventive role in "bush-fire" operations, but it is also foreseen by the U.S. as assisting to eliminate the causes of insurgency "through appropriate humanitarian and sociological missions". This again harks back to the general-purpose aircraft of the 1920s, and it can be seen that there is as much transport as strike aircraft in the COIN type as currently conceived.

In the United States, despite the attachment of COIN to the roles of the ground forces, development responsibility has been allocated firmly to the U.S.A.F., although there is an associated Navy requirement for the Marine Corps. U.S.A.F. experience with COIN dates back to the end of 1961, when the first contingent of B-26 Invaders and A-1 Skyraiders was sent to Vietnam to counter growing Communist pressure from the North. With the experience gained from these veteran aircraft, a Special Air Warfare Centre was established at Eglin Air Force Base, Florida, on April 27, 1962, under Tactical Air Command. The SAWC was developed from the 4400th Combat Crew Training Squadron, which had been formed at Eglin in July 1961, after an initial order to the U.S.A.F. Tactical Air Command to develop counter-insurgency capability, and comprising two main formations. The 1st Air Commando Group was given the primary job of instructing and advising aircrews of allied nations in all phases of airborne operations against insurgent forces, while the 1st Combat Applications Group was formed to develop, test and evaluate equipment and tactics for use in special air warfare missions. Both units were supplied by the 4420th Combat Support Group.

When the SAWC assembled its first aircraft equipment, its inventory read like an availability report from World War II. The U.S.A.F. "graveyard" at Davis-Monthan AFB, Ariz., more officially known as the 2704th Air Force Aircraft Storage and Disposition Group, was raided for such veterans as Curtiss C-46s and Douglas C-47s, later joined by the Fairchild C-123B and

Helio U-10 Courier, for transport tasks, while for offensive operations a number of the well-tried Douglas B-26 Invaders were returned to service. For really close support, the SAWC selected the North American T-28 which had not long been redundant as a U.S.A.F. trainer, and possessed the necessary manoeuvrability plus much of the lifting capability for COIN-type operations.

TRAINER ADAPTATIONS

Modifications to develop current operational capabilities for these veteran aircraft were undertaken by the Combat Applications Group, which undertook considerable redesign and armament changes. The T-28, for example, changed from a training to an offensive role by a general strengthening of the airframe to permit the underwing carriage of offensive stores, and an increase in gross weight from 6,760 lb. to 12,100 lb. The 800 h.p. Wright R-1300-1 radial engine of the T-28A was replaced by a 1,300 h.p. Wright R-1820-56S in the resulting T-28D, which also had a strengthened undercarriage, crew armour and many other changes. The addition of three pylon stations beneath each wing permitted a maximum ordnance load of 3,500 lb., including two 0.5-in. Browning M-3 machine-guns in detachable pods, two 500-lb. or 750-lb. HE, incendiary or napalm bombs, and two MA-3 eight-

tube 2.75-in. rocket launchers. Two self-sealing 174 U.S. gal. fuel tanks were installed in the wing centre-section, with smaller tanks outboard. In mid-1966, the U.S.A.F. initiated an evaluation programme in S.E. Asia with 14 T-28Ds under the code name "Lucky Tiger". The aircraft utilised for this programme were essentially similar to the T-28D-5, which featured in-wing ammunition storage, apart from additional avionics.

By July 1966, when a contract was placed for a further 13 conversions, 223 of the 1,193 T-28A trainers originally built had been modified by North American Columbus to T-28D-1 and D-5 standards for service with the 1st Air Commando Group and numerous overseas air forces, including those of South Vietnam, Laos, Thailand, Bolivia, and the Congolese Republic. Of 130 similar T-28A conversions undertaken in France under the name Fennec, 45 have been supplied to Argentina's Navy to replace its Corsairs.

T-28s are still used operationally in Laos, but have been replaced in Vietnam by heavier strike aircraft. An attempt to modernise the T-28 by the installation of a 2,445 s.h.p. Lycoming YT55-L-9 turboprop, plus such additional changes as a taller fin and rudder, and LW-2 ejection-seats for the crew of two, was abandoned after the construction of three prototype YAT-28Es. A parallel SAWC evaluation was conducted with the Cessna YAT-37D, a COIN adaptation of the widely-used U.S.A.F. basic jet trainer with two 4,800 lb.s.t. J85-J2 turbojets, but this was also abandoned.

Following the increased attrition resulting from escalation of the war in Vietnam, however, Cessna revived flight demonstrations of the YAT-37D in mid-1965, and offered production aircraft within about fourteen months for a unit cost of less than $300,000 (£107,000 approx.), and on August 22, 1966 Cessna received an initial U.S.A.F. contract for the conversion of 39 T-37Bs to AT-37D standards for delivery to Vietnam. Further orders have also been placed with Cessna for T-37C armed trainers for delivery to friendly nations under the U.S. Military Assistance Programme.

Most other international jet trainers have been proposed for COIN duties, carrying light ground attack armament, and the armed trainer now has a well-established place in many of the smaller air forces' inventories. Modifications are less extensive than those proposed for such types as the AT-37D and in most cases simply comprise underwing attachment points for external stores, plus the addition of suitable gun, rocket and bomb sights. One of the most widely used of the armed trainers is the Macchi M.B.326, and it has been reported that the R.A.A.F. will probably re-equip some of its Sabre units with M.B.326H armed trainers, locally-built, for light ground attack, while an extensive COIN role is obviously envisaged for its nationally-produced Impala version of the M.B.326 by the South African Air Force.

Canadair has produced a counter-insurgency version of its Tutor jet trainer known as the CL-41G, with up-rated (2,950 lb.) General Electric J85-J4 turbojets, two 0.3-in. General Electric Miniguns under the fuselage and 3,500 lb. of underwing ordnance. A prototype CL-41G has been flying since June 1964, and has been extensively demonstrated in Europe and South America. In Sweden, a special light ground attack version of the Saab 105 jet trainer, known as the A 60, has been ordered by *Flygvapnet* for support of naval and military forces, although in an emergency the entire training fleet of 130 Sk 60s could be used for similar duties.

From the widely-used Jet Provost trainer, itself sold as an armed aircraft to Ceylon, Sudan, Kuwait, Venezuela and Iraq in its T.Mks.51 and 52 forms, BAC is developing a COIN version of the pressurised T.Mk.5, known as the BAC 167. Powered by a 3,410 lb. Bristol Siddeley Viper 20 Mk. 522 turbojet, the BAC 167 will have a gross weight of 10,500 lb., compared with 7,400 lb. for the standard Jet Provost T.Mk.4, and will carry up to 3,100 lb. of external stores on six underwing hard points.

The Macchi M.B.326 has been widely adopted for the dual training and counter-insurgency role, the armed version being designated M.B.326B, this having provision for two 0.5-in. gun pods and four 260-lb. bombs or MATRA 125 launchers each with six 2.75-in. rockets. The version to be manufactured in Australia, the M.B.326H, will be fitted with the General Electric six-barrel 7.62-mm. Minigun. The model assembled in South Africa is known as the Impala, and the M.B.326F of the Ghana Air Force is illustrated right.

Above and below) A COIN version of the CL-41A Tutor, the CL-41G, with two 7.62-mm. Minigun pods beneath the fuselage, and two 500-lb. and two 250-lb. bombs beneath the wings.

A little-known development in the armed trainer field is that of the Lockheed AT-33, which is a new COIN derivative of the T-33A trainer. Great attention is now being paid by the OAS (Organisation of American States) to building up counter-insurgency forces with U.S. assistance, and armed versions of the T-33, presumably reverting to F-80 Shooting Star weapons arrangements, are now being supplied to several Central and South American countries under the MAP. One of the first recipients of the Lockheed AT-33 is the *Fuerza Aérea Columbiana*, which is also being supplied with a squadron of Bell UH-1B helicopters specifically for COIN duties.

RESURRECTING VETERANS

An even more remarkable COIN conversion from the U.S.A. which is now being operationally employed against the Viet Cong is that of the venerable Douglas C-47 transport—undoubtedly the most elderly aircraft ever to see combat. To meet a field requirement for a heavy weight of airborne machine gun fire to be available during long endurance missions, the U.S.A.F. modified five C-47s in 1965 to mount various combinations of 0.3-in. Browning guns and General Electric Miniguns firing laterally through window and door apertures. Evaluation of these ground strafing aircraft—initially known as FC-47s, and giving the versatile C-47 its first-ever fighter appellation—soon proved their value in delivering a heavy and sustained weight of fire against ground targets during night missions, and their armament layout was standardised by the installation of three 7.62-mm. Miniguns in self-contained pods within the fuselage.

Each Minigun is provided with 18,000 rounds of ammunition, which represents three minutes of continuous firing. The guns are remotely controlled by the pilot, who is provided with a special gunsight attachment on the port wing, to fire his armament during tight left-hand turns over the target area. Associated equipment, also developed by the Air Force Systems Command, includes new navigational aids and a flare launcher for target illumination.

The Saab 105, which entered service with Flygvapnet in 1966, is intended for both training and light attack tasks. The attack version, the A 60, will carry two Robot 05A ASMs, two 12.7-mm. or 30-mm. gun pods, twelve 13.5-cm. rockets or two 550-lb. bombs.

Following the success of the initial trials, twenty stored C-47s were drawn from the Military Aircraft Storage and Disposition Centre at Tucson, Arizona, to be modified by Air International (Miami) for the most glamorous role ever undertaken in the long career of the "Gooney Bird", emerging as heavily-armed Douglas AC-47s.

These were used to equip the 4th Air Commando Squadron (Fire Support) of the SAWC, which arrived in Vietnam in November 1965. In the U.S.A.F. the AC-47 has earned the name "Puff, the Magic Dragon" from its fire-breathing association with a fairy-story character, but at $120,000 (£43,000) unit cost ($60,000 or £21,500 for conversion, plus $20,000/£7,150 for each of the Mini-gun pods), it is undoubtedly the cheapest weapons system in the U.S.A.F. inventory. By flying at about 3,000 ft., the AC-47s can apparently stay out of range of most small arms fire from the ground, although retaining the effectiveness of their own armament. Another C-47 conversion for Vietnam, extending still further the

versatility of the remarkable Dakota, is the installation of vertical and oblique cameras in the fuselage, resulting in the appearance of the RC-47. The eight-hour low-altitude endurance of the RC-47 gives the inestimable advantage of continuous long-term coverage of a particular area.

Continuing the modernisation theme as a low-cost solution to COIN requirements, an attempt was made in 1962–63 by the U.S.A.F. to extend the effective lives of the veteran Douglas B-26B and B-26C Invaders which were being used in Vietnam for bombing and close support missions. Following a series of in-flight structural failures, all U.S.A.F. B-26s were grounded early in 1964, but a face-lift programme was tried with a trial batch of forty Invaders for the 1st Air Commando Group. Twenty-seven B-26Bs were withdrawn from storage at Davis-Monthan AFB, plus a further thirteen from the Tactical Air Command, and sent to the On Mark Engineering Corporation at

Van Nuys, California, for rebuilding and modification to B-26K Counter-Invader standard.

Main changes to the B-26K included a completely remanufactured airframe for a new fatigue life, plus the installation of 2,500 h.p. Pratt & Whitney R-2800-103W engines driving three-bladed Hamilton Standard reversible-pitch airscrews with automatic feathering. Gross weight was increased to 43,380 lb., which included up to 8,000 lb. of external stores, in addition to the standard 4,000 lb. carried in the bomb bay. Permanent wing-tip tanks brought the total internal fuel capacity to 1,230 U.S. gal. (1,024 Imp. gal.), and with maximum armament load the B-26K had a 90-min. loiter capability at a combat radius of 575 miles. The B-26K was designed to carry quickly-changed underwing pod armament in addition, with any combination of 0.5 in. guns, bombs, rockets, napalm, fuel tanks or flare dispensers. For reconnaissance, cameras and equipment could be pallet-mounted in the bomb bay. All forty B-26K Invaders were delivered to the

1st Air Commando Group, but the only overseas service achieved was by a batch of aircraft taken by the U.S.A.F. to the Congo during the Simba rebellion. After operational service there, nine B-26Ks were taken over by the Congolese Air Force, and others have since been passed to Laos.

The B-26 has been replaced in the U.S.A.F. inventory by its stablemate, the Skyraider, which can carry approximately the same external load and entered U.S.A.F. service in 1963, some seventeen years after starting its long career with the U.S. Navy. In its search for suitable coin types, the SAWC, and in particular the Combat Applications Group, borrowed several Skyraiders from the Navy and found that their load-carrying capability, coupled with the two-man cockpit of the A-1E (the rules of engagement in Vietnam at that time required that a South Vietnamese pilot be technically in control of combat aircraft, with a U.S.A.F. pilot permitted to "accompany" him) made them ideal for the type of operations envisaged. The U.S.A.F. therefore obtained some 150 surplus A-1Es for service with the SAWC from excess Navy stocks. There they were used for training U.S.A.F. pilots on type, being fitted with dual control for this purpose. This was highly necessary, since many U.S.A.F. pilots had never flown a piston-engined aircraft, nor one with a tailwheel undercarriage. After training, the U.S.A.F. pilots were sent to Vietnam, originally to fly with Vietnamese personnel operating with the 34th Tactical Group in Skyraiders supplied from the U.S.A. to replace the T-28Ds and B-26s. The rules of engagement restricting operations in Vietnam were abandoned by the U.S.A.F. in February 1965, to permit overt missions by American personnel, and the use of turbine-powered aircraft for the first time. The U.S.A.F. operates about fifty two-seat A-1E Skyraiders in Vietnam, while the Vietnamese have around 130 single-seat A-1Hs and A-1Gs. The U.S. Navy is also operating A-1H and A-1J Skyraiders from its carriers around Vietnam, and it is safe to say that the "Spad" is contributing a greater workload in the COIN campaign against the Viet Cong than any other individual aircraft type.

Since the Skyraider cost only about $285,000 (£101,800) when its production was completed in 1957, after completion of 3,180 aircraft, it represents unparalleled cost-effectiveness. Its replacement, the A-7A Corsair II, will cost at least $1.7m. (£607,000), and will carry almost as much ordnance at far higher speeds, but its time over the target will be very much shorter.

THE U.S. SERVICES' LARA

The turboprop conversion of the A-1 by the installation of a 4,050 h.p. Allison T-56 has been proposed, to increase the maximum speed to 375 m.p.h. at sea level, but it seems that the days of the Skyraider are now probably numbered by more sophisticated COIN developments. These principally derive from a 1963 design contest to produce an up-to-date COIN type for common use by all the U.S. services involved. A specification was evolved by the Navy, as systems manager, based on a requirement of the U.S. Marine Corps for a Light Armed Reconnaissance Aircraft (LARA). This was conceived as falling somewhere between the Cessna O-1 observation aircraft, which is performing an invaluable reconnaissance and forward air controller post role in Vietnam, and the armed helicopter. Its mission profiles were to cover armed reconnaissance, close air support, helicopter escort, personnel and cargo transportation, photographic and target reconnaissance, forward air controlling and so on, and its specification included two-place tandem seating, twin turboprop engines, light weight, STOL operation from unimproved runways or open fields, aircraft-carrier compatibility, amphibious capacity, and minimum size, complexity and cost.

This was in essence the "colonial" aircraft of the 'thirties brought right up to date. Maximum specified speed was not less than 315 m.p.h., with minimum flight speeds of 46 m.p.h. power on, and 70 m.p.h. power off, while the minimum on-station loiter was laid down as two hours. Take-off and landing distances over 50 ft. had to be a maximum of 800 ft., and the single-engine service ceiling specified was 10,000 ft. minimum. The LARA specification demanded extreme ruggedness, with an acceptable landing sink rate of no less than 20 ft./sec., and a design load factor of 8 g. Ferry range was to be a minimum 1,380 miles and in addition to four 7.62-mm. machine guns, the aircraft was to carry up to 2,000 lb. of high-density internal stores as well as other ordnance on five external stations.

Four alternative powerplants were recommended by the U.S. Government—the Continental YT72, the Canadian Pratt & Whitney YT74-CP-4/6, the Garrett (AiResearch)YT76-G-2/4, or the Turboméca Astazou II. In fact, only two of the recommended engines—the T74 and the T76—were specified by all nine companies submitting design studies in early 1964 to the LARA/COIN contest, which was to include the construction and flight-testing of seven prototypes of the selected design for a total cost of up to $15m (£6.35m). Original target price for unit production was only $100,000 (£35,700), but this was not regarded by most competing manufacturers as realistic.

On August 15, 1964, North American Columbus Division was announced as winner of the LARA design contest, and authorisation was given for the construction of the seven prototypes. The NA-300 submission was a relatively conventional twin-boom high-wing monoplane of all-metal structure except for glass-

Cessna O-1 Bird Dog light observation aircraft employed for the forward air controller task by the U.S.A.F. in Vietnam are now being fitted with an M-60 machine gun (left) which, fired from the port rear window, is operated by the pilot. The O-1 will be succeeded in the FAC role by the North American OV-10A.

fibre fairings, although among the thirty–forty design studies undertaken by North American before its finalisation were a compact twin-turboprop biplane, a tandem-engined twin-boom layout, a tail-first co-axial pusher, a three-quarter scale T-28, various V/STOL projects and several small aircraft reminiscent of pre-World War II racing types. With the inclusion of appropriations for 234 OV-10As, as the NA-300 has been designated, in the Fiscal 1967 budget, several long-standing disputes concerning the status and hardware of the COIN programme appear to have been settled. Although the North American design had been selected as winner of the COIN contest, General Dynamics/Convair had gone ahead beforehand with the construction of a prototype of its Model 48 Charger design submission and, with the support of Army and U.S.M.C. factions, had pressed for a competitive

evaluation against the OV-10A. The U.S. Department of Defense was persuaded to award a $500,000 (£178,500) contract to Convair to assist flight-testing of the Charger, which was already being built as a $3.5m. (£1.25m.) private venture. Powered by two 650 s.h.p. Pratt & Whitney YT74-CP-8 and -10 engines, and bearing a close general similarity in configuration to the OV-10A, the sole prototype Charger was completed in short time and made its first flight on November 25, 1964, at San Diego. It was subsequently evaluated by N.A.S.A. and military pilots, and was being flown by a naval officer when it crashed at San Diego on October 9, 1965, during an attempted single-engine landing. At the time of the accident, the Charger had completed 193 hours' flying, of which 162 were by company pilots, ten by N.A.S.A. and twenty-one by the military. Sufficient data was obtained to permit a comparative evaluation with the OV-10A, and a list of modifications, including a longer fuselage, had been prepared for a production prototype. The U.S.A.F. and U.S.M.C. request for Fiscal 1967 appropriations for the OV-10A, however, appears to have decided the competitive evaluation issue. Convair had costed its aircraft at about $150,000 (£53,600), less engines and electronics, which would have been Government furnished for a further $50,000 (£17,850) per Charger for a 500 run. Latest cost figures for the OV-10A indicate a unit price of around $300,000 (£107,000) complete.

The OV-10A appropriations also appear to have decided the status situation of the COIN programme, so far as the LARA element is concerned. Neither the U.S. Defense Secretary nor the U.S.A.F. had apparently been keen on LARA, on the basis that higher speeds and greater load-carrying abilities were required, and the air force persisted with "Super COIN" proposals for simplified standard jet fighters such as the Northrop F-5 and Douglas A-4. U.S.A.F. "Super COIN" requirements were crystallised in November 1965 by the issue of a new proposal known as SOR (Specific Operational Requirement) 222, for a "family concept" combination light cargo transport and strike-reconnaissance aircraft for COIN duties. The commander of the SAWC at Eglin was instrumental in framing the SOR 222 specification, which includes a maximum speed of about 460 m.p.h., a 315 m.p.h. cruise, a range of some 1,150 miles on internal fuel, or 3,000 miles for ferrying, and a maximum take-off distance of 1,800 ft. A twin-turboprop design was envisaged using engines of about 1,000 h.p., with a maximum ordnance load of about 4,000 lb. in a 7.33 g airframe.

Studies have been made to scale up the North American OV-10A to meet SOR 222, which covers a proposal for about 300 strike-reconnaissance versions and some sixty transports. A transport development of the OV-10A, the NA-301, has been prepared by North American, using a completely new fuselage nacelle with side-by-side seating for a crew of two and accommodation for twelve or more passengers or a 4,500-lb. payload. Gross weight would be increased from 10,550 lb. for the close air support version to 12,500 lb., and to maintain good short-field performance the plank-like wing would simply be extended from 40 ft. 3 in. to about 50 ft. Beaver-tail rear loading between the tail booms would make the transport OV-10A a useful bush freighter for both military and civil use.

Whether SOR 222 will ever get off the ground remains to be seen, but having accepted the OV-10A as a replacement for its Cessna O-1F Bird Dog light aircraft, with additional strike potential, the U.S.A.F. is vulnerable to escalation proposals from North American for a more potent version for the "Super COIN" requirement. This would bridge the gap between the basic COIN concept and the diversification of counter-insurgency effort represented by faster but still simple strike aircraft, such as the Northrop F-5, and the Lockheed AAFSS armed helicopter.

Most other strike fighters have been looked at by the U.S.A.F. and SAWC for the heavier COIN role, and at the other extreme the Defense Department directed the U.S.A.F. in mid-1965 to evaluate several current production light planes, including a Bonanza/Debonair hybrid from Beech, a Cessna 206 Super Skywagon, a Piper Cherokee Six and a UH-6A Beaver, as interim strike/utility types for COIN use. Once again, the evaluation of these aircraft carrying underwing pod-mounted armament, including bombs, rockets, napalm tanks and Miniguns, was undertaken by the SAWC at Eglin, for a potential requirement totalling 170 aircraft initially, perhaps for overseas air forces procurement under the MAP. No more has been heard of this light COIN exercise, which has been eclipsed by the still smaller Malmö armed Militrainer version of the Junior two-seater in Sweden. But from the range of types now available, it is evident that the COINs of today and tomorrow will continue to be of all denominations.

Probably the smallest aircraft offered for the counter-insurgency role is the MFI-9B Mili-Trainer produced in prototype form by the AB Malmö Flygindustri. The Mili-Trainer is primarily a military primary trainer capable of carrying various light ordnance loads on two underwing stations for COIN and policing roles. It is seen below with four 7.5-cm. rockets. The aircraft of this type were ordered by Flygvapnet in 1966.

Known in Vietnam as the "Spad", the Douglas Skyraider has proved itself the most effective of existing combat aircraft in the counter-insurgency role. The U.S.A.F. A-1E two-seat version (Bu.No.134989) illustrated left and seen during a mission against the Viet Cong is carrying 14 fragmentation bombs in addition to a centre-line drop tank. The Skyraider's combination of endurance, ruggedness and load-carrying capability is second to no aircraft in its category.

DOUGLAS A-1 SKYRAIDER

In some respects the rugged, piston-engined Skyraider is one of the most remarkable combat aircraft to have been produced since the end of the Second World War. Rescued from relative obscurity by the Korean conflict, the Skyraider, designed as a single-seat shipboard attack bomber, has undertaken every task from troop-carrying to target-towing, from airborne early warning to anti-submarine warfare, from close-support to electronic countermeasures. In fact, no one basic aircraft has ever before filled such a multitude of roles, and when the last of 3,180 Skyraiders was delivered on February 18, 1957, no fewer than 28 variants had appeared. Indeed, today, 10 years later, its primary task is that of counter-insurgency warfare, having embarked on an entirely new career with the U.S.A.F. and Vietnamese Air Force 20 years after its conception.

For the COIN task the Skyraider is as yet unsurpassed, and since the appearance of the two-seat A-1E version of the aircraft in

Vietnam in 1964 with the 1st and 602nd Air Commando Squadrons of the U.S.A.F.'s 34th Tactical Group, the Skyraider has been used continuously against targets in both North and South Vietnam outside the surface-to-air missile envelope. It is also serving in Vietnam in its single-seat A-1G and A-1H versions, equipping five squadrons and one group of the Vietnamese Air Force, and the five carriers of the U.S. Navy's Task Force 77 committed to the Vietnam war each carry an A-1H or A-1J squadron, the Skyraider's heavy payload capacity, excellent endurance, relative invulnerability to small arms fire, and the ability to operate in weather that grounds most jets proving invaluable attributes in the type of warfare being waged in Vietnam.

GENERAL ARRANGEMENT DRAWING: *An A-1H Skyraider (39714) of the 83rd Special Air Group of the 33rd Wing, Vietnamese Air Force, based at Tan Son Nhut*

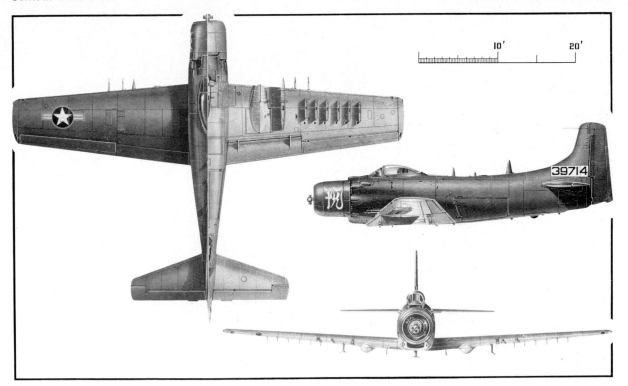

Development of the Skyraider was begun early in 1944, and on July 6th of that year 25 aircraft were ordered for development and evaluation, the first of these flying on March 18, 1945. The initial production model, the single-seat AD-1, was deployed aboard the U.S.S. *Midway* with VA-1B late in 1947, and 242 examples of this model were followed by 35 AD-1Q counter-measures aircraft with a second crew member in the fuselage aft of the pilot. The AD-2 and -2Q, 156 and 22 examples of which were built respectively, exchanged the 2,500 h.p. R-3350-24W engine of the initial version for the 2,700 h.p. -26W, and embodied some structural strengthening and an increase in fuel capacity

from 365 to 380 U.S. gal. (304 to 316 Imp. gal.), and yet further structural strengthening characterised the AD-3, of which 194 examples, including 23 AD-3Qs, 15 AD-3N night attack aircraft and 31 AD-3W early warning aircraft, were built before this type was supplanted on the assembly lines by the AD-4 in mid-1949.

The AD-4 brought to an end the long series of structural modifications that had marked every Skyraider variant to that time, and equipment included new APS-19A radar, a P-1 automatic pilot, etc. A year later, in June 1950, when North Korean forces crossed the 38th parallel, the phasing out of the Skyraider and its replacement aboard U.S. Navy carriers by jet attack aircraft

(Below) Two Vietnamese A-1H Skyraiders flying escort for a Fairchild C-123B Provider transport of the U.S.A.F. over Vietnam.

appeared imminent, but the discovery that no turbojet-powered attack aircraft could orbit on station during close-support missions for a comparable length of time, or carry the large and varied offensive load of the Skyraider endowed it with a new lease on life, and the AD-4 remaining in production until the late summer of 1953 when a total of 1,032 examples of this model had been delivered. Redesignated A-1D in 1962, when the AD-4 version of the Skyraider had long since been out of first-line U.S. Navy service, this model still serves with the *Armée de l'Air* and the Royal Khmer Aviation of Cambodia. Eighty-eight examples were supplied to France for use in Algeria, and a number still equip the *Escadrons d'Avions d'Appui* 1/21 and 2/21, the remainder having been presented to the Cambodian government. While production of the AD-4 alias A-1D was proceeding, an even more versatile version of the Skyraider was under test, the AD-5 which was later to be redesignated A-1E.

A-1E: First flown on August 17, 1951, the A-1E embodied extensive redesign although retaining much of the structure of earlier models. The forward fuselage was widened to permit side-by-side seating in the cockpit; overall length was increased from 38 ft. 2 in. to 40 ft. 1 in.; vertical tail surface area was increased by 50 per cent; a single dive brake supplanted the multiple surfaces, and interchangeable kits permitted the rapid conversion of the basic aircraft from A-1E day attack to EA-1E early warning, EA-1F countermeasures, or A-1G night attack models. A total of 670 examples of this multi-purpose version of the Skyraider was built for the U.S. Navy, and the A-1E had been withdrawn from first-line U.S. Navy service when, in 1963, the U.S.A.F. Tactical Air Command's Special Air Warfare Center, after extensive evaluation of several types for the COIN role, selected the A-1E, some 150 aircraft of this type subsequently being transferred from Navy stocks to the Tactical Air Command. These are operated by the 1st and 602nd Air Commando Squadrons in Vietnam, and the 603rd Air Commando Squadron at Hurlburt Field in the

(*Above*) *A-1H Skyraiders of the Vietnamese Air Force which has received* 106 *aircraft of this type to equip the bulk of its combat elements.*

Eglin A.F.B. Special Air Warfare Center complex for training purposes.

The A-1E has a built-in armament of four wing-mounted 20-mm. cannon, and its 15 stores attachment points are capable of lifting a maximum of 8,000 lb. of ordnance, offensive loads of three 1,000-lb., six 500-lb. and six 250-lb. bombs, or eight 1,000-lb. bombs being commonplace for sorties in Vietnam, maximum overload weight being 25,000 lb. The only modifications to the A-1E found necessary by the U.S.A.F. to adapt it for its new COIN warfare role were the introduction of dual controls, and the substitution of radio and navigational equipment compatible with U.S.A.F. operation. Twenty-six examples of the A-1G single-seat night attack equivalent of the A-1E have been supplied to the Vietnamese Air Force, but the principal Skyraider model employed by that air arm is the A-1H.

A-1H: Manufactured in parallel with the A-1E, the single-seat

(Left) An A-1H Skyraider (Bu.No. 137552) of VA-115, a component of Carrier Air Wing 11 aboard the U.S.S. Kitty Hawk which was deployed off the Vietnamese coast early in 1966.

and differs in having strengthened wing attachment points to improve fatigue life for low-level operations with heavy underwing loads. Other changes include the introduction of the improved -26WB engine and some strengthening of the undercarriage. Seventy-two examples of the A-1J had been manufactured when Skyraider production finally terminated on February 18, 1957.

A-1H differs from the earlier A-1D primarily in having a strengthened wing centre section and simplified electronics, and deliveries to the U.S. Navy began in 1953 and terminated in 1956 with the 713th example. Powered by a similar R-3350-26WA engine to the A-1E and carrying a similar quartette of 20-mm. cannon and underwing ordnance loads, the A-1H is gradually giving place in U.S. Navy attack squadrons to the A-6A Intruder, but a number of units will retain the piston-engined Skyraider through 1967, and 106 have been delivered to the Vietnamese Air Force. Together with the smaller quantity of A-1Gs, the Vietnamese A-1Hs equip one squadron in each of the 41st Wing (Da Nang), the 62nd Wing (Nha Trang), and the 74th Wing (Bihn Thuy), two squadrons of the 23rd Wing (Bien Hoa), and the 83rd Special Air Group of the 33rd Wing (Tan Son Nhut).

A-1J: The final production version of the Skyraider, the A-1J serves side by side with the A-1H in U.S. Navy attack squadrons,

Power Plant: *One Wright R-3350-26WA (-26WB) 18-cylinder radial air-cooled engine rated at 2,700 h.p. (dry) and 3,050 h.p. with water injection.*
Performance: *Max. speed, 318 (311) m.p.h. at 18,500 (18,000) ft.; econ. cruise, 188 (200) m.p.h. at 6,000 ft.; tactical radius (with one 150 U.S. gal./125 Imp. gal. drop tank and eight 750-lb. bombs), 650 (600) mls.; range (clean), 900 mls.; ferry range, 2,900 (2,750) mls.; initial climb, 2,380 (2,300) ft./min.; service ceiling, 32,000 ft.*
Weights: *Empty, 12,100 (12,313) lb.; normal loaded, 19,000 (18,799) lb.; max., 25,000 lb.*
Dimensions: *Span, 50 ft. 9 in.; length, 38 ft. 10 in. (40 ft. 1 in.); height, 15 ft. 8¼ in. (15 ft. 10 in.); wing area, 400.33 sq. ft.*
Note: *Specification relates to A-1J, data in parentheses applying to the A-1E.*

NORTH AMERICAN OV-10A

Developed initially under a U.S. Navy contract to meet a Marine Corps requirement for an aircraft capable of performing both utility and ground support missions from semi-prepared strips in forward combat zones, the NA-300 was pronounced the winner in August 1964 of the U.S. services' jointly-sponsored LARA (Light Armed Reconnaissance Airplane) intended for COIN-type operations, seven prototypes being ordered under the designation OV-10A. The first OV-10A flew on July 16, 1965, five prototypes having joined the test programme by July 1966 when long lead-time funds were released for the procurement of 134 OV-10As for the U.S.A.F. and 100 for the U.S.M.C. The seventh prototype has been fitted experimentally with United Aircraft of Canada YT74 turboprops. In U.S.A.F. service, the OV-10A will replace in the forward air control role the O-1F Bird Dog light observation aircraft currently fulfilling this task in Vietnam. In the FAC role,

the O-1F is limited to four 2.75-in. rockets and seven smoke bombs for target marking, and no ordnance is carried for attacking small targets for which it is not worth summoning a strike. The OV-10A, on the other hand, can carry a variety of ordnance, and will, therefore, be able to perform both the FAC and light strike tasks in one mission, and the U.S.M.C. plans to employ the aircraft primarily for close air support of ground forces.

For the required slow speed and short-landing performance, the OV-10A enjoys substantial lift augmentation by having much of its wing-span bathed by the airscrew slipstream, the double-section, double-slotted flaps thus being, in effect, 'blown'. The small ailerons are boosted by spoiler sections above the wing for lateral control, and the minimum sustained flight speed is of the order of 55 m.p.h. With a 1,200-lb. ordnance load and fuel for three hours, the OV-10A can take-off and clear a 50-ft. obstacle

(Right) The second prototype OV-10A (Bu.No.152880) which, first flown on November 30, 1965, was subsequently employed for initial armament trials. It is seen here carrying bombs on the Aero 65A pylons on each of the sponsons, and on the outboard fuselage stations. Each sponson can mount four 7.62-mm. M-60C machine guns and house 2,000 rounds of ammunition per gun. An additional 20,000 rounds may be carried in the cargo bay and arranged to feed through the fuselage to the guns. The first production OV-10As are scheduled to be delivered during the spring of 1967, and initial requirements call for 134 aircraft for the U.S.A.F. and 100 for the U.S.M.C.

(Above and below) The first prototype OV-10A (Bu.No.152879). Five OV-10A prototypes had logged more than 300 flights by mid-1966.

container for 24 M83 anti-personnel bombs on each station, a 75 U.S. gal. (62.4 Imp. gal.) Mk.77 napalm bomb on each station, or, on the centreline station only, three Mk.81 Snakeye, three AN-M88 fragmentation bombs, or two AN-M64A1 general-purpose bombs. The two crew members are seated in tandem LW-3B zero-zero ejection seats, and 86° over-the-side visibility is provided by the cockpit.

Current procurement of the OV-10A is from Fiscal 1967 appropriations, and production deliveries to both the U.S.A.F. and U.S.M.C. are expected to commence in the spring of 1967. However, U.S. Navy evaluation of the OV-10A on behalf of the latter service during 1966 revealed shortcomings in design performance which have dictated aerodynamic changes to reduce drag. Despite drag reduction measures, it was anticipated mid-1966 that maximum low-level speed requirement would have to be reduced from 305 to 288 m.p.h. A modified OV-10A embodying some of the changes proposed for the production model was flown on August 15, 1966, this featuring a 10 ft. increase in wing span. T76 turboprops of 715 s.h.p. will now be fitted.

Power Plants: *Two Garrett AiResearch T76-G-6/8 turboprops each rated at 660 s.h.p.*
Performance: *Max. speed (design), 305 m.p.h. at sea level; tactical radius (maximum offensive load), 58 mls.; ferry range (with max. auxiliary fuel), 1,380 mls.; normal endurance, 2 hr.; initial climb (clean), 3,400 ft./min.; service ceiling, 27,000 ft.*
Weights: *Empty, 5,257 lb.; loaded (close support), 10,170 lb.; max. overload, 13,264 lb.*
Dimensions: *Span, 30 ft. 3 in.; length, 40 ft. 0 in.; height, 15 ft. 1¼ in.; wing area, 218 sq. ft.*

---

within 600 ft., and it is able to fly turns of only 500 ft. radius. Possessing a structure stressed to 8 *g* and a maximum diving speed of 530 m.p.h., the OV-10A can lift up to 3,270 lb. of ordnance. Small stub wings or sponsons can mount either four 7.62-mm. M-60C machine-guns, or two 0.5-in. guns as fixed forward armament, and each sponson also carries a 600-lb. capacity Aero 65A bomb rack. Three more racks can be attached to strong points beneath the fuselage, the centreline rack being of 1,200-lb. capacity and the outboard racks each being of 600-lb. capacity type. Typical armed reconnaissance mission offensive loads include an M28A2

GENERAL ARRANGEMENT DRAWING: *The second North American OV-10A prototype (152880) which has been used for armament trials.*

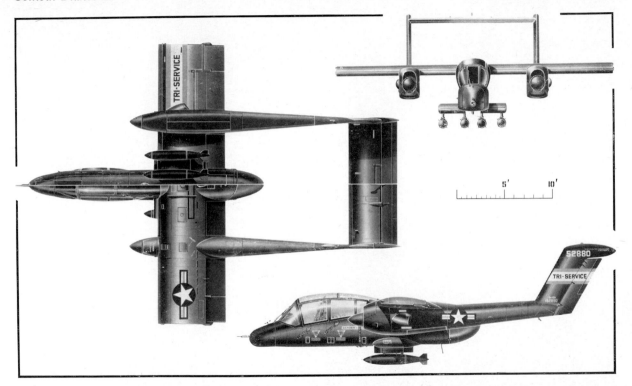

COMBAT HELICOPTER DEVELOPMENT

DURING their 20 or so years of military operation, helicopters have been mainly associated with transport, rescue and communications, although their offensive potentialities have been known from the

beginning. The first recorded trials with an armed helicopter took place in mid-1942, when the prototype Sikorsky XR-4 was adapted for bombing experiments at the U.S.A.A.F. Materiel Center, Wright Field. Initial testing was simply on the basis of a 25-lb. practice bomb being carried on the lap of the XR-4's passenger who heaved it overboard while hovering above a chalked target. The XR-4 was soon modified, however, for a more sophisticated arrangement, this involving under-fuselage racks for five 25-lb. practice bombs released via a trigger on the stick, and aimed by means of a pendulum-type bomb sight.

These early experiments confirmed the offensive potential of the helicopter, and also that greater accuracy could be achieved during forward flight than when hovering, but the limited payloads of early rotorcraft restricted further armament development for some considerable time. Another limiting factor was the low maximum speeds of early helicopters for combat roles, coupled with restricted applications foreseen at that time for their unique flying qualities so far as offensive operations were concerned. In fact, the lack of stability and excessive vibration of initial production rotorcraft gave discouraging results during the first tentative applications of fixed forward-firing armament.

One operational role which could obviously make use of the unique qualities of the armed helicopter, was that of anti-submarine warfare, as an extension of search and strike measures from surface vessels. Here was a field in which only the speed and manoeuvrability of the helicopter could keep pace with the submerged performance of modern, powerful submarines, and

(Left) An Agusta-Bell 204B of Italy's Marinavia seen in the automatic sonar cable hovering mode. The ASW version of the AB-204B has been produced in small series for the Italian Navy, and with auxiliary tanks is capable of extended sonar missions of up to four hours. The new Italian cruiser Vittorio Veneto will carry nine AB-204B ASW helicopters.

(Right) A Sud-Aviation-assembled Sikorsky SH-34G (No. 45) of France's Aéronavale. Sud-Aviation assembled 135 S-58 helicopters and manufactured a further 166 for the French services, a substantial proportion of these being the anti-submarine warfare SH-34G model. Of 1,901 S-58s produced by the parent company, 341 were ASW SH-34G or SH-34J Seabats for the U.S. Navy, the latter version featuring Ryan Doppler radar and an automatic hover coupler. The SH-34 is powered by a 1,525 h.p. Wright R-1820-84B or D radial engine.

where its hover capabilities could be uniquely employed by lowering sonar into the sea for effective search and detection. These capabilities added to its platform take-off and landing qualities for operation from even the smallest ocean-going ship rendered the helicopter made-to-measure where short-range anti-submarine operations were concerned.

The first rotorcraft combat application evolved, therefore, in the home of the helicopter, the U.S.A., where the Sikorsky S-55 represented the initial rotary-wing conversion for ASW operations. Because its payload was still relatively small, the first HO4S-1, as the S-55 was then designated by the U.S. Navy, could be modified for either the "hunter" ASW role, carrying detection and special navigation equipment, or as a "killer" armed with homing torpedoes, but not for both tasks simultaneously. The principal search equipment of the "hunter" version was the AQS-4 "dunking" sonar, combining hydrophonic and echo-ranging systems, and used in conjunction with a radar altimeter and a hovering position indicator. The idea was that "hunter" and "killer" helicopters should hunt in pairs, and the U.S. Navy undoubtedly pioneered the development and application of helicopter ASW with the HO4S-1 and its derivatives.

In an initial attempt to combine "hunter/killer" capability in a single helicopter, the U.S. Navy held an ASW design competition in 1950, when the tandem-rotored Bell XHSL-1 was selected as winner. The XHSL-1 was Bell's first departure from its standard single-rotor configuration, and was powered by a 1,900 h.p. Pratt & Whitney R-2800-50 engine. Three prototypes were ordered, the first flying initially on March 4, 1953, and these were used to develop a helicopter ASW weapon system, including a Bell auto-pilot permitting the helicopter to hover for long periods during search operations. The production HSL-1 also had the latest dipping sonar for submarine detection, and was designed for such lightweight homing weapons as the Fairchild Petrel for the "killer" part of its dual role.

Although fifty-three HSL-1s were built, the characteristics of the Bell helicopter proved unsuitable for operational service, and the main U.S. Navy successor to the Sikorsky HO4S series was the Sikorsky S-58, or HSS-1. The big S-58, powered by a 1,525 h.p. Wright R-1820-84 engine, first flew on March 8, 1954, and ASW was just one of the many military and civil roles for which it was subsequently developed. The HSS-1, later redesignated the SH-34G Seabat, originally took over most of the specialised anti-

submarine equipment of the HO4S-3, but added a pair of Mk.43 acoustic homing torpedoes to give the U.S. Navy its first operational "hunter/killer" helicopter. Most of the U.S. Navy ASW helicopter squadrons re-equipped with the HSS-1 before its further development resulted in the HSS-1N, or SH-34J as it later became, fitted with more sophisticated equipment. This was principally directed towards all-weather operation, and included Ryan APN-97A c.w. Doppler radar to measure ground speed and drift, a radar altimeter, automatic engine r.p.m. controller and an autopilot and hover coupler. With this equipment, it was possible to bring the helicopter from cruising flight at 92 m.p.h. and 200 ft. to a zero groundspeed hover at 50 ft. at a preselected location completely automatically.

A number of SH-34G and SH-34J helicopters have been supplied under MAP to NATO and friendly foreign countries, and some of the later ASW systems were incorporated in the Westland-built version of the S-58, known as the Wessex. Following the 1956 installation of two General Electric T58 shaft turbines in the

(Above, left) A Sikorsky SH-3A Sea King amphibious ASW helicopter of the Japanese Maritime Self-Defence Force, and (left) a similar helicopter of the Royal Canadian Navy (by which service it is known as the CHSS-2). The SH-3A is powered by two 1,250 s.h.p. General Electric T58-GE-8B turbo-shafts, and deliveries of the improved SH-3D to the U.S. Navy began in July 1966. The SH-3D, which is to be manufactured under licence by Westland in the U.K. and by Agusta in Italy, has the 1,400 s.h.p. T58-GE-10 turboshafts, improved avionic equipment, and a longer cable for the new sonar system which allows placement of the transducer below the deepest isothermal layer.

(*Right*) *The amphibious Sud-Aviation SA-321G Super Frelon ASW helicopter currently in process of delivery to France's Aéronavale. The example illustrated is the fourth pre-production model, and initial orders call for 17 production examples of the ASW model for the Aéronavale and 16 for South Africa. The SA-321G has Sylphe search radars in the floats, dunking sonar, homing torpedoes, and other ASW stores. It is powered by three 1,500 s.h.p. Turboméca Turmo IIIC3 turboshafts.* (*Below, right*) *One of four Boeing-Vertol Model 107-II-15 (HKP 4) helicopters employed by Sweden's Marinen for the ASW role.*

nose of an experimental HSS-1F (SH-34H) airframe, which made its first flight on January 30, 1957, Westland fitted a U.S.-built S-58 with a 1,100 s.h.p Napier Gazelle N.Ga.11 shaft turbine. This first became airborne on May 17, 1957, and was developed to meet a Royal Navy requirement for a replacement for the Whirlwind, the licence S-55, in the ASW role. The first Westland-built example fitted with anglicised ASW equipment flew on June 20, 1958, powered by a 1,450 s.h.p. Gazelle N.Ga.13 (161), and as the Wessex H.A.S. Mk.1 entered Royal Navy service.

Progressive development of the basic Wessex for the Royal Navy has produced the H.A.S. Mk.3 version with a further increase in power from a Gazelle N.Ga.22 Mk.165 engine de-rated to the transmission limit of 1,550 h.p. from a one-hour rating of 1,750 h.p. The H.A.S. Mk.3 also has new electronic equipment. The ASDIC or sonar equipment for the Wessex, derived from the American AQS-5 and later series, is manufactured in the U.K. under licence, as is also the Lear Mk.19 autostabilising system.

When used by a number of helicopters, dipping sonar can provide an ASDIC barrier round a fleet or convoy to provide

(Left) A Westland Wessex H.A.S.Mk.3 (XM328) anti-submarine warfare helicopter of the Royal Navy. This model is currently supplanting the H.A.S.Mk.1 from which it differs primarily in having an up-rated turboshaft, automatic flight control systems, and a more advanced ASW system than the Newmark-made -1N. The Wessex H.A.S.Mk.3 is powered by a 1,600 s.h.p. Rolls-Royce Gazelle N.Ga.22, and has empty equipped and normal loaded weights of 8,900 lb. and 14,000 lb. respectively. Performance includes maximum and minimum cruise speeds of 127 and 121 m.p.h., and maximum range with standard tankage is 300 miles. Twenty-seven basically similar ASW helicopters have been delivered to the Royal Australian Navy as Wessex Mk. 31s.

bearing and range information. It can also be used for underwater ultrasonic communication. Dipping sonar comprises an electric-acoustic transducer suspended from a cable hoist, and can be rotated from the control station in the helicopter. It uses the normal sonar system of reflected pulses from submerged objects, the signals being amplified and fed to presentation circuits giving visual and aural target data. The transducer is housed in a protective dome, which also contains a flux valve compass forming part of a remote positioning system. The transducer can therefore be directed and maintained at a fixed compass bearing selected on the azimuth indicator unit in the helicopter.

In an alternative mode of operation, the transducer can be automatically rotated step by step between signal pulses to permit a rapid and systematic search over a wide area. When submerged, a pressure transducer indicates the precise depth of the dome, and information is also provided on the height of the helicopter above water level.

Sonar and its associated ASW equipment can be readily fitted to any helicopter with the necessary payload capability, and the Royal Swedish Navy, for example, has used ten Vertol V-44s and four Vertol 107-II rotorcraft from 1958 onwards in the ASW role. In France, the SA-321 Super Frelon has been developed for both transport and ASW duties, and twenty-three SA-321Gs are being delivered to the *Aéronavale* for the latter role. In addition to the normal U.S.-derived ASW avionics housed in the cabin, plus Sylphe search radar in radomes on each of the outboard sponsons, the amphibious ASW version of the Super Frelon carries two homing torpedoes on twin racks each side of the fuselage for "hunter/killer" operations. The Soviet Navy is known to use various types of helicopter for ASW duties, including, allegedly, the Kamov Ka-20 fitted with chin and tail radomes, and carrying an air-to-surface missile on each side of the fuselage.

Sikorsky is continuing as main supplier of U.S. Navy ASW helicopters, and the SH-34 has now been largely replaced in the permanent navy squadrons by the S-61B in its SH-3A and -3D Sea King forms. Representing a completely new generation of helicopter design, the S-61 series was first developed for the U.S. Navy to meet a 1957 specification for a "hunter/killer" type with an endurance of four hours, a cruise speed of 152 m.p.h. over a 276-mile radius carrying a crew of four, full ASW equipment and 840 lb. of weapons, and allowing half the mission time for hovering close to the sea. Among the integrated flight and attack equipment installed was Ryan APN-130 Doppler navigation system, an APN-117 radar altimeter, coupled Bendix AQS-10 sonar, and Hamilton Standard automatic stabilisation equipment (ASE). The first operational SH-3As entered service with Helicopter Anti-Submarine Squadrons HS-2 and HS-10 in 1962.

The Royal Navy has now selected the later SH-3D version of the Sea King, for the eventual re-equipment of its Wessex ASW squadrons, and at the time of closing for press an order was imminent for up to sixty of these rotorcraft anglicised and licence-built by Westland for the naval portion of the British OR.358 specification. The anglicised SH-3D will be powered by two

(Above) The Kamov Ka-20, known in the West as the "Harp", is the only specialised ASW helicopter to have been revealed by the Soviet Union, and its present service status is uncertain. The Soviet Navy used an ASW weapon-carrying version of the Ka-15 during the 'fifties.

(Right) A Vertol Model 44A (HKP1) of Sweden's Marinen. Four Model 44As modified for ASW operations with dipping sonar, radar and flotation equipment were acquired by the Marinen in 1958, five more being purchased in 1960. In 1964, five ex-New York Airways Model 44Bs were acquired, two being modified to ASW HKP1 standards and the remaining three being cannibalised.

(Left) The Westland Wasp A.S.Mk.1 is a small anti-submarine weapon-carrying helicopter operated from platforms aboard Royal Navy frigates equipped with long-range asdic. In this role the Wasp is normally crewed by a single pilot and carries two 270-lb. torpedoes. Power is provided by a Bristol Siddeley Nimbus 103 turboshaft rated at 710 s.h.p., and performance includes a maximum speed of 121 m.p.h. and a cruising speed of 110 m.p.h., normal range being 303 miles. Empty and loaded weights are 3,384 and 5,500 lb. respectively. The Wasp has also been acquired by the Brazilian, Netherlands and South African navies.

1,500 s.h.p. Bristol Siddeley Gnome H.1400 turboshafts, and will carry homing torpedoes and sonar equipment manufactured by the Marine Systems Division of the Plessey Electronics Group. Ekco will be responsible for the radar and tactical co-ordination equipment, Marconi will provide the Doppler navigation equipment, and Louis Newmark the all-weather flight control system. The German Navy is also interested in the SH-3D, and a joint procurement and production plan with the U.K. has been proposed. Among the new equipment installed in the SH-3D is Bendix AQS-13 sonar with longer range and greater reliability than previous systems.

SMALLER ASW HELICOPTERS

Other ASW helicopter development includes smaller types with weapons but no search capability, to operate from frigates, destroyers and cruisers as virtual extensions of the ship's armament. Principal examples of this class are the Westland Wasp H.A.S. Mk.1, which carries a pair of Mk.43 or Mk.44 homing torpedoes weighing around 550 lb., and the Gyrodyne DASH (Drone Anti-Submarine Helicopter) weapon system. Like the Wasp,

the co-axial Gyrodyne QH-50 carries two Mk.44 acoustic torpedoes, but it is unmanned and is guided to its target by radio control. After launching, the QH-50 drone is tracked by radar and its course, speed and altitude is adjusted as necessary to position it for weapon release over the submarine target located by the ship's sonar.

After initial development from 1960 onward of the QH-50A and B using Porsche piston-engines, Gyrodyne began production of the QH-50C (formerly DSN-3) powered by a 300 h.p. Boeing T50-BO-8A shaft-turbine. First unmanned flight of the QH-50C took place on January 25, 1962, and several hundred have since been delivered to the U.S. Navy to operate from more than fifty destroyers. Production is now continuing with the QH-50D. This is powered by a 330 h.p. Boeing T50-BO-10 turbine, and can carry an alternative warload of a Mk.46 acoustic homing torpedo and one sonobuoy. The Mk.46-O is a larger high-speed torpedo for use from aircraft and helicopters, powered by a solid rocket hot-gas propulsion system. It weighs 570 lb. and is 8 ft. 4 in. long. A later version, the Mk. 46 Mod. 1, is being introduced with a more reliable liquid propulsion system.

One major shortcoming of the Gyrodyne DASH drone ASW helicopter concept has proved to be the state-of-the-art guidance techniques which prohibit the deployment of the QH-50 beyond line-of-sight ranges, a fact which, together with the introduction of longer-range sonars such as the SQS-26, is forcing the U.S. Navy to reconsider the need for a small *manned* helicopter which, carrying both weapons and sensors, can be operated from platforms aboard destroyers and other small vessels. In Italy, Costruzioni Agusta, which has built for the Italian Navy a number of ASW-weapon-carrying AB-47J-3 helicopters for operation from the frigates *Rizzo*, *Fasan*, *Margottini* and *Bergamini*, has evolved a light turbine-powered single-seat ASW helicopter, the A.106, capable of combining both search and attack roles. Powered by a 320 s.h.p. Turboméca—Agusta TAA 230, the A.106 can carry two Mk.44 torpedoes and has provision for search radar in the nose. Its normal empty and maximum take-off weights are 1,300 and 3,000 lb. respectively; it has maximum and cruising speeds of 124 and 115 m.p.h. at 2,866 lb., and its maximum cruise range is 174 miles.

HELICOPTERS FOR STRIKE

It is difficult to trace early rotorcraft armament installations, but the French can probably claim the first combat application of helicopter strike with their deployment, in what was then French Indo-China around 1950, of Vertol H-21s fitted with a 20-mm. cannon. The armed H-21s were employed to break up enemy troop concentrations, and then to encircle them while other helicopters brought up supporting infantry for ground engagement. Similar tactics were also employed by the French in Algeria, where most of the helicopters used, including Djinns, Alouette IIs, Sikorsky S-58s and Vertol H-21s, were fitted from time to time with machine guns, rocket pods and wire-guided short-range missiles, and these field experiments provided much of the basic data for the current concept of the armed helicopter.

Similar field experience was accumulated by the U.S. Army and U.S. Marine Corps with their helicopters in Korea, where the UH-34Ds of HMM-361, for example, were armed with M-60 light machine guns firing from the doorway and beam windows to suppress enemy small arms fire during assault landings. Marine Experimental Squadron HMX-1 began tests in 1949 at the Quantico training school in equipping Sikorsky helicopters with all types of armament, extending even to mortars and bombs, but the strongest capability of the piston-engined rotorcraft at that time was considered to be transport rather than strike.

Systematic development of the armed helicopter to evolve new tactical doctrines for flying cavalry units was undertaken by the U.S. Army in 1956–57 at Fort Rucker, Alabama, with most of the rotorcraft types then in service. A small group of volunteer pilots assembled at the Army Aviation School in June 1956 to begin

(Below) The Agusta A.106 light single-seat ASW helicopter, which began its flight test programme early in 1966, can carry two Mk.44 torpedoes for the attack role.

(*Left*) *An SE-3130* Alouette II *equipped for the attack role with four* SS-11 *missiles, and* (*below, left*) *similarly equipped SE-3160* Alouette IIIs *of the French Army.*

armament experiments, using 0.3-in. and 0.5-in. AN/M-2 Browning machine guns, 80-mm. rockets and folding-fin 2.75-in. rockets, as well as 3.5-in. and 5-in. HVARs, recoilless rifles, and chemical bombs. It was determined that the Vertol H-21 could mount a turret containing two 0.5-in. machine guns forward of the nose-wheel, and it was considered that some traverse and elevation of forward-firing armament was desirable in all except the lighter helicopters. The vibration of the latter resulted in a considerable spread of fire from fixed guns. The tandem rotor configuration was found to offer more stability along the pitch axis for weapon aiming and firing. Another finding was that the only flying machine which would be effective against a helicopter would be another helicopter.

Implementation of the recommendations for armed helicopters for the U.S. Army was assured in mid-1962 by the report of the Howze Board, more accurately known as the Army Tactical Mobility Requirements Board, led by Lt.-Gen. Hamilton H. Howze commanding the Strategic Army Command and the 18th Airborne Corps at Fort Bragg. Among other things, the Howze Board shaped the future of Army aviation around a new air mobility concept based on an "air assault division", in which helicopters were to replace ground vehicles. This paved the way for the U.S. Army's 1st Cavalry Division (Airmobile), which has had the task of proving the Howze concepts in Vietnam.

The Howze Board compared helicopter development at that stage with the early days of the fixed-wing aircraft, and foresaw a corresponding development in offensive capability, starting with the addition of light machine-guns, and continuing with increasingly heavy armament loads, including special guided missiles. Transport helicopters would be required to be escorted by armed rotorcraft to provide "a mobile elevated platform for immediate and continuous fire support in mobile situations". The armed helicopters would have to engage ground targets, eliminate them and then rejoin the convoy, necessitating "dash" speeds of up to 160 m.p.h.

The Board also forecast the use of advanced TV, radar-seeking and infra-red homing missiles by armed helicopters by 1972, with a requirement for quick convertibility for the attack mission so that one type of rotorcraft would be capable of carrying a wide range of weapons systems and yet still be able to undertake reconnaissance and other missions. Aircraft weapons recommended by the board were two 0.3-in. M-37 machine-guns with 650 rounds of ammunition for the Bell OH-13 and Hiller OH-23; four 7.62-mm. M-60 or XM-2 machine-guns for the Bell UH-1B, Vertol CH-21 and Sikorsky CH-34; and a General Electric XM-138 40-mm. grenade launcher, 48 2.75 in. rockets for an area fire system, or up to six SS-11 wire-guided missiles for the Bell UH-1B. These were designed to meet three specific armed helicopter requirements, for an Army Helicopter Light Weapons System, an AH Area Weapons System, and an AH Point Weapons System, although it was considered that these last two could be combined.

The widespread use of rotorcraft in Vietnam accelerated development of the armed helicopter, with the Bell UH-1 Iroquois becoming easily the most widely-used type in the theatre. By the end of January 1966, the U.S. Army alone had approximately 1,400 helicopters in service in Vietnam—mostly UH-1s—and its Fiscal 1967 procurement is for a further 1,500 UH-1 Iroquois and CH-47 Chinook helicopters, while in July 1966, the U.S. Army Aviation Materiel Command awarded a definitive contract for no fewer than 2,115 Iroquois. The Iroquois are used mainly to escort the transport Chinooks, although some of the Bells are also operated in the assault role themselves. When the Iroquois was first armed in Vietnam, it was fitted with only two fixed forward-firing 0.3-in. machine-guns, but a standard offensive version was evolved fitted with two 7.62-mm. M-60 automatic weapons on

(*Above*) *A UH-1A Iroquois firing a burst of 0.3-in. machine gun fire. It is also equipped with 2.75-in. rockets.* (*Below*) *A UH-1B with the XM-3 weapon system comprising a total of 48 2.75-in. rockets.*

comprising twenty-four rockets on each side of the fuselage, and these armed Iroquois were known locally as "Hogs". Even the standard troop-carrying Iroquois, referred to in Vietnam as "Slicks", were given an M-60 machine-gun mounted in each cabin door for additional suppressive fire when required, and the normal 25-rotorcraft establishment of a UH-1 company was made up of nine "Cobras" or "Hogs", and sixteen "Slicks".

In operation, the "Cobras" usually arrive over the landing zone about two minutes before the "Slicks" to make a final survey and begin suppressive fire. Their batteries of rockets have been found particularly effective, and have resulted in an experimental conversion of one UH-1B to take even greater numbers of these weapons. Because the "Cobras" are able to operate using the U.S. Army's "nap of the earth" technique, which involves taking advantage of trees and other natural cover, and only popping up for a brief reconnaissance or strike, their close support is more immediately effective, although far lighter, than that of the U.S.A.F. ground attack aircraft.

Although the UH-1B "Cobras" have been fitted with the same 1,100 s.h.p. Lycoming T53-L-11 turbines as the later UH-1D "Slicks", they are naturally slower, cruising at around 85–95 m.p.h., compared with 98–104 m.p.h. of the troop carriers. Nevertheless, their use is considered by the U.S. Army to provide complete justification of the armed helicopter concept, which has now been given considerable priority. Specialised attack helicopters are being developed, and production of the Iroquois has been increased to around 160 per month. Other armed versions have also been developed, including sixteen with Nord SS-11 missiles, and one with a General Electric M-5 chin turret containing a 40-mm. M-75 automatic grenade launcher. Development of the M-5 system was sponsored by the Springfield Armoury, and added a total weight of 208 lb. without the 107 rounds of 40-mm. ammunition.

outriggers on each side of the fuselage with traversing capability, aimed and operated via a reflector gunsight control in front of the co-pilot. The traversing system was manufactured by Emerson, well-known during World War II for its power-operated gun turrets, and the M-60s were belt fed from ammunition boxes in the rear of the cabin.

The armed Iroquois, known in Vietnam as "Cobras", also carry eight 2.75-in. rockets on each of the outriggers, sometimes replaced by pods with seven of these projectiles, and the first twenty with factory-fitted Emerson Electric M-60s and rocket racks arrived in S.E. Asia towards the end of 1962. A few UH-1Bs were also fitted with rocket pods only in an M-3 installation

(Right) An M-61 Vulcan triple-barrelled 20-mm. automatic cannon mounted on a UH-1 Iroquois.

Rate of fire of the M-75 is 220 r.p.m., and it has a peak recoil force of 2,000 lb. The turret can be rotated through plus or minus 60° in azimuth, plus 15° up in elevation and 35° down. The M-5 system has been evaluated operationally in Vietnam, and has been described as "the most effective helicopter weapons system in use today".

For U.S. Marine Corps UH-1E Iroquois helicopters, previously fitted with only fixed forward-firing armament, Emerson Electric has evolved a modification of the TAT (Tactical Armament Turret) -101, originally developed for the experimental Bell 207 Sioux Scout referred to later. The U.S.M.C. turret contains twin 7.62-mm. M-60C machine guns with 1,000 rounds, and can swivel through a 220° arc, 110° left or right of the centreline. It can also be deflected 45° downward and 15° upward, and is slaved to a sight manipulated by the co-pilot on the port side of the helicopter.

General Electric's Missile and Armament department has also proposed and developed offensive systems for the Bell UH-1, including several based on the use of either its Vulcan or Minigun rotating multi-barrelled cannon and machine guns. These weapons are basically similar apart from size and calibre, and range from 5.56-mm./10,000 r.p.m., through 7.62-mm./6,000 r.p.m. to 20-mm./3,000 r.p.m. for the M-61 cannon. The M-61 has also been produced in modified lightweight form for helicopter use, with three instead of six barrels, and a rate of fire of up to 2,000 r.p.m. Extensive test firings of the three-barrelled M-61 have been made from the Bell UH-1D during Army evaluation.

GE has also proposed a belly-mounted remotely-controlled turret for helicopter installation, mounting a six-barrelled 20-mm. M-61 Vulcan cannon with 1,000 rounds of ammunition, and rotating through 240°. The General Electric XM-30 armament system for the UH-1B involves mounting a 30-mm. XM-140 cannon on each side of the fuselage with traverse and elevation facilities, while in the XM-21 system, these high-velocity cannon are replaced by two 7.62-mm. Miniguns and seven-tube Chromecraft Corporation 2.75-in. rocket pods. Other GE armed helicopter systems include the XM-7 for the Hughes OH-6A, comprising twin 7.62-mm. Miniguns on each side of the fuselage with elevating facilities; the XM-8 which adapts an M-75 grenade launcher to the OH-6A, and the XM-9, a now-abandoned twin M-75 installation for the UH-1B. Alternative helicopter armament is offered by the midget Hughes 7.62-mm. Heligun, a 30-in. twin-barrelled 30-lb. weapon with a revolving breech block, firing at up to 6,000 r.p.m., and proposed for an armed version of the Hughes OH-6A.

(Above) A swivelling turret housing a 40-mm. anti-personnel grenade launcher. This weapon system, known as the M-5, is seen mounted on a UH-1 Iroquois.

In Europe, the French have continued their armed helicopter experiments to evolve a standard version of the Alouette III for the Army, carrying four Nord SS-11 wire-guided missiles on fuselage outriggers. More extensive modifications added additional strike capability in the form of either a side-mounted swivelling 20-mm. MG 151 cannon fired from the cabin, or a similar nose-mounted cannon sighted periscopically through the roof. The latter arrangement resulted in development of the experimental SA-3164 three-seat armed version of the Alouette III, with a

"stepped" cabin profile and an Artouste IIIB turbine, which made its first flight on June 24, 1964.

In the U.K., both the Whirlwind and the Wessex have been modified to carry armament. The standard modification kit for the Gnome-engined Whirlwind H.A.R.Mk.10s of the R.A.F. permits the installation of two Nord SS-11 anti-tank missiles on each side of the fuselage, or Vickers Vigilant anti-tank missiles, also wire-guided, plus two 0.303-in. Browning Mk.II* machine-guns with 1,000 rounds of ammunition. The bigger Wessex has been modified by the R.A.F. to carry Nord anti-tank missiles, machine-guns, and even 100 Imp. gal. (120 U.S. gal.) drop tanks each side of the fuselage, and following extensive trials, the Royal Navy has equipped all the Wessex H.U.Mk.5s of No. 845 Squadron for the armed assault role. Standard armament comprises two SS-11s with effective ranges of 400–3,800 yards, and an optimum distance of 2,500 yards; two seven-tube Thomas French/MATRA No. 6 Mk.1* 2-in. rocket launchers with ranges of 1,000 yards; two fixed 0.303-in. Browning machine-guns with ranges of 800 yards and 500 r.p.g. of ball/tracer ammunition fired at 1,150 r.p.m.; and a 7.62-mm. GPMG swivel-mounted machine-gun each side of the cabin firing at 1,200 r.p.m. All these weapons can be carried together outboard of the mainwheels, with light bomb racks aft for either strike or marker missiles.

ADVANCED AERIAL FIRE SUPPORT SYSTEM

With the success of the armed helicopter in Vietnam there came a requirement for a faster and more powerful type to act as a convoy escort and suppressive firepower vehicle. In requesting appropriations for development of such a type at the beginning of 1963, General Dwight E. Beach, U.S. Army chief of research and development said, "a helicopter will for the first time be designed around existing components as a pure fire support aircraft. Such a vehicle is required to support transport helicopters in combat operations not favourable to fixed-wing aircraft. Plans call for development of prototypes by 1965 as an interim aircraft aimed at fulfilling this requirement."

Even before a specification evolved for this requirement, most U.S. helicopter manufacturers began modification programmes to arm their production types, or to develop new versions for the interim programme of what soon became known as the U.S. Army's Advanced Aerial Fire Support System or AAFSS. In mid-1963, Bell proposed an armed version of the UH-1 known as the Warrior, with stub wings and a cleaned-up airframe to provide the necessary high speed, and flew a streamlined Iroquois even without wings at more than 175 m.p.h. Later in 1963, Bell flew an extensively modified Model 47, which was called the Sioux Scout, as a prototype helicopter "fighter". The Model 207 Sioux Scout featured a tandem two-seat cockpit, with the pilot seated above and behind the gunner who controlled an Emerson Electric TAT

(Tactical Armament Turret) -101 chin turret containing two 0.3-in. machine-guns. Powered by a 260 h.p. Lycoming TVO-435-A1A engine, the Sioux Scout did not have the necessary performance to provide an effective helicopter escort, but it gave Bell invaluable experience towards the evolution of an interim AAFSS design.

On August 1, 1964, the U.S. Army invited a number of companies to submit designs for the AAFSS specification before November 23, 1964. Project Definition Phase contracts were then expected to be awarded to between two and four manufacturers in January for a six-month period, followed by two months of evaluation before final hardware contracts to the successful contender in mid-1965. The AAFSS specification laid down a maximum speed of around 260 m.p.h., plus a 10-minute hover requirement in its main mission profile, but the U.S. Army did not specify the use of rotary-wing aircraft for its achievement. This

(Right) The Sud-Aviation SA-3164 is a derivative of the Alouette III (see page 180) intended for counter-insurgency, escort and armed reconnaissance roles. First flown on June 24, 1964, the SA-3164 features a redesigned forward fuselage mounting a 20-mm. MG 151 cannon in the nose, this, a 250-round ammunition tank and the gunner's seat being mounted on a special shock-absorbing plate attached to the cabin floor. SS-11 or SS-12 missiles may be attached to pylons on the fuselage sides. The SA-3164 has a 550 s.h.p. Turboméca Artouste IIIB turboshaft, and at 4,189 lb. its maximum and cruising speeds are 130 and 121 m.p.h., range being 367 miles.

(Left) The Bell Model 207 Sioux Scout tandem two-seat attack-fighter helicopter was in some respects the progenitor of the current production AH-1G interim AAFSS helicopter. First flown in 1963, the Sioux Scout featured an Emerson Electric TAT-101 gun turret controlled by a gunner who sat ahead and below the pilot. Powered by a 260 h.p. Lycoming TVO-435-A1A engine, its performance was inadequate to enable it to fulfil the escort and fire suppression roles effectively, and the sole example of the Sioux Scout is currently serving as a test-bed for the Vipre Fire-1 "hands-free" tracking gun sight which is being developed for use by the AH-1G.

(Below) A small number of CH-47A Chinook helicopters have been armed and armoured for U.S. Army evaluation. A 40-mm. M-5 grenade launcher is mounted beneath the nose, plus two fixed forward-firing 20-mm. cannon, and five swivelling 7.62-mm. machine-guns.

meant that V/STOL aircraft were not excluded, although the terms of the specification favoured the helicopter configuration, as did the time-scale, 1970 service being a requirement.

It became apparent that a compound helicopter would probably offer the best solution for the AAFSS, and the two finalists for the production contract, from Sikorsky and Lockheed, were both projects of this type. One of the main features of the Sikorsky proposal for its projected S-66 AAFSS design was the use of a swivelling tail-rotor, or "Rotoprop", which could function sideways in hovering flight, and as a pusher airscrew in cruise. The "Rotoprop" was successfully flight-tested on an S-61 from July 1965 onward, but the Lockheed submission was selected in preference for the AAFSS contract on November 1, 1965.

Ten prototypes have initially been ordered of the Lockheed AAFSS through an initial contract of $12.7m. (£4.54m.), although this is expected to increase rapidly to about $86m. (£30.7m.), as a major share of the $92.6m. (£33m.) which comprises the U.S. Army's Fiscal 1967 research and development budget. Few details of the Lockheed design have been released, apart from the fact that it is a compound helicopter powered by a 3,400 s.h.p. General Electric T64-S4A gas turbine, and will employ the rigid rotor concept. This has already been tested on the Lockheed XH-51A, which has also been equipped experimentally with a 7.62-mm. M-60 machine-gun to assess its stability as a gun platform. The Lockheed AAFSS is unusual in employing a pusher airscrew in the tail, as well as a normal tail rotor mounted on one end of its tailplane.

The crew of two will be seated in tandem, and will operate a variety of equipment for all-weather, day and night missions, in addition to machine-guns, grenade launchers, rockets and an airborne version of the TOW anti-tank missile. Apart from its primary roles of escort and suppressive fire, it will also engage and destroy area and point targets, including fixed emplacements and armoured vehicles. The Lockheed AAFSS will have a maximum speed of 260 m.p.h., a hover ceiling of 6,800 ft., and an endurance of more than three hours. Initial climb rate will be 3,720 ft./min. and ferry range will be 2,900 miles. Its lift capability is reported to be formidable, with six attachment points on the wings and

fuselage for 2,000 lb. stores. Representative armament will probably comprise an M-75 grenade launcher in a chin turret,

(Right and above, right) The prototype Model 209 "Hueycobra", or AH-1G interim AAFSS, currently in production for the U.S. Army, the first of 100 production examples being expected to commence its test programme in May 1967. Based on the UH-1B Iroquois, the AH-1G can attain speeds in excess of 190 m.p.h. at 1,000 ft. In the prototype, the pilot is seated 11 ft. 4 in. aft and 10 in. higher than the gunner, but the cockpit layout of the production model will embody a number of changes. The gunner controls the Emerson Electric TAT-102 gun turret.

plus a 30-mm. XM-140 cannon in a ventral turret with 360 degrees of traverse, and six TOW anti-tank missiles. The Lockheed AAFSS will incorporate the IHAS (Integrated Helicopter Avionics System) currently under development. The IHAS, which is being evolved by Teledyne Systems, is designed to perform the various airborne avionics functions of navigation, flight control, terrain following, and avoidance, station-keeping, etc., the heart of the system being a central computer complex. For fire control purposes, it may be presumed that the IHAS will carry pre-assigned stored ballistic data for the weapons, and will accept inputs from the laser rangefinder, a low-light-level TV camera, and the gunner's optical sight. It will be capable of directing two weapons simultaneously at two different targets. Unit cost of the Lockheed AAFSS will be in the region of $500,000 (£178,500).

The first Lockheed prototype is likely to fly during early 1967, and the initial production run is expected to be about 200 machines, but in the meantime the U.S. Army has been confronted with the problem of 90 m.p.h. UH-1B "Cobras" in Vietnam having to escort 138 m.p.h. Chinooks, now operating as the main transport helicopters. An interim AAFSS became increasingly urgent during the latter part of 1965, and a committee was formed under Colonel H. L. Bush to evaluate current production rotorcraft in the U.S.A. for possible adaptation as armed high-speed helicopters. Principal requirements were availability, to enter service in Vietnam during the next 18–24 months, high speed and high payload capacity.

Four types were assessed by the "Bush Board" for interim AAFSS use: a conversion of the Chinook itself, the Sikorsky S-61 Sea King, the Kaman UH-2A Sea Sprite and a radical development of the Bell UH-1 known as the Model 209, or "Hueycobra". The armed CH-47A involved installation of four 0.5-in. or 7.62-mm. machine-guns firing forward from each of two fuselage stations, plus a 40-mm. grenade launcher beneath the fuselage, and two 20-mm. cannon and two 19-tube 2.75-in. rocket launchers or Minigun pods. The Chinook could also accommodate one or two 0.5-in. machine-guns firing aft from its rear loading ramp, to

defeat current Viet Cong tactics of waiting until the "Cobras" have flown past before emerging from cover to fire at them. The Chinook could also carry up to 2,000 lb. of armour plate, and four were reported to have been modified to the armed configuration for operational evaluation with the 1st Cavalry Division (Air-mobile) in Vietnam early in 1966.

Sikorsky planned the installation of 3,600 lb. of armament on its S-61 interim AAFSS, including waist guns in the cabin, which retained its cargo floor and fittings for twenty troop seats to serve as a back-up troop and freight carrier. Kaman proposed extensive modifications of its armed UH-2A, known as the "Tomahawk", and powered by a 2,650 h.p. Lycoming T55-L-7 instead of the standard 1,250 s.h.p. General Electric T58-8B. The "Tomahawk" project included 1,536 lb. of armament, comprising one 20-mm. M-3 cannon with 750 rounds in the nose; two 7.62-mm. M-60 waist guns with 3,000 rounds, and one 40-mm. M-5 grenade launcher with 150 rounds in the nose. Normal top speed of the Tomahawk would have been 167 m.p.h., but at the cost of some performance, it could also have carried rocket pods, TOW missiles or SS-11s at wing-tip stations. Take-off gross weight would have been 11,781 lb. and the unit cost $340,000 (£123,000), which was almost certainly too expensive for an interim type.

The Bell Model 209 "Hueycobra" was finally selected in March, with a requirement for 100 examples (compared with 500–1,000 Lockheed compound helicopters), and initial deliveries are scheduled to start mid-1967 as the AH-1G. Bell gained a consider-able advantage in the interim AAFSS contest by producing a PV prototype of its "Hueycobra" which first flew on September 7, 1965. The AH-1G bears an obvious relationship to the Model 207 Sioux Scout in its seating and armament arrangements, but it is otherwise closely related to the Iroquois with a reported 85 per cent commonality. Principal change is in fuselage cross-section, with a width of only 36 in. compared with about 8 ft. for the UH-1. Coupled with the clean profile, this contributes greatly to the 160 m.p.h. cruise with an armament including a 7.62-mm. Minigun in an

Emerson Electric TAT-102 swivelling "chin" turret which, like the TAT-101, permits the gun to swivel 220° but allows increased elevation and depression of 20° and 60° respectively. The Minigun will have a derated fire rate of 4,000 r.p.m., but later versions of the AH-1G are likely to carry the XM-28 weapon system in the nose turret, mounting one 40-mm. grenade launcher plus one 7.62-mm. Minigun, alternatives being two grenade launchers or two Miniguns. Two underwing stores stations are expected to carry XM-18 rocket launchers. A "hands-free" tracking gunsight, the Vipre Fire-1 (Visual Precision Fire control equipment), is currently under development for the AH-1G, and was being evaluated on the Bell Sioux Scout during 1966. The Vipre Fire-1 is intended to permit the AH-1G pilot to train his guns on a target merely by looking at it through a bull's-eye sight mounted on his flying helmet, an electro-mechanical linkage between the helmet and the airframe measuring head movement relative to the helicopter's axis, thus keeping the guns constantly aimed at whatever the pilot sees through the sight in the guns' field of fire.

Like current UH-1Bs and -1Ds, the AH-1G is powered by the 1,400 s.h.p. Lycoming T53-L-13 turbine, de-rated to 1,100 s.h.p. for maintaining its output under "hot and high" conditions, and this will drive Bell's new Model 540 wide-chord "door hinge" type of rotor introduced on the Iroquois production line towards the end of 1965. The skid-type landing gear of the AH-1G prototype is retractable, but this feature is being eliminated from the production model, and the crew seats are made from Ausform steel armour. When it attains service, the AH-1G will reach the target area in half the time taken by a UH-1B over a 57-mile radius, and remain on station for three times as long. With a design load limit factor of 3.5 *g*, the AH-1G promises to revolutionise the tactical applications of the armed helicopter, which may become as significant a weapon as the fixed-wing fighter.

Somewhat surprisingly, the Soviet Union as yet seems to have devoted little energy to the development of specialised combat helicopters, although armed versions of such standard types as the

The artist's impression (above) depicts an early conception of the Lockheed AAFSS, 10 prototypes of which have been ordered for evaluation. The 40-mm. M-75 grenade launcher can be seen in the extreme nose with an optical sight immediately aft. Just forward of the bulged fairings beneath the stub wings is what appears to be the 30-mm. 360° swivelling XM-140 gun system. There are six 2,000-lb. capacity external stores stations, two beneath each stub wing and one beneath each lateral fairing, and it may be presumed that one of these stations will be occupied by the forward-looking terrain-following radar. All-weather day and night operational capability is one of the requirements of the specification to which the AAFSS has been designed, and service introduction is expected during the late 'sixties, total U.S. Army requirement for this type possibly totalling four figures. Prototype trials are expected to commence during 1967.

Mil Mi-4 have been supplied to such countries as Algeria for counter-insurgency tasks. However, there can be little doubt that Soviet rotorcraft designers are watching such development as the AAFSS with considerable interest, and it is highly likely that comparable developments will be undertaken in the Soviet Union if they are not already proceeding.

POWER PLANTS FOR COMBAT AIRCRAFT

THE 1960s are witnessing two profound changes in the military aircraft engine scene. First the gradual down-grading of the military engine from its dominant role as the progenitor of all power units, both for military and for civil duties, reflecting the slowly diminishing status of the manned aircraft as a weapons system versus the increasing expansion of world air transport. Second, the spread of the turbofan into virtually all military fixed-wing aircraft roles apart from those at the small, low speed end of the scale.

The consequence of the first trend is that whereas, until the advent in 1959 of the Rolls-Royce **RB.141 Medway** which was originally intended for the Trident commercial transport, all civil aero engines were derived from original military designs, today there are new designs of civil and military turbines being developed concurrently. Such is the strength of this trend that engines such as the Rolls-Royce **RB.168** and the Pratt & Whitney **TF33** are military derivatives of earlier civil engines, namely the **RB.163 Spey** and the **JT3D**. Of the second trend, its major influence has been to bring virtually to an end the development of new designs of turbojet. For the small/medium, moderate-speed aircraft the turboprop is likely to meet all but a few special requirements. Above these the turbofan of varying by-pass ratio and with or without afterburning will hold sway. The turbojet has now been all but eliminated from new military applications. The Lockheed YF-12A and SR-71 powered by the very advanced Pratt & Whitney **J58** could well be the last refuge of the turbojet in major new military aircraft.

The target of every military engine is first and foremost high performance. This is in contrast to the demands for economy and reliability in a civil engine. Both of these latter features are necessary in the military power unit, but come lower down on the scale of priorities. The civil Rolls-Royce **Conway R.Co.12,** for example, gives 17,500 lb. thrust for a specific fuel consumption (SFC) of 0.735 lb./lb./hr., and a time-between-overhauls (TBO)

of 8,000 hours. Equivalent figures for the military counterpart engine, the **R.Co.17,** are 20,370 lb., a higher (and classified) SFC and a TBO of around 1,000 hours, this last figure being lower both because of the higher rating and the much lower military utilisation.

For recent new-project specifications, such as that for the American advanced manned strategic aircraft (AMSA), there is, however, an increased emphasis on a low SFC. This is required throughout virtually the aircraft's full mission, including take-off, cruise, climb and loiter. Supersonic dash at high or low altitude is likely to be required, and this, coupled with other desirable characteristics, will almost certainly call for the development of a new generation of variable-cycle turbofans.

For the military engine in general, high performance is demonstrated by three basic factors, the values for which have to be as high as possible. These are its specific thrust which is the thrust produced per pound of air mass flow/sec., its thrust/weight ratio (the *aircraft* designer is more interested in the reciprocal of this, the specific weight, which is the weight/lb. thrust), and thirdly its thrust/unit frontal area. For turboprop and turboshaft engines the same performance factors apply in general, but measured against power as opposed to thrust. A high specific thrust means that the engine produces a high thrust for its size—it therefore enhances both the thrust/weight and thrust/unit frontal area ratios. It is attained primarily by operating the engine at a high turbine entry temperature (TET). This enables the engine to extract the maximum thrust (or power) from the airflow inducted. It was this advantage which persuaded Rolls-Royce in 1955 to pioneer the introduction of air-cooled turbine rotor blading in military Avon turbojets, and then in later engines, to permit them to operate at higher TETs. During World War II, the Germans also used cooled rotor blading in the BMW 003 and Junkers Jumo 004 turbojets but more to make up for deficiencies in their wartime turbine materials than to obtain increased thrust.

(Above) The Pratt & Whitney TF30 turbofan for the General Dynamics F-111. A French version, the TF-306, will power the Mirage F and G.

High thrust/weight and thrust/unit frontal area ratios mean a lighter, smaller engine leading to an increased military load or a smaller, less expensive aircraft to perform the required role. Thrust/weight ratio is enhanced by the use of advanced engine design techniques and advanced materials. Titanium, lighter than aluminium and as strong as steel, is already extensively used in the compressor and by-pass duct components of engines. Beryllium, as an even lighter material, is now being investigated for such items as compressor discs and blades. Because of its very high strength/weight ratio, beryllium enables the compressor to operate at considerably higher tip speeds such that the necessary pressure ratio can be achieved in markedly fewer stages than hitherto. This permits engines of outstandingly small size and low weight to be designed. Bristol Siddeley Engines and Rolls-Royce in the United Kingdom, and Pratt & Whitney and General Electric in the U.S.A. are engaged in research and development on beryllium engine components.

Thrust/unit frontal area benefits from a high specific thrust and the use of a high compressor pressure ratio. Special effort is also made to minimise engine carcase diameter. For military turbojets to provide maximum air throughout for a given intake diameter, they are frequently designed to be of near constant diameter throughout their length. This configuration normally entails the use of a fully annular combustion system. Examples of this type of engine include the General Electric **J79**, **J85** and **J93**, the Pratt & Whitney **J58**, the Bristol Siddeley **Gyron Junior** and the SNECMA **Atar 8** and **9**.

AIRCRAFT REQUIREMENTS

Because of the very considerable financial investment involved in the development of a modern aircraft engine, it is normal for a power unit that was initially conceived for one type of application to be subsequently employed in other roles. Outstanding instances of this practice are the Pratt & Whitney **J57** and Rolls-

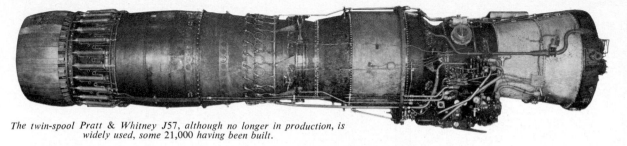

The twin-spool Pratt & Whitney J57, although no longer in production, is widely used, some 21,000 having been built.

Royce **Avon** turbojets which, in their various versions, have each powered fighters, bombers, transports, reconnaissance aircraft, airliners and naval fighter and strike aircraft. They are both also used for industrial power generation purposes.

Thus, although an engine may be designed to meet a specific requirement, its capabilities are normally of sufficient flexibility to permit its modification to meet the needs of other applications. The widespread use of the **J57** and **Avon** effectively illustrate that the propulsion characteristics ideally sought for the various categories of combat aircraft do not in fact vary to any major extent. The exception which makes the rule may be the specialist V/STOL engine, but even this is capable of some variety of application. However, an indication of what may in future prove to be a trend in the opposite direction can be seen in the current development of specialist engines for individual multi-purpose military aircraft in the fashion of the TFX and AMSA projects.

FIGHTER ENGINES: Undoubtedly the most demanding of all combat aircraft propulsion requirements, the fighter engine must give maximum all round performance. Turbine entry temperature is therefore normally in advance of that in other categories of engine. Its compressor, combustion system and turbine are highly rated throughout and SFC and TBO are not so vital as thrust output for size and weight. To facilitate a rapid take-off, climb to altitude and acceleration to interception speed, an afterburner is invariably fitted, and this must be designed to give maximum thrust boost for the added weight and length.

The engine's flight envelope, in terms of maximum speed and altitude, tends to exceed that for other aircraft, although the bomber, in turn, is always attempting to exceed the fighter's performance in these respects. It is significant, however, that the current holder of the world's speed and altitude records is the Lockheed YF-12A interceptor. The high manoeuvrability of the fighter within its flight envelope means that its engine handling flexibility and reliability have to be of the highest order, a characteristic made all the more difficult to attain by reason of the high rating of the compressor and its need to accept a wide variety of intake airflow distortions.

The high manoeuvrability of the fighter also imposes excessive *g* and gyroscopic loads, requiring the adoption of robust forms of engine construction and the use of advanced mechanical design techniques. To minimise or largely eradicate the resultant gyroscopic loads in twin-spool engines, recent turbofans, such as the Rolls-Royce/MAN **RB.193,** are designed with contra-rotating low and high pressure rotors. This technique is also used in single-shaft turboprops by arranging the reduction gear train to give contra-rotation between the propeller and engine.

The frequently defensive role of the fighter requires a quick-start capability in its engine with, in some instances, only ten seconds being allowed between depressing the start button and the engine attaining idling speed. To enable the engine to meet this stringent requirement without the necessity for external ground services, the engine is normally designed to utilise a cartridge starter or some other form of high energy turbine drive.

Until the early 1960s all fighter aircraft were turbojet powered. Following the advent of the Rolls-Royce **Conway** turbofan, however, this more advanced form of power unit has progressively taken over as the standard fighter engine. The changeover is based on the lower all-round SFC of the turbofan and the considerably greater afterburner thrust boosts it is capable of providing. While the turbojet afterburner has been developed to give up to forty or fifty per cent static thrust boost, the turbofan, even with a by-pass ratio of only unity, is able to produce seventy to seventy-five per cent thrust boosts.

BOMBER ENGINES: With the steady closing of the performance gap between the fighter and bomber, the engine for the latter aircraft is only rarely designed specifically for bomber duties, and is more often an adaptation of an existing fighter power plant. A current exception to this trend is the General Electric **J93** turbojet powering the North American XB-70A Valkyrie which began life as a Mach 3.0 experimental strategic bomber. The **J93** as initially specified was designed to operate on high energy chemical fuel, thus requiring the development of special combustion systems and turbines.

The bomber engine differs from the fighter engine primarily in its need for a lower SFC and an extreme altitude operating capability in keeping with the bomber's needs for range and avoidance of interception. Where a low altitude role is specified, as with the Bristol Siddeley **Olympus 22R** turbojet for the ill-fated BAC TSR-2 tactical reconnaissance bomber, the task of the engine designer is greatly increased. A low SFC becomes markedly more difficult to attain, and sustained flight at high Mach numbers and low altitude incurs major problems from the high ram air temperature rise into the engine.

As with the fighter, the bomber's engine has traditionally been a turbojet and in more recent Mach 2.0 to 3.0 aircraft, such as the

(Right) The twin-spool Bristol Siddeley B.Ol.21 Olympus Mk.301 turbojet rated at 20,000 lb.s.t. without afterburning currently powers the Hawker Siddeley Vulcan B.Mk.2 strategic bomber (see pages 55–57). Apart from the ill-fated BAC TSR-2, the Olympus has found no other military application, although the Olympus 593B with a current into-service rating of 32,500 lb. has been evolved to power the Concorde supersonic transport. The Olympus 593B is, to all intents and purposes, a new engine.

(Left) The axial twin-spool Rolls-Royce Tyne turboprop, seen here being prepared for testing with the 18-ft. airscrew of the Transall C.160 transport, powers the Atlantic maritime patrol aircraft.

XB-70 Valkyrie, the B-58 Hustler and the Mirage IV, use is made of afterburning. The superior capabilities of the turbofan, its higher afterburner performance and the possibility of optimising the design by-pass ratio to suit the combat mission, is virtually certain to result in any future bomber project being powered by this type of engine.

STRATEGIC RECONNAISSANCE AIRCRAFT: The engine for the strategic reconnaissance aircraft is a logical extension of the bomber power plant. There is even greater need for extreme altitude operation, low fuel consumption and, for such ultra-long range single-engine aircraft as the Lockheed U-2, reliability becomes a particularly vital factor. For this special duty, high-altitude variants of existing bomber engines are normally developed, these incorporating modified compressor and combustion equipment.

MARITIME RECONNAISSANCE AIRCRAFT: Maritime reconnaissance represents a different propulsion requirement to that of strategic reconnaissance. For the current airscrew-driven maritime aircraft, the markedly lower consumption of the turboprop or piston engine enables them to operate for long periods and over considerable ranges. For later projects such as the Hawker Siddeley HS.801 and succeeding designs, the turbofan offers the possibility of high thrust for the "dash" to the search area, and an adequately low cruising consumption at lower search altitudes and speeds. Where (as is being considered for potential successors to the HS. 801) the addition of afterburning is planned, then an even wider ratio of maximum thrust to economic low cruise thrust becomes practicable.

OBSERVATION AND COIN AIRCRAFT: Both these aircraft types require engines with the characteristics of reliability and robustness, for both operate at low level in forward battle areas where the failure of an engine purely as a result of poor reliability is likely to have immediate and dire consequences. Rapid, low altitude manoeuvring also calls for a power unit highly responsive to throttle change. Robustness of design is vital to withstand the affects of heavy, high *g* handling in rough air conditions, and to minimise susceptibility to small-arms fire damage. Because of these needs, piston engines power the majority of observation aircraft today but are gradually being replaced by turboprops. This latter type of power plant is also specified for virtually all COIN aircraft projects.

HELICOPTERS: The requirements for a helicopter engine are not unlike those for observation and COIN aircraft, but accentuated by the helicopter's normal operation at high throttle opening. The turboshaft's low weight, compact size and flexible response under change of helicopter rotor load make it an ideal power unit for rotorcraft. To provide twin engine reliability and to enhance the helicopter's operating capabilities, coupled turbo-shafts are now used in many medium and heavy designs.

CURRENT MILITARY ENGINES

The military turbine is by a large margin the major product of the aero engine industry today—a situation aided by the fact that whereas civil power units are rarely licence built, military engines are often the sole product of a nation's industry, working under licence. Thus, in countries such as Belgium, Italy, Spain, Australia, Japan, India, Sweden, and Switzerland, the major aero engine production is based entirely on licence-built military designs. Initially, in the early post-war years, these were all turbojet licences, later supplemented by turboprop and turboshaft licences, and most recently by turbofans, which are now, without doubt, the most important category of military power plants.

TURBOFANS: The first turbofan to be developed for military duties was the 17,250 lb. thrust Rolls-Royce **Conway R.Co.11** in 1958. This engine represented the first serious attempt to produce an operational engine of this configuration and to take advantage of the lower SFC it offered. Because of its wing-root installation in the Handley Page Victor B.Mk.2 and for other reasons, the

(Right) The Rolls-Royce RB.153 turbo-fan was originally developed jointly with MAN-Turbo for the cancelled VJ 101D V/STOL strike and reconnaissance fighter, and a number of experimental units have been tested. The RB.153 is rated at 6,850 lb.s.t. boosted by some 70 per cent with afterburning. A form of switch-in thrust deflector was evolved for this turbofan for VJ 101D application, swivelling nozzles enabling thrust to be vectored 15° either side of the vertical.

(Left) The Bristol Siddeley/SNECMA M45G turbofan rated at 7,100 lb.s.t. and 12,230 lb. with afterburning is the proposed power plant of the projected Anglo-French variable-geometry strike and reconnaissance fighter. The M45G employs the same high-pressure rotor and combustion systems as the commercial M45H turbofan for the German VFW 614 short-haul transport. Development and manufacture of the M45G is to be shared on a 50-50 basis between Bristol Siddeley and SNECMA.

R.Co.11 had a by-pass ratio (BPR) of only 0.3:1. Even so it provided a significantly lower SFC than its turbojet contemporaries.

Entry into service of the **Conway** quickly spurred the American industry to follow suit with turbofan derivatives of their major turbojets. Most important of these was the Pratt & Whitney **J57** which was modified to a front fan configuration for civil and military purposes, with the designations **JT3D** and **TF33**. With more freedom in choice of BPR, Pratt & Whitney gave the **TF33** a higher than unity ratio enabling the engine to more than equal the **Conway** on SFC. The TF33 is installed in the Boeing B-52H Stratofortress and the Lockheed C-141A Starlifter, and has take-off ratings covering 17,000 to 21,000 lb.

Following the initial round of turbofan developments and related improvements thereof, both Rolls-Royce and Pratt & Whitney are now heavily engaged in their successors, the **RB.168** and the **TF30**. The **RB.168** is the military variant of the civil **RB.163 Spey** powering the Hawker Siddeley Trident and BAC One-Eleven, and is produced in two basic series—the **RB.168-1** of 11,500 lb. thrust for the subsonic Hawker Siddeley Buccaneer S.Mk.2, and the more recent **RB.168-25** with afterburner of 12,500 lb. basic

rating, rising by seventy per cent under reheat. This latter engine powers the McDonnell F-4K and F-4M Phantoms. A version without afterburner, the **RB.168-20**, has been chosen for the Hawker Siddeley HS.801 maritime reconnaissance aircraft. The **RB.168-1** first ran in December 1961 and has a BPR of unity, this falling to 0.7:1 in the **RB.168-25**.

The **TF30** is a much modified military derivative of the early Pratt & Whitney **JTF10** civil engine of around 1959. Earliest military variant of the **JTF10** was the French SNECMA **TF-104** of 10,500 lb., the subsonic predecessor of the supersonic derivative of the same turbofan, the **TF-106**, which was originally intended to provide forward propulsion for the Mirage IIIV. The **TF-104** was the initial technical outcome of the SNECMA-Pratt & Whitney agreement of 1959 in which the American company acquired a ten per cent holding in SNECMA. The later variant, the **TF-106**, the A3 version of which in the Mirage IIIV-01 offered 11,680 lb. and 16,755 lb. thrust with duct burning, was superseded in 1965 by the **TF-306**, virtually a direct counterpart of the American military TF30 engine, and in **TF-306C** form is rated at 20,500 lb.thrust with afterburning, basic thrust being similar to that of the **TF-106A3**.

The **TF30** is under development by Pratt & Whitney to power the General Dynamics F-111 and FB-111, and the Ling-Temco-Vought A-7A Corsair. The **TF30-P-3** in the F-111 incorporates duct burning and is in the 19,000 lb. thrust category, while the **TF30-P-6** in the A-7A is rated at 11,350 lb. thrust. Although it has experienced development problems, the **TF30**, in view of its stringent propulsion role in the F-111, is probably the most advanced engine flying today.

Other Rolls-Royce military turbofans are: (a) the 19,750 lb. Conway **R.Co.43** powering later Victor B.Mk.2s; (b) the **R.Co.12** of 22,500 lb. installed in the R.A.F.'s VC10 C.Mk.1 transports, which is essentially a civil **R.Co.12** but with a larger low pressure rotor giving the higher BPR of 0.6:1; (c) the **Medway** in the 17,000 to 22,000 lb. thrust bracket with the designations **RB.142, RB.176** and **RB.177,** which was originally the engine designed for the Trident transport and was later uprated and fitted with a Rolls-Royce switch-in thrust deflector for use in the Hawker Siddeley HS.681, both airframe and engine being cancelled in 1965; (d) the **RB.153** of 6,850 lb. thrust developed in conjunction with MAN-Turbo for the subsequently abandoned EWR VJ 101D V/STOL strike and reconnaissance fighter in which installation it was to have been fitted with a switch-in thrust deflector of MAN design; (e) the **RB.172/T-260 Adour,** smallest Rolls-Royce turbofan and under joint Anglo-French sponsored development with Turboméca to power the SEPECAT Jaguar—basic rating is 4,200 lb. rising with afterburning to 6,835 lb., and (f) the **RB.178** as a military derivative of Rolls-Royce's new 44,000 lb. thrust high BPR transport engine which is also proposed as the main propulsion unit for the Boeing-Bölkow variable-geometry fighter project.

Pratt & Whitney's military turbofans following the **TF30** and **TF33** include: (a) the large 41,000 lb. thrust **JTF14** with a 7-ft. diameter single-stage front fan, reportedly of 3.5:1 BPR. Two **JTF14**s were built as demonstrators for the U.S. competition to power the Lockheed C-5A transport and are continuing under limited company-financed development; (b) the **JTF16,** a scaled-down derivative of the **JTF14** which is being developed in demonstrator form for the Advanced Manned Strategic Aircraft (AMSA) project, no details of this engine having been revealed, and (c) the **JT8D** transport turbofan which in its -22 version is under development by Svenska Flygmotor (SFA) in Sweden as the **RM 8** with afterburner for the Saab 37 Viggen. In this form the engine gives 26,400 lb. thrust, or almost twice the normal civil rating.

While Rolls-Royce and Pratt & Whitney are the leading suppliers of military turbofans, a significant challenger is emerging in the shape of the mighty General Electric **TF39** engine, chosen power unit for the Lockheed C-5A. Being developed under a massive $459 m. U.S.A.F. contract, the **TF39** is an 8:1 BPR turbofan of more than 41,000 lb. thrust based on the smaller experimental

(*Below*) *A mock-up of the Rolls-Royce/Turboméca RB.172/T-260 Adour being developed for the Anglo-French Jaguar (see Vol. I page 53) which has a 4,200 lb. basic rating and 6,300 lb. with reheat.*

GE1/6 engine. It is the first derivative to be officially sponsored of General Electric's new GE1 family of 'building-block' engines in which a basic design of gas generator is used in conjunction with a variety of other fan, turbine and exhaust systems to produce a range of power unit configurations at reduced cost in development time and money.

The only other military turbofans of importance in the West are the Turboméca A**ubisque** and the SNECMA/Bristol Siddeley **M45G**. The **Aubisque** has a take-off rating of 1,640 lb. thrust and comprises the basic Turboméca gas generator unit driving a single-stage axial fan via reduction gearing. This engine powers the Saab 105 trainer and light attack aircraft. The **M45G** is a joint design and development project by SNECMA and Bristol Siddeley for use in the forthcoming Anglo-French variable-geometry fighter. The engine is one of a family of civil and military turbo-jets and turbofans originally of SNECMA design, but which, in its definitive configuration, will have major contributions from Bristol Siddeley. A number of sub-series of **M45G** have been pro-jected, covering a basic thrust range of 7,000 lb. basic, to 13,000 lb. with afterburning.

In the Soviet Union, civil transports such as the Ilyushin Il-62 and Tupolev Tu-124, 134 and 154 are fitted with turbofans produced by the Kuznetsov and Soloviev design bureaux. These have thrust ratings extending from the 11,905 lb. of the Soloviev **D-20P** and 14,990 lb. of the **D-30** which power the Tu-124 and Tu-134 respectively, to the Kuznetsov **NK-8** of 20,944–23,150 lb. in the Il-62 and Tu-154, and the 28,600 lb. of its derivative, the **NK-144,** for Russia's supersonic transport. A newcomer to the field of turbo-fans is the Ivchenko bureau which is developing the 3,307 lb. **AI-25** for the Yak-40. Thus while no turbofan-powered combat aircraft have yet been identified with certainty, the availability of this category of engine almost certainly means that advantage has been taken of its unique performance gains in powering the Soviet Union's newer military aircraft. The thrust bracket covered by the Kuznetsov and Soloviev civil engines corresponds very closely to that of the western countries' first and second generation turbofans.

The Turboméca Aubisque (right) geared twin-spool turbofan is currently being manufactured for the Saab 105 trainer and light ground attack aircraft (see page 159) at a rating of 1,543 lb.s.t. Weighing only 550 lb., the Aubisque consists of a single-stage low-pressure compressor, a high-pressure compressor with one axial and one centrifugal stage, an annular combustion system and a two-stage turbine.

(Right) The Bristol Siddeley Orpheus single-shaft turbojet, illustrated in its 803 form of 5,000 lb.s.t., has found its principal military application in the Fiat G.91 (see Vol. I, pages 84–86). In its 701 form it powers the Gnat lightweight fighter (see Vol. I pages 98–100) with a rating of 4,700 lb.

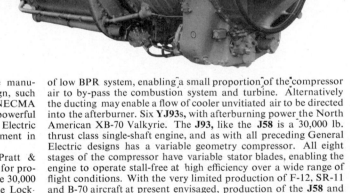

TURBOJETS: There are currently close on thirty types of turbojets powering military aircraft in the West, with thrust ratings ranging from 3,000 lb. up to as high as 30,000 lb. The majority of these engines are of axial flow configuration and only the older and lower-rated designs have centrifugal compressors.

Major twin-spool engines such as the Pratt & Whitney **J57** and **J75** and the Bristol Siddeley **Olympus** have now all completed their production runs, and only the smaller and later 3,500 lb. thrust Pratt & Whitney **J52** continues to be manufactured. By contrast, earlier engines of single-shaft design, such as the Rolls-Royce **Avon**, General Electric **J79** and SNECMA **Atar** are still in production. Development of more powerful variants continues to some extent, primarily at General Electric which company has a considerable engineering investment in three turbojets, the **J79**, **J85** and **J93**.

The most advanced turbojets flying today are the Pratt & Whitney **J58** and the General Electric **J93**, both designed for propulsion at Mach 3.0. The **J58** is a single-shaft engine in the 30,000 lb. thrust class, two of which with afterburning power the Lockheed YF-12A and SR-11. In its later versions the **J58** has a series of six large-diameter external ducts extending from the combustion section aft to down-stream of the turbine. No details of the engine have been revealed, but the ducting would appear to act as a form of low BPR system, enabling a small proportion of the compressor air to by-pass the combustion system and turbine. Alternatively the ducting may enable a flow of cooler unvitiated air to be directed into the afterburner. Six **YJ93s**, with afterburning power the North American XB-70 Valkyrie. The **J93**, like the **J58** is a 30,000 lb. thrust class single-shaft engine, and as with all preceding General Electric designs has a variable geometry compressor. All eight stages of the compressor have variable stator blades, enabling the engine to operate stall-free at high efficiency over a wide range of flight conditions. With the very limited production of F-12, SR-11 and B-70 aircraft at present envisaged, production of the **J58** and **J93** is unlikely to extend much beyond the small quantities already built.

Two other General Electric turbojets of which development is continuing are the **J79** and **J85**. The **J79** with afterburning has ratings extending from 16,150 lb. to 17,000 lb., and has major applications in the F-104 Starfighter, the F-4 Phantom II and the B-58 Hustler, all of Mach 2.0 capability. Primarily in these aircraft the **J79** has logged well over two million flight hours. Company-funded development work has been undertaken to raise the maximum rating to 17,900 lb. in a version designated **J79-J1Q**. This provides an engine for later versions and extended production of the Starfighter and Phantom, and is being assembled in Italy by Alfa Romeo and Fiat for the F-104S version of the former. It is also intended to combat competition from Pratt & Whitney and Rolls-Royce turbofans.

Similar work is underway in uprating the **J85** from its normal top rating of 4,300 lb. to 5,000 lb. in the **J85/J1A**. Major uses of the J85 include the Northrop F-5 and T-38A Talon, the Canadair, CL-41 Tutor and the Fiat G.91Y. Pratt & Whitney's military turbojets, in addition to the **J58**, include the **J57**, **J75**, **J52** and **J60**. More than 21,000 twin-spool **J57**s were built during the engine's production life from 1951 to 1965. With ratings ranging from 10,000 lb. to 18,000 lb. with afterburning, the **J57** powers early Century series fighters, the B-52 Stratofortress, and such U.S. Navy aircraft as the F-6A Skyray and A-3 Skywarrior and F-8 Crusader. Its design successor, the larger **J75**, also of twin-spool layout, extended the thrust range up to 26,500 lb. with afterburning. Markedly fewer **J75**s were built to power second generation Century series fighters, in particular the F-105 Thunderchief and F-106 Delta Dart, and certain versions of the Lockheed U-2. The two smaller Pratt & Whitney engines are the twin-spool **J52** of 8,500 lb. to 9,300 lb. thrust, and the single-shaft **J60** of 2,900 lb. to 3,300 lb. The **J52** powers the A-6 Intruder and later versions of the A-4 Skyhawk, and the **J60** is essentially a trainer and light transport engine.

In Britain only two military turbojets remain under active development, the single-shaft Rolls-Royce **RB.146 Avon** and the Bristol Siddeley **Viper**. The **Avon**, as Rolls-Royce's only axial turbojet, has evolved through three basic versions, the 100, 200 and 300 series, covering a thrust range, including afterburning, of 6,500 lb. to 17,100 lb. A multiplicity of fighter, bomber, trans-

(Left) The Bristol Siddeley Viper turbojet has found many military applications. In its licence-built 2,500 lb.s.t. Viper 22-1 form it powers the Macchi MB.326 trainer and light attack aircraft (see page 157), and as the Viper 20 Mk.522 offering 3,410 lb.s.t., it powers the BAC 167 trainer and counter-insurgency derivative of the Jet Provost.

port, reconnaissance and naval strike aircraft have been powered by the **Avon,** and the **RB.146** version is currently in production for the Lightning T. Mk.5 and F. Mk.6, and in Sweden as the **RM 6C** for the Saab 35D and 35F variants of the Draken.

The **Viper,** like the **Avon,** an engine with a wide variety of applications, is primarily a trainer engine, but is also projected for use in light ground attack or COIN versions of the BAC Jet Provost and the Aermacchi MB.326. Thrust ranges from 1,750 lb. to 3,410 lb. Other Bristol Siddeley turbojets are the single-shaft 4,520 lb. to 5,000 lb. thrust **Orpheus,** the **Sapphire** with ratings from 6,500 lb. to 12,000 lb., and the larger twin-spool **Olympus** with 100, 200 and 300 series versions covering a thrust range of 11,000 lb. to 20,000 lb. Sole application of the **Olympus,** apart from the **Olympus B.0l.6. 22R** of 33,000 lb. with afterburning for the short-lived BAC TSR-2, is the Hawker Siddeley Vulcan B.Mks.1 and 2. The **Orpheus** powers such light fighters as the Hawker Siddeley Gnat, Hindustan HF-24 Marut and Fiat G.91, and the **Sapphire's** last major service application was the Javelin.

Only two turbojets of any significance have emerged from the European Continent—the SNECMA **Atar** installed in all production Mirage series of fighters and bombers, all of Mach 2.0 capability, and the Turboméca **Marboré** powering a variety of trainer aircraft. The **Marboré** has also been produced under licence in America by Continental's Gas Turbine Division as the **J69** for trainers, missiles and drones. The single-shaft **Atar,** derived originally from the wartime BMW 003, has evolved through two basic series, the **Atars 101A** to **G,** and **Atars 8** and **9,** covering an overall thrust bracket with afterburning of 6,000 lb. to 14,770 lb. and with the Mirage as their primary application. The latest version, the **Atar 9K,** powers the Mirage IIIE2 strike fighter and Mirage IVA bomber.

Turbojets in the Communist bloc are as diverse in size and application as their Western counterparts. A consequence no doubt of the belated Russian entry into the turbofan field is the Soviet Union's more extensive use of high thrust turbojets.

Examples of these are the single-shaft Mikulin **AM-3M** developing up to 19,180 lb. thrust which powers the Tupolev Tu-16 and Myasishchev Mya-4 bombers and strategic reconnaissance aircraft, and the latest commercial derivative of this engine, the 21,385 lb. **RD-3M-500;** the **TRD** series engine of some 22,000 lb. thrust installed in the Mikoyan Ye-166 and other experimental interceptors, and the huge Type **D15** turbojet of 28,660 lb. thrust in the experimental Myasishchev-designed 103-M and 201-M aircraft. Other Russian design groups producing turbojets are the Klimov and Tumanski bureaux. Klimov, who was largely responsible for Russian development of Rolls-Royce **Derwent** and **Nene** derivatives, appears to have concentrated on low thrust engines such as the **RD-5** to **RD-9** series, commencing with a basic thrust of 4,800 lb. and rising in late variants to 7,850 lb. with afterburning, and installed in the Yak-25 and MiG-19. Klimov engines have also been built under licence in Poland and China. Tumanski have designed even smaller engines and his **TRD-29** turbojet has ratings extending from 1,764 lb. to 2,315 lb., powering the Yak-30 and -32 trainers.

Other Iron Curtain countries have also developed small turbojets, notably the Czechoslovak 1,962 lb. thrust **M-701** of centrifugal design powering the L-29 Delfin trainer, and the Polish **TO-1** centrifugal engine of 882 lb. which found no application, and small axial units also of Polish design, such as the 1,700 lb. **HO-10** and 2,200 lb. **SO-1,** the latter having replaced the former in the TS-11 Iskra trainer.

TURBOPROPS: The major military turboprop in the West is the Allison **T56** axial single-shaft engine of 4,050 to 5,325 e.h.p. This, in addition to powering all C-130 Hercules transports, is installed in the P-3A Orion and the E-2A Hawkeye. The more powerful axial twin-spool Rolls-Royce **Tyne** powers several types of military transports, and is also installed in the Breguet 1150 Atlantic in its 5,955 e.h.p. **R.Ty.20 Mk.21** version. The outstanding single-shaft Rolls-Royce **Dart** with its two-stage centrifugal com-

(Left) The Rolls-Royce Dart has been under continuous development since 1945, and this centrifugal-flow turbo-prop's principal military applications are the Argosy and Andover transports, and the Breguet Alizé (see pages 136–7) in which it is installed in its R.Da.7 Mk. 21 form with a rating of 2,020 e.s.h.p.

pressor, powers, in its **R.Da.21** version of 2,100 e.h.p., the Breguet 1050 Alizé. Other versions of the Dart power various military transport aircraft. In the same power category as the **Dart** are the axial, free turbine General Electric **T64** of 2,850 to 3,400 s.h.p. which powers the Buffalo tactical transport, and the 2,529 e.h.p. axial-cum-centrifugal Lycoming **T55,** also of free turbine layout, which has been installed in the North American YAT-28E but has found no production application so far. Next down the scale rating is the Lycoming **T53** turboprop of 1,100 to 1,400 s.h.p.installed in the Grumman OV-1 Mohawk and Canadair CL-84 Dynavert.

Below these medium/high power turboprops are two strongly competing engines, the United Aircraft of Canada **T74** and the Garrett/AiResearch **T76,** both in the 500 to 700 s.h.p. bracket. The T74 in its 650 s.h.p. **YT74CP-8/10** version powered the Convair Model 48 Charger, and the **T76** at 660-715 s.h.p. powers the North American OV-10A, both COIN aircraft.

Russia's major contribution to turbo-prop technology is the mighty axial single-shaft Kuznetsov **NK-12M** of 14,795 e.h.p. which powers the Tupolev Tu-20 bomber and strategic reconnaissance aircraft and Tu-114 commercial transport and, in its 15,000 e.h.p. **NK-12MB** version, the Antonov An-22. Down the size scale, the Ivchenko bureau produces a range of turboprops for both civil and military transports, the most important of these being the **AI-20** for the Il-18 and An-10 commercial transports and the An-12 military transport. Production of the **AI-20** began in 1957, and current versions include the **AI-20K** which develops 4,015 e.h.p. and the AI-20M of 4,250 e.h.p. which now have a TBO of 4,000 hrs. The smaller **AI-24,** which has been in production since 1960 and powers the An-24, offers 2,550 e.h.p., and is currently running with a TBO of 3,000 hrs.

TURBOSHAFTS: With the rapid growth of rotary-wing technology, there are now almost as many types of military turboshaft engine as there are turbojets. First to be conceived from the outset as a helicopter prime mover was the General Electric **T58** which covers the power range 1,000 to 1,800 s.h.p. More powerful and offering a variety of mechanical drive arrangements, is the General Electric **T64** to which reference has already been made in its turboprop form. In general competition with these two engines are the Lycoming **T53** and **T55** of similar ratings to their previously mentioned turboprop variants.

Other American turboshafts are the Continental **T65** of 310 s.h.p. and **T67** comprising two coupled **Model 217** engines of 770 s.h.p. each; also the 300 to 330 s.h.p. Boeing **T50**, the 500 s.h.p. Garrett/AiResearch **T76**, the 250 s.h.p. Allison **T63,** and the most powerful of all turboshafts in the West, the Pratt & Whitney **JFTD12** of 4,050 s.h.p. Collectively, engines by these seven companies power the vast majority of American military helicopters.

In Europe, two manufacturers predominate in the turboshaft sector, Turboméca and Bristol Siddeley. The French company produces a range of helicopter engines, from the 310 s.h.p. joint Turboméca/Agusta **TAA 230,** through the **Oredon III** (a joint project with Bristol Siddeley) of 350 s.h.p. and the 550 s.h.p. **Artouste,** to the **Turmo IIIC** and **D** series of 1,200 to 1,400 s.h.p. Bristol Siddeley's major turboshaft is the **Gnome,** an anglicized licence-built version of the General Electric **T58** covering the same 1,000 to 1,800 s.h.p. bracket as the American engine. Bristol Siddeley has also developed a coupled version of the **Gnome.** Its other turbo-shaft engines are the **Nimbus** of near to 1,000 s.h.p. and the **T64** for which the company has a licence.

Russia has made major advances in the development of turboshafts, in parallel with its extensive work on heli-copters. Among its engines are the Soloviev **D-25V** of 5,500 s.h.p. two of which power the Mil Mi-6 and Mi-10 helicopters, the Isotov **TB-2-117** of 1,500 s.h.p., two of which are installed in the Mil Mi-8 helicopter, and the small Isotov-designed **GTD-350** of 400 s.h.p. in the Mil Mi-2 helicopter, which is also being manufactured in Poland.

V/STOL ENGINES: Nowhere does the extreme adaptability of the gas turbine show to better advantage than in the field of V/STOL propulsion. Already in being are three fundamentally different systems of providing vertical thrust with a turbine engine, and studies are being made of as many more. Basic systems in use today are the lift jet or turbofan, the vectored thrust turbofan and deflected thrust engine, and the remotely-energised lift fan or fan-in-wing system. The lift engine concept was evolved by Rolls-Royce, while the vectored thrust engine and the lift fan were of French origin but developed to a practical stage in Britain and America respectively.

While originally there were two extremes of concept—the Rolls-Royce composite propulsion system combining batteries of

(Below) The Bristol Siddeley H.1400 Gnome, an anglicised version o the General Electric T58, is to power the Westland-built Sikorsky SH-3D ASW helicopter (see page 174) to be delivered to the Royal Navy. With an emergency rating of 1,500 s.h.p., the H.1400 has a maximum rating of 1,400 s.h.p. and a maximum continuous rating of 1,250 s.h.p.

(Below) Three generations of lift jets: 2,300 lb.RB.108 (centre), 4,400 lb.RB.162 (right) and future 9,000 lb. unit (left).

specialised lift engines with a cruise-sized main propulsion engine, and the Bristol Siddeley single, oversize vectored thrust turbofan— these have now been merged to form a more rational concept. Thus for interceptors there is a trend towards the use of one or two cruise-sized forward propulsion engines with vectored thrust or deflected thrust capabilities, suitably supplemented in vertical flight by lift jets, or lift turbofans in numbers varying inversely with the cruise speed of the aircraft.

To date, Rolls-Royce is the only European company to have developed lift jets—starting with its 2,030 lb. thrust **RB.108** powering the Short SC.1 and sundry European hover rigs, thence to its present **RB.162** of 3,640 lb. thrust installed in the Mirage IIIV and the 6,000 lb. of the **RB.162-81** specified for numerous international projects such as the, VAK 191B and the developed Fiat G.222. The **RB.108** had a thrust/weight ratio of 8:1, raised to more than 16:1 in the **RB.162-81** by the use of plastic intake and compressor components and advanced design techniques. A later design is the **RB.189** of even higher T/W ratio and of much reduced volume for its output. This engine is specified for the U.S.-German variable-geometry fighter project, and will form the basis of the forthcoming Anglo/American lift jet to be developed jointly by Rolls-Royce and Allison.

In America, Continental has run a demonstrator lift jet under contract to the U.S.A.F., but does not appear to have taken the project to the flight test phase. Six General Electric **YJ85** turbo-jets are used in a lift jet role in the Lockheed VTOL simulator.

The lift turbofan has not been taken to such an advanced stage. Rolls-Royce has proposed the **RB.175,** a front fan version of the **RB.162.** Bristol Siddeley test ran but did not develop the **BS. 59** of 5,000 lb., and Allison is working on the **D.610** of 6,000 lb. thrust, also of front fan design. As an adaptation of a main propulsion engine, the General Electric **CF700** turbofan has been used to provide vertical lift for the Bell Aerosystems Lunar Landing Research Vehicle. The turbofan offers a quieter, lower sfc, lower exhaust velocity engine, but a bulkier and more complex one.

Vectored thrust turbofans were pioneered by Bristol Siddeley first with the 15,300 lb. thrust **Pegasus** for the Hawker Siddeley P.1127, then with the **BS.100** for the ill-fated Hawker Siddeley P.1154. The **BS.100,** closely derived from the **Pegasus,** incorporated Bristol Siddeley's plenum chamber burning (PCB) technique which raised lift-off thrust by 30 per cent. This enabled the engine to be sized closer to cruise thrust requirements and operate at a more economic cruise consumption, thus countering one of the major objections to the single-engine system. Development work continues on the 18,000–19,000 lb. **Pegasus Pg.6** to meet the needs of the initial R.A.F. production version of the P.1127.

Rolls-Royce entry into the vectored thrust field was via their twin Spey proposal for the P.1154 in which cross-over exhaust ducts between the two turbofans were designed to minimise thrust imbalance in the event of an engine failure. Currently the company is working in conjunction with MAN-Turbomotoren under a German government contract to develop the 10,000 lb. **RB.193** vectored thrust turbofan for the VAK 191B VTOL strike fighter.

In the U.S.A., Pratt & Whitney is engaged in developing a vectored thrust version of its **TF30** turbofan which powers the F-111. General Electric has also indicated an interest in vectored thrust engines through two variants of its **GE1** 'building-block' series. This includes a turbojet with swivelling nozzles, and a turbofan with main and by-pass flow combustion and thrust vectoring.

The Ryan XV-5A is the only project flying with General Electric's lift fan system. Two General Electric **J85** turbojets power the aircraft in both forward or vertical flight. General Electric-designed fans in the wings and nose have tip-mounted turbines energized by exhaust gases diverted from the **J85s.** The fans are designed to provide either vertical thrust, or diagonal thrust for transition. Following transition, the **J85's** exhaust is directed rearwards in the normal manner for forward propulsion. The two 5 ft. 2½ in. diameter fans in the wing are designated **X-353-5B** and the small nose fan is the **X376.**

Only other company engaged in lift fan work is Curtiss-Wright which as yet does not appear to have taken its interest further than design studies.

TRENDS: Major areas of engine development in the near future are likely to concern the turbofan and the lift jet—the turbofan to become even more versatile and the lift jet to enhance its already high thrust/weight and thrust/volume ratios. Seven new designs of turbofan are being developed for six of the major new international military aircraft projects, namely the Pratt & Whitney **JTF16** and its General Electric equivalent (for the AMSA pro-

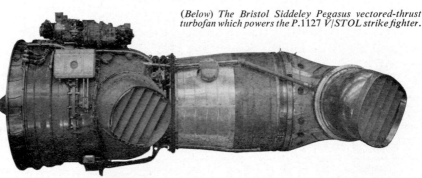

(Below) The Bristol Siddeley Pegasus vectored-thrust turbofan which powers the P.1127 V/STOL strike fighter.

(Left) The Rolls-Royce RB.193 lift-cruise turbofan for the VAK 191B VTOL strike fighter. Being developed in collaboration with MAN-Turbo, the RB.193 has four thrust-vectoring nozzles similar in concept to those of the Pegasus (see page 205), and is in the 10,000 lb.s.t. category. The VAK-191B (see Vol. 1, page 56) is scheduled to fly in 1968, and is so far the only announced application for the RB.193.

climb and take-off, and is soon likely also to be needed during supersonic dash, be it at low or high altitude. By providing a turbofan of variable by-pass ratio, this parameter can be varied in flight to 'tune' the engine to each sector of the aircraft's mission.

Most likely means of attaining the variable cycle engine is by non-mixed flow turbofans with variable area nozzles, in most instances only the inner nozzle. By designing the engine with a fixed outer nozzle (thereby assisting airframe installation) and a variable inner nozzle, the back pressure on the fan duct can be varied to reduce the by-pass airflow and increase the 'engine' airflow, thus effectively reducing the BPR. This configuration requires that the duct airflow and turbine exhaust be kept separate (and not mixed as they are in Rolls-Royce turbofans).

Because of the increased variation in airflow through the major rotating components, i.e., the fan, compressor, and turbine, these will have to be developed with variable 'pumping' capabilities and much flatter efficiency curves than hitherto. This requirement will almost certainly dictate the need for variable geometry compressors as an extension of General Electric's work on variable stator compressors.

Lift jet development is likely to be directed primarily at increasing the thrust/volume ratio and the installed thrust/weight

ject), the General Electric **TF39** (Lockheed C-5A), the Rolls-Royce/Turboméca **RB172/T-260 Adour** (Jaguar), the Bristol Siddeley/SNECMA **M-45G** (Anglo-French variable geometry project), the SFA/P.&W. **RM 8** (Saab Viggen), and the Rolls-Royce **RB.193** (VAK191B).

In contrast, the major effort in lift jet development seems likely to centre on one engine only, the Anglo-U.S. advanced project, work on which was scheduled to start during 1966. Application of the new lift jet is likely to be widespread among U.S. and European projects, especially as this type of unit has now been widely accepted as being vital to virtually all forms of V/STOL aircraft.

Major trend in turbofan development is the need for a variable cycle capability to meet the increasingly stringent requirements of new combat specifications—in particular their emphasis on a low specific fuel consumption over virtually the entire flight spectrum. An economic performance is now demanded during loiter, cruise, ratio. This will call for shorter compressors, combustion systems, and turbines of special design, and minimum-length intake and exhaust ducts. Material advances, such as beryllium, will be used to aid this and the need for minimum weight. To give maximum pressure ratio and minimum number of stages, compressors are likely to be twin-spool contra-rotating units. Engine height and diameter will tend to become equal, giving a very squat profile more amenable to fuselage and pod installation.

In the early 1960s it was widely thought that the aircraft gas turbine had reached a plateau of evolution— an impression subsequently revised following the advent of such projects

General Electric's lift fan system has undergone considerable flight testing in the Ryan XV-5A experimental V/STOL aircraft, derivatives of which have been proposed for the counter-insurgency role. This cutaway drawing of the XV-5A shows the General Electric X376 pitch control fan in the nose with the nose fan inlet louvres open; the X-353-5 lift fan in the port wing, and the port J85 gas generator.

as the General Electric **TF39** and the Rolls-Royce **RB.189**. Further progress will undoubtedly take place, although for engines such as the turboprop and turboshaft these seem unlikely to be radical. Already such advances as the modern regenerative turboprop appear to have been surpassed by recent improvements in the turbofan—development, for example, of the Allison **T78** regenerative engine started in 1962 was cancelled in 1966. Undoubtedly, though, the propulsion requirements of military aircraft will continue to stimulate development of more complex and sophisticated forms of aero engine.

INDEX TO AIRCRAFT TYPES

Page numbers in **bold type** indicate primary coverage of the aircraft concerned.

A-1 Skyraider, Douglas
    9, 10, 155, 160, 161, **164–168**
A-3 Skywarrior, Douglas   27, 28, **43–46**
A-4 Skyhawk, Douglas .   13
A-5 Vigilante, North American   29
A-6A Intruder, Grumman .   15
A-7A Corsair II, Ling-Temco-Vought 161
A-11, Lockheed .   78, 79
A 32A Lansen, Saab .   14
A 60, Saab .   157, **159**
AAFSS, Lockheed 163, 186, 187, 188, **189**
AC-47, Douglas .   158, 159
Aermacchi M.B.326 .   **157**
AF-1 Fury, North American .   13
Agusta-Bell AB 47J-3 .   178
Agusta-Bell AB 204B .   172
AH-1G, Bell   186, 187, **188, 189**
AJ 37 Viggen, Saab .   14
Alizé, Breguet   126, **133–135**
Alouette II, Sud-Aviation SE-3130   180
Alouette III, Sud-Aviation SE-3160   180
Argus, Canadair .   124, **138–140**
AT-33, Lockheed .   158
AT-37D, Cessna .   157
Atlantic, Breguet .   28, 126, **133–135**
Avro 730 .   32
Avro Shackleton .   123, **127–129**

B-26 Invader, Douglas
    29, 154, 155, 159, 160
B-36, Convair .   26, 31, 73
B-45 Tornado, North American   26
B-47 Stratojet, Boeing   29, 30, 31, 73
B-52 Stratofortress, Boeing
    9, 10, 14, 15, 16, 23, 30, 31, 32, **33–36**, 81
B-57, Martin   27, 28, **60–62**
B-58 Hustler, Convair   9, 15, 32, **37–39**
B-70 Valkyrie, North American   32
BAC 167 .   157
BAC-Breguet Jaguar   14
BAC Jet Provost .   157
BAC Lightning F.Mk.6 .   24
BAC TSR-2 .   29, 32
Badger (Tu-16) 16, 31, **63–65**, 74, 122
Barge (Tu-85) .   26
Beagle (Il-28)   26, 27, 28, **58–59**
Bear (Tu-20)   16, 26, **66–69**, 74, 122
Bell 207 Sioux Scout   185, 186, 189
Bell AH-1G   186, 187, **188, 189**
Bell HSL-1 .   173
Bell OH-13 .   181
Bell UH-1 Iroquois
    7, 181, 182, 183, 184, 185
Bell Warrior .   185
Beriev Be-6 (Madge) .   **119**

Beriev Be-10 (Mallow)   122, **130–132**
Beriev Be-R1 .   130
Beriev LL-143 .   122, 130
Bison (Mya-4) .   31, **81**, 122
Blinder (Tupolev) . 16, 25, 32, **70–72**
Blowlamp (Il-54) .   58
Boeing B-47 Stratojet   29, 30, 31, 73
Boeing B-52 Stratofortress
  9, 10, 14, 15, 16, 23, 30, 31, 32, **33–36**, 81
Boeing-Vertol 107-II-15 .   175, 176
Boeing-Vertol CH-47 Chinook
    181, 186, 188
Bounder (Myasishchev) .   31, **32**
Breguet Alizé   126, **136–137**
Breguet Atlantic   125, **133–135**
Brewer (Yakovlev)   28
Buccaneer, Hawker Siddeley   14, 27, 28
Bull (Tu-4) .   25

Canadair CF-104 .   116
Canadair CL-28 Argus   124, **138–140**
Canadair CL-41G .   **157**, 158
Canberra, English Electric
    27, 28, 47–51, 79, **81–84**
Cessna AT-37D .   157
Cessna O-1 Bird Dog   161, 162, 163
Cessna T-37C .   **156**, 157

CF-101B Voodoo, McDonnell 10
CF-104, Canadair . 116
CH-47 Chinook, Boeing-Vertol
181, 186, 188
Charger, Convair 48 . 162
Chinook, Boeing-Vertol CH-47
181, 186, 188
CHSS-2, Sikorsky . 174
CL-28 Argus, Canadair 124, **138–140**
CL-41G, Canadair . **157,** 158
Convair B-36 . 26, 31, 73
Convair B-58 Hustler 9, 15, 32, **37–39**
Convair F-102A Delta Dagger 24, 26
Convair F-106A Delta Dart . 20
Convair Model 48 Charger . 162
Corsair II, Ling-Temco-Vought A-7A 161
Crusader, Ling-Temco-Vought F-8E
11, 24
Crusader, Ling-Temco-Vought RF-8
91, **98–100**
CS2F Tracker . . **121**

Dassault Etendard IVM . 14
Dassault Mirage IIIC . 24
Dassault Mirage IIIE . 14
Dassault Mirage IIIO . 24
Dassault Mirage IIIR . **92–94**
Dassault Mirage IVA 14, 32, **40–42**
Dassault Mystère IVA . 10
Delta Dagger, Convair F-102A 24, 26
Delta Dart, Convair F-106A 20
Destroyer, Douglas RB-66 . 116
Douglas A-1 Skyraider
9, 10, 155, 160, 161, **164–168**
Douglas A-3 Skywarrior 27, 28, **43–46**

Douglas A-4 Skyhawk . 13
Douglas AC-47 . . 158, 159
Douglas B-26 Invader
29, 154, 155, 159, 160
Douglas RB-66 Destroyer . 116
Douglas RC-47 . . 159
Draken, Saab J 35 . 23, 24
Draken, Saab S 35E **110–112,** 116

EA-3B Skywarrior, Douglas . **46,** 81
EB-47H Stratojet, Boeing . 73
English Electric Canberra
27, 28, **47–51,** 79, **81–84**
Etendard IVM, Dassault . 14

F-4 Phantom II, McDonnell
8, 9, 14, 15, 22
F-8E Crusader, Ling-Temco-Vought
11, 24
F-80 Shooting Star, Lockheed 7
F-84 Thunderjet, Republic . 7
F-86 Sabre, North American 7, 91
F-89 Scorpion, Northrop . 26
F-100 Super Sabre, North American 9, 91
F-101B Voodoo, McDonnell . 10, 24
F-102A Delta Dagger, Convair 24, 26
F-104 Starfighter, Lockheed 9, 11, 14, 24
F-105 Thunderchief, Republic 9, 91
F-106 Delta Dart, Convair . 20
Fagot (MiG-15) . . 8, 27, 73
Fairey Gannet A.S.Mk.4 . 126
Farmer (MiG-19) . 20, 77
FB-111, General Dynamics . 15, 32
Fiat G.91 . . 14, 21

Fishbed (MiG-21) . 23, 28
Fishpot (Su-9) . . 20
Flashlight-D (Yak-28) 58, 91, **113–115**
Fresco (MiG-17) . 9, 10, 20, 23
Fury, North American AF-1 . 13

G.91, Fiat, . . 14, 21
Gannet A.S.Mk.4, Fairey . **126**
General Dynamics F-111 . 15, 24, 32
General Dynamics FB-111 . 15, 32
GK-210, Kawasaki 122, **123,** 125
Grumman A-6A Intruder . 15
Grumman OV-1 Mohawk 95–97, 116
Grumman S-2 Tracker 120, 126, 140–143
Gyrodyne QH-50 . . 176, 177

H-21, Vertol . . 179
Handley Page Victor 31, **51–54,** 80
Hawker Siddeley Buccaneer . 14, 27,28
Hawker Siddeley HS.801 14, 123, **124,** 127
Hawker Siddeley Vulcan 16, 31, **55–57**
Hawker Hunter F.R.Mk.10 . 91
Hercules, Lockheed RC-130A 81
Hiller OH-23 . 181
HKP 1 (Vertol 44A) . 177
HKP 4 (Boeing-Vertol 107) . 175, 176
HS.801, Hawker Siddeley 14, 123, **124,** 127
HSL-1, Bell . . 173
HSS-1, Sikorsky . . 174
Hughes OH-6A . . 183
Hunter F.R.Mk.10, Hawker . 91
Hustler, Convair B-58 9, 15, 32, **37–39**

Ilyushin Il-28 (Beagle) 26, 27, 28, **58–59**
Ilyushin Il-46 . . 63

Ilyushin Il-54 (Blowlamp) . 58
Impala, M.B.326 . . **157**
Intruder, Grumman A-6A . 15
Invader, Douglas B-26 **29**, 154, 155, 159, 160
Iroquois, Bell UH-1 7, 181, 182, 183, 184, 185

J 35 Draken, Saab . 23, 24
Jaguar, BAC-Breguet . 14
Jet Provost, BAC . . 157
JOV-1A Mohawk, Grumman 95

Kaman UH-2 SeaSprite . 188
Kamov Ka-20 (Harp) . 176, 177
Kawasaki GK-210 (P2V-Kai) 122, **123,**125

Lansen, Saab-32A . 14
Lightning F.Mk.6, BAC . 24
Ling-Temco-Vought A-7A Corsair II 161
Ling-Temco-Vought F-8E Crusader 11, 24
Ling-Temco-Vought RF-8 Crusader 91, **98–100**
LL-143, Beriev . . 122, 130
Lockheed A-11 . . 78, 79, 85
Lockheed AT-33 . 158
Lockhead AAFSS 163, 186, 187, 188, **189**
Lockheed F-104 Starfighter 9, 11, 14, 24
Lockheed P-3 Orion 12, 120, 125, 126, 148, **149–151**
Lockheed RB-69A . 81
Lockheed RC-130A Hercules 81
Lockheed SP-2H Neptune 117, 122, 123, **144–148**

Lockheed SR-71 . . **85–87**
Lockheed YF-12A . 24, 85

Magister, Potez-Air Fouga . 160
Mallow (Be-10) . 122, **130–132**
Malmö MFI-9B Mili-Trainer **163**
Mandrake (Yakovlev) . **77**
Marlin, Martin SP-5 122, **152–153**
Martin B-57 . 27, 28, **60–62**
Martin P6M SeaMaster . 28, 121
Martin RB-47 . . **78–80**
Martin SP-5 Marlin 122, **152–153**
Martin XB-51 . 28
M.B.326, Aermacchi . **157**
McDonnell F-4 Phantom II 8, 9, 14, 15,22
McDonnell F-101B Voodoo . 10, 24
McDonnell RF-4 Phantom II **100–103**, 116
McDonnell RF-101 Voodoo 91, **104–106**
MiG-15 (Fagot) . . 8, 27, 73
MiG-17 (Fresco) . 9, 10, 20, 23
MiG-19 (Farmer) . 20, 77
MiG-21 (Fishbed) . 23, 28
Mirage IIIC, Dassault . 24
Mirage IIIE, Dassault . 14
Mirage IIIO, Dassault . 24
Mirage IIIR, Dassault . **92–94**
Mirage IVA, Dassault 14, 32, **40–42**
Mohawk, Grumman OV-1 . **95–97,** 116
Myasishchev Bounder . 31, 32
Myasishchev Mya-4 (Bison) 81, 122
Mystère IVA, Dassault . 10

Neptune, Lockheed P-2 1117, 122, 123, **144–148**
North American A-5 Vigilante 29

North American AF-1 Fury . 13
North American B-45 Tornado 26
North American B-70 Valkyrie 32
North American F-86 Sabre 7, 73, 91
North American F-100 Super Sabre 9, 91
North American OV-10A 162, 163, **169–171**
North American RA-5C Vigilante **88–90**
North American RF-86F Sabre **91**
North American T-28D 154, 156, 161
North American YAT-28E . 166
Northrop F-5 . . 183
Northrop F-89 Scorpion . 26

O-1 Bird Dog, Cessna 161, 162, 163
OH-6A, Hughes . . 183
OH-13, Bell . . 181
OH-23, Hiller . . 181
Orion, Lockheed P-3 12, 120, 125, 126, 148, **149–151**
OV-1 Mohawk, Grumman . **95–97,** 116
OV-10A, North American 162, 163, **169–171**

P-2 Neptune, Lockheed 117, 122, 123, **144–148**
P-3 Orion, Lockheed 12, 120, 125, 126, 148, **149–151**
P-5 Marlin, Martin 122, **152–153**
P6M SeaMaster, Martin . 28, 121
P2V-Kai, Kawasaki (GK-210) 122, **123**, 125
Phantom II, McDonnell F-4 8, 9, 14, 15, 22

Phantom II, McDonnell RF-4 **100–103**, 116
Potez-Air Fouga Magister . 160
PX-S, Shin Meiwa **121**, 122, 125

QH-50, Gyrodyne . 176, 177

RA-3B Skywarrior, Douglas 44, 46
RA-5C Vigilante, North American **88–90**
RB-47 Stratojet, Boeing . 73
RB-57, Martin . **78–80**
RB-66 Destroyer, Douglas . 81, 116
RB-69A, Lockheed . 81
RC-47, Douglas . 159
RC-130A Hercules, Lockheed 81
RC-135A, Boeing . . 81
Republic F-84 Thunderjet . 7
Republic F-105 Thunderchief 9, 91
Republic RF-84F Thunderflash 91, **107–109**
RF-4 Phantom II, McDonnell **100–103**, 116
RF-8 Crusader, Ling-Temco-Vought 91, **98–100**
RF-84F Thunderflash, Republic 91, **107–109**
RF-86F Sabre. North American 91
RF-101C Voodoo, McDonnell 91, **104–106**

S-2 Tracker, Grumman 120, 126, **140–143**
S 35E Draken, Saab **110–112**, 116
S 37 Viggen, Saab . 14
SA-321G Super Frelon, Sud-Aviation 174, **175**, 176

Saab-32A Lansen . 14
Saab-35E Draken . **110–112**, 116
Saab-37 Viggen . 14
Saab-105 . 157, **159**
Sabre, North American F-86 7, 73, 91
Sabre, North American RF-86F **91**
Scimitar, Vickers Supermarine 13
Seabat, Sikorsky SH-34 (S-58) **173**, 174, 178
Sea King, Sikorsky SH-3A (S-61) **174**, 178
SeaMaster, Martin P6M . 28, 121
SeaSprite, Kaman UH-2 . 188
Sea Vixen, Hawker Siddeley . 13
Shackleton, Avro . 123, **127–129**
Shin Meiwa PX-S . **121**, 122, 125
Short Sperrin . . 30
Sikorsky S-55 . 173
Sikorsky S-66 . . 186
Sikorsky SH-3 . **174**, 178
Sikorsky SH-34 Seabat **173**, 174, 178
Sioux Scout, Bell 207 185, 186, 189
Sk 60, Saab . 157, **159**
Skyhawk, Douglas A-4 . 13
Skywarrior, Douglas A-3 . 27, 28
Skyraider, Douglas A-1 9, 10, 155, 160, 161, **164–168**
Starfighter, Lockheed F-104 . 9, 11, 14,24
Stratofortress, Boeing B-52 9, 10, 14, 15, 16, 23, 30, 31, 32, **33–36**, 81
Stratojet, Boeing B-47 29, 30, 31, 73
Sud-Aviation SA-321G Super Frelon 174, **175**, 176
Sud-Aviation SA-3164 . 184, **185**
Sud-Aviation SE-3130 Alouette II 180

Sud-Aviation SE-3160 Alouette III 180
Sukhoi Su-9 (Fishpot) . 20
Supermarine Scimitar . 13
Supermarine Swift F.R.Mk.7 21
Super Sabre, North American F-100 9, 91
Swift F.R.Mk.7, Supermarine 21

T-28D, North American **154**, 156, 161
T-37C, Cessna . . **156**, 157
TA-3B Skywarrior, Douglas . 46
Tarzan, Tu-91 . . 126
TB-58A Hustler, Convair . 37
Thunderchief, Republic F-105 9, 91
Thunderflash, Republic RF-84F 91, **107–109**
Thunderjet, Republic F-84 . 7
Tornado, North American B-45 26
Tracker, Grumman S-2 120, 126, **140–143**
TSR-2, BAC . . 29, 32
Tupolev Tu-4 (Bull) . . 25
Tupolev Tu-14 (Bosun) . 26, **27**, 58
Tupolev Tu-16 (Badger) 16, 31, **63–65**, 74, 122
Tupolev Tu-20 (Bear) 16, 26, **66–69**, 74, 122
Tupolev Tu-85 (Barge) . 26, 66
Tupolev Tu-88 (Badger) . 63
Tupolev Tu-91 Tarzan (Boot) 126
Tupolev Tu-95 (Bear) . 66
Tupolev Blinder . 16, 25, 32, **70–72**

U-2, Lockheed . . **74–76**
UH-1 Iroquois, Bell 7, 181, 182, 183, 184, 185

Valiant, Vickers . . 28, 30, 41
Valkyrie, North American B-70 32
Vautour, Sud-Aviation . 27, **28**
Vertol H-21 . . 179
Vertol V-44 . . 176, 177
Vickers Valiant . . 28, 30, 31
Victor, Handley Page 31, **51–54,** 80
Viggen, Saab-37 . . 14
Vigilante, North American A-5 29
Vigilante, North American RA-5C **88–90**
Voodoo, McDonnell F-101B 10, 24

Voodoo, McDonnell RF-101C
                                          91, **104–106**
Vulcan B.2, Hawker Siddeley
                                          16, 31, **55–57**

Warrior, Bell . . 185
Wasp A.S.Mk.1, Westland . 178
Wessex, Westland . 175, 176, 184
Westland Wasp A.S.Mk.1 . 178
Westland Wessex 175, 176, 184
Westland Whirlwind . 175, 184

Whirlwind, Westland . 175, 184

XB-51, Martin . . 28

Yakovlev Brewer . . 28
Yakovlev Mandrake . **77**
Yakovlev Yak-25 (Flashlight-A) 28
Yakovlev Yak-28 (Flashlight-D)
                                          58, 91, **113–115**
YAT-28E, North American . 156
YF-12A, Lockheed . 24